Craig Claiborne

The New York Times Guide to Dining Out in New York

Atheneum

New York

1970

Library of Congress catalog card number 67–30689
Published simultaneously in Canada by McClelland and Stewart Ltd.
Composition by Clarke & Way, New York
Printed and bound by The Murray Printing Company
Forge Village, Massachusetts
Designed by Harry Ford
First Printing November 1967
Second Printing February 1968
Third Printing March 1968
Fourth Printing April 1968
Fifth Printing July 1968
Sixth Printing September 1968
Seventh Printing January 1969
Eighth Printing April 1969
Ninth Printing July 1969
Tenth Printing October 1969
Eleventh Printing September 1970

FOREWORD

This edition of *The New York Times Guide to Dining Out in New York* varies in several respects from its predecessor. About 700 restaurants are now reviewed in the book, and more than 200 of these listings are new—restaurants that have opened since the last edition went to press, as well as restaurants not covered in earlier editions. There have been approximately 60 deletions, the vast majority of which are restaurants that have closed within the past year or so.

This new edition also indicates new telephone numbers, new addresses and the revised prices of various restaurants. There has been an appreciable increase in the cost of dining in the city—in many instances, the increase amounts to between 5 and 15 percent.

A further and important addition to this edition is an indication of major credit cards honored by each restaurant.

By a modest estimate, this book represents eating or sitting at a table and contemplating food for nearly 4,000 hours. That is based on the fact of going to two restaurants a day, five days a week, for nearly six years. It has involved dining on such delicacies as squabs and truffles and champagne sauce and sampling such oddities to the native scene as sea urchins eaten raw with lemon, and sea slugs in numerous Chinese preparations. The span has gone from some of the thinnest new wines to the finest vintages of the century in old bottles; from the subtlest of cream soups to powerfully condimented dishes that all but enrage the palate. Oddly enough, this has involved not a single remembered case of crise de foie and only an occasional bout with the stomach.

One of the questions that is most frequently asked of me in this wildly hedonistic occupation is whether or not I am recognized when I visit restaurants. The answer is—

with rare exceptions—a firm no. When reservations have been necessary, they have invariably been made in the name of another guest, and for some peculiar reason my face apparently has the look of utter anonymity. I have waited in line with the best of them, been abused by head-waiters and busboys, placed in the dim corners of restaurants, corners that the help ignores and calls Siberia, had my toes stepped on and jacket drenched with black bean soup (in lieu of apology the waiter said, "Watch out!").

This desire for anonymity is not purely altruistic. It is something to be cultivated for the sake of personal privacy. I do not like being fawned over, with or without the circumstance of my job. And most restaurateurs, if they do discover that you are a restaurant chronicler, are more garrulous than taxi drivers. The moment arrives when you feel you should bill them for listening.

To pursue the point, I went to dine on a recent evening at one of my favorite Chinese places, the Shun Lee Dynasty. I had been there many times and always with the comfortable cloak of anonymity. On this evening, however, I wanted their chicken with spinach, a personal favorite, and river shrimp. Alas, the captain came up and greeted me by name. "Let us order frogs' legs," he proposed and in such a manner it would have seemed rude to refuse. The frogs' legs came in lieu of the shrimp and the chicken dish had been altered. I wanted beer as a beverage since I think it is ideal for Chinese food. Instead the management, in utter goodwill and generosity, deposited a bottle of iced champagne next to my table. Perhaps it is difficult to understand, but with Chinese food I prefer beer to Dom Pérignon.

New York has, of course, the finest restaurants in America, although I will go to my grave declaring that they do not have a French restaurant to compare with the finest of France. The finest French restaurant in Manhattan is La Caravelle for classic cooking, and the best for bourgeois cooking is Le Veau d'Or. There is a point here, too. I have a great affection for Le Veau d'Or, for I happen to like the ambiance as well as the food. It has a middle-class decor, the tables are cloth-by-cloth together, and there is frequently a wait for a table. When the principal chef, Lucien Guillemaud, is away for the summer, the food can be ordinary. There are many people to whom the crowd and crush of Le Veau d'Or and the waiting are anathema, and it is the age-old question of chacun à son goût.

Similarly there is no question in my mind that La Grenouille has one of the finest kitchens in New York and the management is dedicated. The flowers on the table are glorious. But I don't enjoy the crowds and the proximity of the tables. The difference is the genre of the restaurant. La Grenouille is grand luxe with grand luxe prices and I want more elbow room. Grand luxe elbow room.

Although most of my training has been in French cooking and I consider it the world's ultimate, most of the French restaurants here are disappointing to me. There is too much sameness about the menus, and the food of one small establishment tastes uncommonly like that of another. You can recite the menu like the responses to a catechism. Sole meunière, coq au vin, boeuf bourguignon, omelet with cheese, omelet with mushrooms and on and on.

Thus, I find myself more often than not going to Chinese restaurants for the sheer pleasure of dining well. You can find here some of the best Chinese cooking this side of Formosa and Hong Kong, and I prefer the Chinese restaurants of New York to those of San Francisco. These restaurants are becoming far more sophisticated than they were ten years ago, and you can find excellent Szechuan cooking in places like the Shun Lee Dynasty, the altogether commendable Pearl's, which opened recently, and at the Four Seas in the Wall Street area. There are excellent Chinese lo mein—that is to say, noodle restaurants—in Chinatown and places with tea lunches such as the

Nom Wah tea parlor there. It is a little on the large, ramshackle side, but the food is interesting and good. In almost all Chinese restaurants you will dine better if you order from the à la carte menu, and if you order chow mein or chop suey and are disappointed, it is no more than anyone deserves.

The greatest disappointment concerning restaurants in New York is the gross lack of a great Italian or a great fish restaurant. Of course, there are some perfectly acceptable places where you can get a decent plate of pasta or sauté of veal, but there is no Italian restaurant of great distinction such as you find in Rome or Florence. The fish restaurants all seem to be cut from the same pattern: quickly broiled and frequently dusted with paprika to compensate for improper broiling. Sweet's, of course, on Fulton Street is a dear place and a landmark, and the fish is as fresh and good as you will find in the city. It is well worth a visit.

New York restaurants, surprisingly, do not change appreciably over the years, although when changes do occur, they can be monumental.

Le Pavillon, long the foremost temple of fine French cooking and the standard by which all other French restaurants could be judged, has become something less than first-rate since the death of the founder and owner, Henri Soulé. The style is missing and so is the spirit. The last time this reporter dined there the present owner was in the middle of lunch and waved goodbye from his table. It was a friendly but not terribly dignified gesture.

On the other hand, when I revisit restaurants that were mediocre five years ago, they seem equally mediocre today.

Finally, a note about wines in restaurants. They are, for the most part, woefully overpriced from one end of Manhattan to the other. A rare exception is The Four Seasons. The wine list is impressive and for one man's money the price is right.

A NOTE ON TIPPING

To all appearances there are many people who wonder about the mechanics of tipping (and tipping today is, unfortunately, by and large mechanical). As a general rule, 15 percent of the food bill is considered an adequate tip for waiters. If there is a captain, he is normally given 5 percent of the bill, and if there is a wine steward, he may be tipped $1 for each bottle served. If there is only a waiter who renders service, the 15 percent should prove adequate.

In theory, of course, tipping is a voluntary act, and if the table service is conspicuously bad, the gratuity should be measured according to conscience. Restaurant-goers might keep in mind that in most restaurants where there are both waiters *and* captains, the tips are not shared. That is to say, if the diner indicates a tip on the bill or leaves a sum of money as gratuity, all of it goes to the waiter even though most of the service may have been performed by the captain. Nor is the money shared with the wine steward.

FOUR, THREE, TWO AND ONE-STAR RESTAURANTS

Four-Star Restaurants

La Caravelle
La Côte Basque
Lafayette
La Grenouille
Le Veau d'Or
Peter Luger
Quo Vadis
Shun Lee Dynasty

Three-Star Restaurants

Baroque
Bo Bo
Café Chauveron
Casa Brasil
Charley O's Bar and Grill
Christ Cella
Coach House, The
Colony, The
Copenhagen
Dinty Moore's
El Faro
El Parador Café
Fountain Café
Four Seasons, The
French Shack, The
Gauguin Room, The
Giordano Restaurant
Isle of Capri
La Toque Blanche
Le Manoir
Le Mistral
Leopard, The
Lüchow's
Lutèce
Mandarin House East
Mon Paris
Palm Restaurant
Pearl's Chinese Restaurant
P. J. Clarke's
Saito
San Marco
Spanish Pavilion, The
Sweet's Restaurant

Two-Star Restaurants

Act I
À la Fourchette
Al Cooper's Herald Square Restaurant
Alfredo of New York
Algonquin Hotel:
The Oak Room
The Rose Room
Antica Roma
Arirang House
Assembly Steak House
Ballato Restaurant
Barbetta Restaurant
Benihana East
Benihana of Tokyo
Billy's
Brasserie
Brazilian Coffee Restaurant
Broadway Joe Steak House
Brussels Restaurant
Café Argenteuil
Café Brittany
Café de France

Café Nicholson
Café Saint Denis
Camillo
Capri Restaurant
Casa Mario
Cattleman, The
Cedars of Lebanon
Champlain Restaurant
Cheshire Cheese Restaurant
Chez Cardinale
Chez Renée
Christo's
Chuan Hong Restaurant
Clos Normand
Copter Club
Crêpes Suzette
Czechoslovakia Praha
Dan Dowd's Steak House
Danny's Hide-A-Way
Dardanelles Armenian Restaurant
Du Midi
Eduardo's
Elizabeth White's Restaurant
El Matador
Emil's
Empire, The
Fleur de Lis
Four Seas
Frankie and Johnnie
Gaetano's Ristorante
Gage and Tollner
Gate of Peiping, The
Gatti's
Gene's
Gino's Restaurant
Giovanni
Gloucester House
Gold Coin
Golden Horn
Granados Restaurant
Great Shanghai, The
Grotta Azzurra
House of Chan
House of Milano
Il Bambino
India House Restaurant
Italian Pavilion
Jai-Alai
Japanese Steak House
Jimmy's Greek-American Restaurant
Jimmy's La Grange
Joe's Restaurant
Joy Garden
Kashmir Restaurant
Keen's English Chop House
Keneret
Kenny's Steak Pub
King Wu
Kitcho Restaurant
Kobe Steak House
La Cabana
La Comédie
La Crêpe Restaurants
La Croisette
La Fortuna
La Grillade
La Groceria
L'Aiglon
La Piazzetta
La Popotte
La Potinière
La Potinière du Soir
L'Armorique
La Stella
La Venere West
Le Biarritz
Le Bistro
Le Chambertin
Le Chanteclair
Le Cheval Blanc
Lee's Restaurant

Le Moal
Le Pavillon
Le Périgord
Le Pont Neuf
Le Poulailler
Le Provençal
L'Escargot
Les Pyrénées
Le Steak
Longchamps
Long River
Lotus Eaters
Lotus Eaters Fifth
Louise Jr.
Mme. Romaine de Lyon
Manganaro's and Manganaro's Hero-Boy Restaurant
Mandarin House, The
Manny Wolf's
Marchi's
Mario
Mark Twain Riverboat
Marnel's Restaurant
Marta Restaurant
Marta's
McSorley's Old Ale House
Mercurio
Mike Manuche
Mirko
Monte's Restaurant
Mont St. Michel Restaurant
Near East Restaurant
New Shun Lee Restaurant
Nicola Paone
Ningpo Restaurant
Nippon
Nom Wah Tea Parlor
Orsini's
Pak-India Curry House
Pancho Villa's
Pantheon Restaurant
Pappas
Paradise Inn
Passy, The
Patricia Murphy's Candlelight Restaurant
Paul and Jimmy's Place
Peking House
Pen and Pencil, The
Peter's Backyard
Philippine Garden, The
Pierre au Tunnel
Pierre, Hotel:
The Café Pierre
The Pierre Grill
Pierre's
Pietro's
Piraeus, My Love
Pizzeria alla Napoletana
P. J. O'Hara
Plaza Hotel:
Oak Room
Rajmahal Restaurant
Red Coach Grill
Renato East
Reuben's
Rex Restaurant
Ruc Restaurant
Rugantino
Running Footman, The
Russian Tea Room
San Marino
Santa Lucia
Sardi's
Sardi's East
Sayat Nova
Say Eng Look
Scandia
Sea-Fare of the Aegean
Sea-Fare Restaurant
Sheik Restaurant, The
Sixty Eight Restaurant

Stage Delicatessen
Steak Casino
Steak Joint, The
Stockholm Restaurant
Stouffer's
Sun Luck Queens
Takeda Restaurant
Tamura Restaurant
Tien Tsin
Tik Tak Hungarian
Tin Lizzie Restaurant, The
Tomaldo Restaurant
Tom's Shangri-La
Tony's Italian Kitchen
Tony's Wife
Toots Shor
Tower Suite
Trader Vic's
Trini
"21"
Unicorn, The
Vasata
Vesuvio Restaurant
Via Margutta
Via Veneto
Victor's Café
Villa Pensa
Vincent Petrosino
Wah Kee Restaurant
Whyte's Downtown
Wo Ping
Xochitl Mexican Restaurant
Ye Olde Chop House
Zetti Hungarian Restaurant
Zum Zum

One-Star Restaurants

Adano
Aki Dining Room
Alamo Chile House, The
Aldo and Eddie Rapallo Restaurant
Alfie's
Amato's Italian Restaurant
Angelina's
Annette's Le Petit Veau
Antlers
Antolotti's
Artist and Writers Restaurant
Athena East
Athenian Restaurant, The
Au Canari d'Or
Au Steak Pommes Frites
Balkan Armenian Restaurant
Beaujolais
Beirut Restaurant
Belcrep
Bernstein-on-Essex-Street
Black Angus
Blaue Donau
Blue Sea
Brittany du Soir
Bronco Restaurant
Budapest Hungarian Restaurant
Ca d'Oro
Café Europa
Café Français
Café Renaissance
Canton Restaurant
Captain's Table, The
Carnegie Delicatessen and Restaurant
Carolina
Casa di Pre
Ceylon India Inn
Chalet Suisse
Chandler's
Charles à la Pomme Soufflé
Charles French Restaurant
Charlie Brown's

Chateaubriand
Chez Napoleon
Chez Vous
Chez Yvonne l'Escargot
China Bowl
Chinese Rathskeller
Chock Full O'Nuts
Coq au Vin
Corner at Margaret's
Daly's Dandelion
Damon's
Dawson's Ha-Penny Bar
Del Pezzo
Delsomma
Dresner's
Due Mondi
Dumpling House
Eating Ho
El Charro
Electra
El Quijote
El Radiante
Empress, The
English Grill
Esplanade, The
Esther Eng
Fagiano Restaurant
Fisherman's Net
500 on 8th Restaurant, The
Flower Drum Restaurant
Fonda la Paloma
Forlini's Restaurant
Fornos
Frank Leone's
Frank's Restaurant
Friar Tuck
Gaiety East
Gallagher's
Giambelli
Giambelli 50th
Gold Coin
Golden Coach
Goldie's New York
Gondola
Grand Central Terminal:
Oyster Bar and Restaurant
Grand Ticino
Ground Floor, The
Hanover Square Restaurant
Harbin Inn
Headquarters Restaurant
Hellenic Pallas
Henry Stampler's Filet Mignon
Hide Sukiyaki
Ho Ho Restaurant
Hong Fat Restaurant
Horn & Hardart Automats
Hoy Yuen
Hyde Park Restaurant
Ida de France
Île de France
International Cheese Club Restaurant
Italianissimo
Jade Palace
Jenedi's
Joe Allen
Joe and Rose
Johnny Johnston's Charcoal Room
John's Restaurant
Jumble Shop Steak House
Kamehachi
Karachi
Katz's Delicatessen
King of the Sea
Kirby Allen Restaurant, The
Kleine Konditorei
Koon Shing Tea House
La Bourgogne
La Fonda del Sol
La Galette
La Locanda

Le Petite Marmite
La Place
Larré's French Restaurant
La Scala
La Strada East
Le Alpi
Le Château Richelieu
Le Gourmet
Le Marmiton
Leone's
Les Champs
L'Étoile
Le Valois
Liborio
Lichee Tree, The
Lindy's
Lin Heong
Little Kitchen, The
Lord & Taylor's Soup Bar
Louise
Lum's Garden
Luna's Restaurant
Mama Laura Restaurant
Mañana
Mario's Villa Borghese
Mario's Villa d'Este
Marsh's Steak Place
Mary Elizabeth's
Mary's
Maud Chez Elle
Max's Kansas City
Mayhews
Michael's Pub
Miller's
Minetta Tavern
Miyako
Molfetas Cafeteria
Mona Trattoria
Mont d'Or
Moon Palace
Morgen's East
Morgen's Restaurant
Nat Simon's Penguin Room
New Moon Inn
O. Henry's Steak House
Old Denmark
Old Forge Steak House
Old Mexico Restaurant
Oriental Pearl
Oscar's Delmonico
Oscar's Salt of the Sea
Oviedo
Pablo's
Pagoda Restaurant
Palladium
Paprika
Parioli, Romanissimo
Parkway East
Paul Revere's Tavern and Chop House
Per Bacco
Pergola des Artistes
Piccolo Mondo
Piro's
P. J. Moriarty
Plush Burger
Port Arthur
Portofino
Press Box
Prime Burger
Publick House
Rattazzi
Rick's Sea Food House
Ristorante Puglia
Rocco Restaurant
Romeo Salta
Rosetta's Restaurant
St. Germain Restaurant
Sam Wo
Savoia
Schaefer's
Schrafft's Restaurants

RESTAURANTS LISTED BY AREA

Wall Street Area

Antlers
Castilla Restaurant and Bar
Chez Yvonne L'Escargot
Chock Full O'Nuts
Coachman Restaurant, The
Eberlin's
Emil's
Four Seas
Fraunces Tavern
Fusco's
Hanover Square Restaurant
Horn & Hardart Automats
International Cheese Club Restaurant
Jimmy's Greek-American Restaurant
Kabuki
La Crêpe Restaurants
Longchamps
Miller's
Oscar's Delmonico
Schrafft's Restaurants
Sloppy Louie's
Son of the Sheik
Sweet's Restaurant
Talisman, The
Tamura Restaurant
Teddy's Restaurant
Vincent Petrosino
Whyte's Downtown
Ye Olde Chop House
Zum Zum

Chinatown

Bo Bo
Canton Restaurant
Chinese Rathskeller
Dumpling House
Eating Ho
Esther Eng
Hong Fat Restaurant
Joy Garden
Joy Luck Coffee Shop
King Wu
Koon Shing Tea House
Lee's Restaurant
Lin Heong
Nom Wah Tea Parlor
Oriental Pearl
Pagoda Restaurant
Port Arthur
Quon Luck Restaurant
Sam Wo
Say Eng Look
Shanghai Village
Tai Yat Low
Temple Garden, The
Tinghatsak
Vincent's Clam Bar
Wah Kee Restaurant
Wo Kee
Wo Ping

Greenwich Village

Albert
Angelina's
Asti

Lower East Side (below 14th Street)

Little Kitchen, The
Luna's Restaurant
Mayhews
McSorley's Old Ale House
Ningpo Restaurant
Parkway East
Ratner's
Ristorante Puglia
Sing Wu
Villa Pensa

Downtown—East Side (34th to 14th Streets)

Balkan Armenian Restaurant
Blue Sea
Brownies
Cedars of Lebanon
Chock Full O'Nuts
El Parador Café
Fisherman's Net
Frank's Spa
Gate of Peiping, The
Golden Coach
Good Table, The
Horn & Hardart Automats
House of Milano
Hye Oriental Food Shop
Italianissimo
La Strada East
Longchamps
Lotus Eaters Fifth
Lüchow's
Marchi's
Max's Kansas City
Mon Paris
Old Forge Steak House
Palace d'Orient
Paul and Jimmy's Place
Per Bacco
Peter's Tavern
Philippine Garden, The
Phil's Cocktail Lounge and Restaurant
Savoia
Schrafft's Restaurants
Sheik Restaurant, The
Shun Lee
Spark's Pub South
Suehiro Restaurant
Tom's Garden Restaurant
Walsh's Steak House
Wards Black Bass
Yen King
Yen Luck
Ying's

Downtown—West Side (34th to 14th Streets)

Beirut Restaurant
Casa Johnny
Cavanagh's Restaurant
Chock Full O'Nuts
El Quijote
Horn & Hardart Automats
Lotus Eaters Fifth
Nautilus, The
Old Garden, The
Old Homestead
Oviedo
Pappas
P. J. Moriarty
San Remo
Schrafft's Restaurants
Solowey's

Midtown—East Side (34th to 72nd Streets)

Al Schacht's Restaurant
Aldo and Eddie Rapallo Restaurant
Annette's Le Petit Veau
Antolotti's
Asian Pearl
Assembly Steak House
Athena East
Au Canari d'Or
Baccarà Restaurant
Baroque
Beef and Bourbon Restaurant
Benihana East
Billy's
Black Angus
Boat House, The
Brasserie
Brass Rail, The
Brussels Restaurant
Café Argenteuil
Café Chauveron
Café Europa
Café Nicholson
Café Renaissance
Café Saint Denis
Camillo
Cattleman, The
Chalet Suisse
Chandler's
Charles à la Pomme Soufflé
Charlie Brown's
Château Henri IV
Chateaubriand
Chez Renée
Chock Full O'Nuts
Christ Cella
Christo's
Clos Normand
Colony, The
Copain
Copter Club
Corner at Margaret's
Daly's Dandelion
Danny's Hide-A-Way
Dawson's Ha-Penny Bar
Dragon Gate
Due Mondi
Eduardo's
Electra
Elizabeth White's Restaurant
El Matador
Empire, The
Empress, The
Esplanade, The
Ferdi's
Flower Drum Restaurant
Fountain Café
Four Seasons, The
Frank Leone's
Friar Tuck
Gaiety East
Gatti's
Giambelli
Giambelli 50th
Gian Marino's
Gino's Restaurant
Giovanni
Gloucester House
Gold Coin
Goldie's New York
Gondola
Grand Central Terminal: Oyster Bar and Restaurant
Hamburg Heavens
Harvey's Sea Food House
Hob Nob Restaurant
Horn & Hardart Automats
India House Restaurant
Inn of the Clock

Isle of Capri
Jade Palace
Janssen's
Jenedi's
Jimmy's La Grange
Jimmie Walker's
Joe and Rose
John Barleycorn Pub
Johnny Johnston's Charcoal Room
Kenny's Steak Pub
King Henri IV
King of the Sea
Kirby Allen Restaurant, The
La Cabana
La Cave Henri IV
La Côte Basque
La Croisette
Lafayette
La Fortuna
La Galette
La Grenouille
L'Aiglon
La Locanda
La Maganette
La Petite Maison
La Piazzetta
La Place
La Popotte
La Reine
L'Armorique
La Toque Blanche
Le Bistro
Le Chanteclair
Le Château Richelieu
Le Cheval Blanc
Le Manoir
Le Marmiton
Le Mistral
Le Moal
Leopard, The
Le Pavillon
Le Périgord
Le Pont Neuf
Le Provençal
L'Escargot
Les Champs
Le Steak
L'Étoile
Le Valois
Le Veau d'Or
Longchamps
Lotus Eaters
Louise
Louise Jr.
Lutèce
Mme. Romaine de Lyon
Mama Laura Restaurant
Mañana
Mandarin House East
Manny Wolf's
Maria
Mario's Villa Borghese
Mario's Villa d'Este
Marnel's Restaurant
Mary Elizabeth's
Mayhews
McCarthy's Famous Steak House
Michael's Pub
Mirko
Mont d'Or
Morgen's East Restaurant
Nicola Paone
Nippon
Nyborg and Nelson
Old Denmark
Old Hungary Restaurant
Original Joe's Restaurant
Oscar's Salt of the Sea
Pablo's
Palladium
Palm Restaurant
Passy, The

Patricia Murphy's Candlelight Restaurant
Paul Revere's Tavern and Chop House
Peking House
Pen and Pencil, The
Piccolo Mondo
Pierre, Hotel
Pierre's
Pietro's
P. J. Clarke's
P. J. Moriarty
P. J. O'Hara
Plush Burger
President
Press Box
Prime Burger
Proof of the Pudding
Publick House
Quo Vadis
Rattazzi
Renato East
Restaurant Laurent
Reuben's
Rex Restaurant
Rick's Sea Food House
Rita Dimitri's La Chansonnette
Roma di Notte
Ruc Restaurant
Running Footman
Russian Bear
San Marino
Sardi's East
Schrafft's Restaurants
Sea-Fare Restaurant
Sempione
Serendipity 3
Shanghai East
Shun Lee Dynasty
Sign of the Dove
Siro's
Six Happiness
Smokehouse, The
Spanish Pavilion, The
Sultan's Table, The
Sun Luck East
Sun Luck Imperial
Three Crowns
Tiki Village, The
Tomaldo Restaurant
Tom's Shangri-La
Tonkatsu
Tony's Wife
Town House, The
Trattoria
Trefner's Restaurant
Unicorn, The
Voisin
Waldorf-Astoria:
The Bull and Bear
Yellowfinger's Butcheria
Zoe Chase
Zum Zum

Midtown—West Side (34th to 72nd Streets)

Absinthe House
Act I
Adano
À la Fourchette
Alamo Chile House, The
Al and Dick's Steak House
Al Cooper's Herald Square Restaurant
Alfredo of New York
Algonquin Hotel
Amato's Italian Restaurant
Arirang House
Artist and Writers Restaurant
Athenian Restaurant, The

Au Steak Pommes Frites
Barbetta Restaurant
Beaujolais
Belcrep
Benihana of Tokyo
Bill Hong's
Billy Gwon's
Blue Ribbon
Brass Rail, The
Brazilian Coffee Restaurant
Brittany du Soir
Broadway Joe Steak House
Bronco Restaurant
Ca d'Oro
Café Brittany
Café de France
Café des Artistes
Café des Sports
Café Français
Café Lucca
Canton Village
Capri Restaurant
Caracalla
Carnegie Delicatessen and Restaurant
Caso Mario
Ceylon India Inn
Champlain Restaurant
Charles V
Charley O's Bar and Grill
Cheshire Cheese Restaurant
Chez Cardinale
Chez Napoleon
China Bowl, The
Chock Full O'Nuts
Copenhagen
Coq au Vin
Crêpes Suzette
Cyrano
Damon's
Dan Dowd's Steak House
D'Angelo's
Davy Jones Sea Food House
Del Pezzo
Delsomma
Dinty Moore's
Du Midi
English Grill
Ershowsky Deli
Famous Kitchen
500 on 8th Restaurant, The
Fleur de Lis
Fonda La Paloma
Fontana di Trevi
Fornos
Forum of the Twelve Caesars
Frankie and Johnnie
French Shack, The
Fuji Restaurant
Fundalor
Gallagher's
Gauguin Room, The
Ginger Man, The
Giordano Restaurant
Golden Horn
Great Wall
Ground Floor, The
Guido
Hacienda La Paloma
Headquarters Restaurant
Hellenic Pallas
Henry Stampler's Filet Mignon
Herb Evans Restaurant
Hide Sukiyaki
Ho Ho Restaurant
Horn & Hardart Automats
House of Chan
House of Louie
Hoy Yuen
Île de France
Italian Pavilion
J. & T. Chili House

Jane Davies
Jim Downey's
Joe Allen
Kamehachi
Karachi
Kashmir Restaurant
Keen's English Chop House
Kippy's
Kitcho Restaurant
Kobe Steak House
La Bourgogne
La Caravelle
La Comédie
La Crêpe Restaurants
La Fonda del Sol
La Grillade
La Petite Marmite
La Potinière
La Potinière du Soir
Larré's French Restaurant
La Scala
La Strada
La Venere West
Le Alpi
Le Berry
Le Biarritz
Le Café Arnold
Le Chambertin
Le Gourmet
Leone's
Le Poulailler
Les Pyrénées
Liborio
Lindy's
Lobster, The
Longchamps
Long River
Lord & Taylor's Soup Bar
Louis Sherry at Philharmonic Hall
Louis Sherry's Plaza Café at Philharmonic Hall
Lum's Garden
Manganaro's and Manganaro's Hero-Boy Restaurant
Mark Twain Riverboat
Marsh's Steak Place
Marta's
Maud Chez Elle
Max's Restaurant
Mayan Room, The
Mercurio
Metropolitan Opera House:
Grand Tier Restaurant
The Top of the Met
Mike Manuche
Miyako
Molfetas Cafeteria
Mont St. Michel Restaurant
Morgen's Restaurant
Orsini's
Pak-India Curry House
Pantheon Restaurant
Paradise Inn
Parisien
Pearl's Chinese Restaurant
Penthouse Club
Pergola des Artistes
Phil Gluckstern's
Pierre au Tunnel
Piraeus, My Love
Pizzeria alla Napoletana
Plaza Hotel:
Edwardian Room
Oak Room
Rainbow Room
Red Coach Grill
Romeo Salta
Rosoff's
Rugantino
Russian Tea Room
St. Germain Restaurant
Saito

San Marco
Santa Lucia
Sardi's
Scandia
Schrafft's Restaurants
Sea-Fare of the Aegean
Sea Hunt
Stage Delicatessen
Steak Place, The
Stockholm Restaurant
Stouffer's
Sun Luck Gourmet
Supreme Macaroni Company
Swiss Inn
Takeda Restaurant
Tavern on the Green
37th Street Hideaway
Tin Lizzie Restaurant, The
Tokyo Sukiyaki House
Toledo Restaurant
Toots Shor
Top of the Six's
Tout Va Bien
Tower Suite
Trader Vic's
Trini
Troll Smorebrod Shoppe
"21"
Un Rincon Argentino
Valentino's
Vesuvio Restaurant
Via Veneto
Victor's Café
Vorst's Century Sea Grill
White's Sea Food Restaurant
Whyte's
Xochitl Mexican Restaurant

Uptown—East Side

Alfie's
Blaue Donau
Budapest Hungarian Restaurant
Café du Soir
Café Geiger
Café Hindenburg
Casa Brasil
Chardas
Czechoslovak Praha
Dresner's
86th Street Brauhaus
Fagiano Restaurant
Fin 'n Claw
Foo Chow Restaurant
Gaetano's Ristorante
House of Meng
Hyde Park Restaurant
Ida de France
Jager House
King Dragon
Kleine Konditorei
Le Boeuf à la Mode
Longchamps
Lorelei
Lotus, The
Pancho Villa's
Paprika
Parioli, Romanissimo
Pilsner Restaurant
Piro's
P. J. Moriarty
Schaefer's
Schrafft's Restaurants
Student Prince
Susy Wong
Three Hussars
Tik Tak Hungarian
Vasata
Villa Doria

White House Restaurant
Zetti Hungarian Restaurant

Uptown—West Side

Aki Dining Room
Chock Full O'Nuts
Chuan Hong Restaurant
Frank's Restaurant
Great Shanghai, The
Green Tree, The
Harbin Inn
La Concha
Moon Palace
New Moon Inn
New Shun Lee Restaurant
Shanghai Café
Shanghai d'Or
Steinberg's
Tien Tsin
Tip Toe Inn
Tony's Italian Kitchen
Tsuruya

Other Boroughs

Carolina
El Radiante
Gage and Tollner
Joe's
La Stella
Mona Trattoria
Near East Restaurant
Old Mexico Restaurant
Peter Luger
Sun Luck Queens

TYPES OF RESTAURANTS

American

Absinthe House
Act I
Alamo Chile House, The
Albert
Al Cooper's Herald Square Restaurant
Algonquin Hotel
Al Schacht's Restaurant
Antlers
Artist and Writers Restaurant
Beef and Bourbon Restaurant
Billy's
Blue Mill Tavern
Blue Ribbon
Brass Rail, The
Bronco Restaurant
Brownies
Café des Artistes
Café Geiger
Café Nicholson
Chandler's
Charlie Brown's
Chock Full O'Nuts
Christo's
Coach House, The
Coachman Restaurant, The
Colony, The
Cookery Lafayette, The
Copter Club
Daly's Dandelion
Dinty Moore's
Dresner's
Eberlin's
86th Street Brauhaus
Elizabeth White's Restaurant
Finale, The
Fountain Café
Four Seasons, The
Frankie and Johnnie
Frank's Restaurant
Frank's Spa
Fraunces Tavern
Ginger Man, The
Goldie's New York
Ground Floor, The
Hamburg Heaven
Headquarters Restaurant
Herb Evans Restaurant
Hob Nob Restaurant
Horn & Hardart Automats
Hyde Park Restaurant
Inn of the Clock
International Cheese Club Restaurant
J. & T. Chili House
Jane Davies
Joe Allen
Kirby Allen Restaurant, The
Le Café Arnold
Lindy's
Little Kitchen, The
Longchamps
Lord & Taylor's Soup Bar
Lorelei
Louis Sherry's Plaza Café at Philharmonic Hall
Mark Twain Riverboat
Mary Elizabeth's
Max's Kansas City
Mayhews
McSorley's Old Ale House
Miller's

Mont d'Or
Morgen's Restaurant
Nat Simon's Penguin Room
Old Garden, The
Pablo's
Pappas
Patricia Murphy's Candelight Restaurant
Paul Revere's Tavern and Chop House
Penthouse Club
P. J. Clarke's
P. J. Moriarty
Plaza Hotel:
Edwardian Room
Oak Room
Plush Burger
President
Press Box
Prime Burger
Proof of the Pudding
Red Coach Grill
Reuben's
Rosoff's
Running Footman
Sardi's
Sardi's East
Schaefer's
Schrafft's Restaurants
Serendipity 3
Sign of the Dove
Stouffer's
Student Prince
Talisman, The
Tavern on the Green
Texas Chili Parlor
Tin Lizzie Restaurant, The
Tip Toe Inn
Tony's Wife
Toots Shor
Top of the Six's
Tower Suite
Town House, The
Trefner's Restaurant
"21"
University Restaurant, The
Waldorf-Astoria:
The Bull and Bear
Washington Square Inn
Yellowfinger's Butcheria
Ye Waverly Inn
Zoe Chase
Zum Zum

English and Irish

Alfie's
Charley O's Bar and Grill
Cheshire Cheese Restaurant
Dawson's Ha-Penny Bar
English Grill
English Pub, The
Friar Tuck
Jim Downey's
Jimmie Walker's
John Barleycorn Pub
Keen's English Chop House
McBell's
Michael's Pub
P. J. Moriarty
P. J. O'Hara
Publick House

Far Eastern

CHINESE

Asian Pearl
Bernstein-on-Essex-Street
Bill Hong's

Billy Gwon's
Bo Bo
Canton Restaurant
Canton Village
China Bowl, The
Chinese Rathskeller
Chuan Hong Restaurant
Dragon Gate
Dumpling House
Eating Ho
Empire, The
Empress, The
Esther Eng
Flower Drum Restaurant
Foo Chow Restaurant
Four Seas
Gate of Peiping, The
Gold Coin
Golden Coach
Great Shanghai, The
Great Wall
Harbin Inn
Ho Ho Restaurant
Hong Fat Restaurant
House of Chan
House of Louie
House of Meng
Hoy Yuen
Jade Cuckatoo
Jade Palace
Joy Garden
Joy Luck Coffee Shop
King Dragon
King Wu
Koon Shing Tea House
Lee's Restaurant
Lichee Tree, The
Lin Heong
Long River
Lotus, The
Lotus Eaters
Lotus Eaters Fifth
Lum's Garden
Mandarin House, The
Mandarin House East
Marco Polo
Moon Palace
New Moon Inn
New Shun Lee Restaurant
Ningpo Restaurant
Nom Wah Tea Parlor
Oriental Pearl
Pagoda Restaurant
Pearl's Chinese Restaurant
Peking House
Port Arthur
Quon Luck Restaurant
Sam Wo
Say Eng Look
Shanghai Café
Shanghai d'Or
Shanghai East
Shanghai Garden
Shanghai Village
Shun Lee
Shun Lee Dynasty
Sing Wu
Six Happiness
Sun Luck East
Sun Luck Gourmet
Sun Luck Imperial
Sun Luck Queens
Susy Wong
Tai Yat Low
Temple Garden, The
Tien Tsin
Tinghatsak
Tom's Garden Restaurant
Tom's Shangri-La
Wah Kee Restaurant
Wo Kee
Wo Ping

Yen King
Yen Luck
Ying's
Young China

JAPANESE

Aki Dining Room
Benihana East
Benihana of Tokyo
Fuji Restaurant
Hide Sukiyaki
Japanese Steak House
Kabuki
Kamehachi
Kitcho Restaurant
Kobe Steak House
Miyako
Nippon
Saito
Suehiro Restaurant
Takeda Restaurant
Tamura Restaurant
Tokyo Sukiyaki House
Tonkatsu
Tsuruya

KOREAN

Arirang House

INDIAN

Ceylon India Inn
India House Restaurant
Karachi
Kashmir Restaurant
Pak-India Curry House
Rajmahal Restaurant

POLYNESIAN

Gauguin Room, The
Tiki Village, The
Trader Vic's

PHILIPPINE

Philippine Garden, The

French, Belgian, Swiss, Dutch

À la Fourchette
Annette's Le Petit Veau
Au Canari d'Or
Au Steak Pommes Frites
Baroque
Beaujolais
Belcrep
Brasserie
Brittany du Soir
Brussels Restaurant
Café Argenteuil
Café Brittany
Café Chauveron
Café de France
Café de Sports
Café du Soir
Café Europa
Café Français
Café Saint Denis
Chalet Suisse
Champlain Restaurant
Charles à la Pomme Soufflé
Charles V
Charles French Restaurant
Châteaubriand
Château Henri IV

Mon Paris
Mont d'Or
Mont St. Michel Restaurant
Parisien
Passy, The
Per Bacco
Pergola des Artistes
Pierre au Tunnel
Pierre Hotel
Pierre's
Quo Vadis
Rainbow Room
Restaurant Laurent
Rita Dimitri's La Chansonnette
St. Germain Restaurant
Siro's
Sutter's French Café
Tant Mieux
37th Street Hideaway
Tout Va Vien
"21"
Voisin

German and Middle-European

Blaue Donau
Blue Ribbon
Budapest Hungarian Restaurant
Café Geiger
Café Hindenburg
Chardas
Corner at Margaret's
Czechoslovak Praha
86th Street Brauhaus
Green Tree, The
Hanover Square Restaurant
Jager House
Janssen's
Kleine Konditorei
La Galette
Lorelei
Lüchow's
Old Hungary Restaurant
Paprika
Pilsner Restaurant
Ruc Restaurant
Schaefer's
Student Prince
Swiss Inn
Three Hussars
Tik Tak Hungarian
Vasata
White House Restaurant
Zetti Hungarian Restaurant
Zum Zum

Italian

Adano
Aldo and Eddie Rapallo Restaurant
Alfredo of New York
Amato's Italian Restaurant
Angelina's
Antica Roma
Antolotti's
Asti
Baccarà Restaurant
Ballato Restaurant
Barbetta Restaurant
Bianchi and Margherita
Bruno's Italian Restaurant
Ca d'Oro
Café Lucca
Café Renaissance
Camillo
Capri Restaurant
Caracalla
Carolina

Casa di Pre
Casa Johnny
Casa Mario
Chez Cardinale
Chez Vous
Christo's
Cyrano
Damon's
D'Angelo's
Delfino
Del Pezzo
Delsomma
Due Mondi
Eduardo's
Esplanade, The
Fagiano Restaurant
Famous Kitchen
Ferdi's
Finale, The
Fontana di Trevi
Forlini's Restaurant
Frank Leone's
Fusco's
Gaetano's Ristorante
Gatti's
Gene's
Giambelli
Giambelli 50th
Gian Marino's
Gino's Restaurant
Giordano Restaurant
Giovanna
Golden Horn
Gondola
Grand Ticino
Grotta Azzurra
Guido
House of Milano
Il Bambino
Isle of Capri
Italianissimo
Italian Pavilion
Jenedi's
Joe and Rose
Joe's
Joe's Restaurant
John's Restaurant
Julius Lombardi
Jumble Shop Steak House
La Fortuna
La Groceria
L'Aiglon
La Locanda
La Maganette
Lanza Restaurant
La Petite Maison
La Piazzetta
La Scala
La Stella
La Strada
La Strada East
La Venere West
Le Alpi
Le Café Arnold
Leone's
Louise
Louise Jr.
Luna's Restaurant
Mama Laura Restaurant
Manganaro's and Manganaro's
Hero-Boy Restaurant
Marchi's
Maria
Mario
Mario's Villa Borghese
Mario's Villa d'Este
Marnel's Restaurant
Marta Restaurant
Marta's
Mary's
Mercurio
Mike Manuche

Minetta Tavern
Mona Trattoria
Monte's Restaurant
Nicola Paone
Original Joe's Restaurant
Orsini's
Oscar's Delmonico
Parioli, Romanissimo
Parisien
Paul and Jimmy's Place
Per Bacco
Pete's Tavern
Phil's Cocktail Lounge and Restaurant
Piccolo Mondo
Pietro's
Piro's
Pizzeria alla Napoletana
Pompeian Café and Restaurant, The
Portofino
Quo Vadis
Rattazzi
Renato
Renato East
Rex Restaurant
Ristorante Puglia
Rocco Restaurant
Roma di Notte
Romeo Salta
Rosetta's Restaurant
Rugantino
San Marco
San Marino
San Remo
Santa Lucia
Sardi's
Sardi's East
Savoia
Sempione
Sixty Eight Restaurant
Spark's Pub South
Supreme Macaroni Company
Teddy's Restaurant
37th Street Hideaway
Tomaldo Restaurant
Tony's Italian Kitchen
Trattoria
Unicorn, The
Valentino's
Vesuvio Restaurant
Via Margutta
Via Veneto
Villa Doria
Villa Pensa
Vincent Petrosino

Jewish

Bernstein-on-Essex-Street
Carnegie Delicatessen and Restaurant
Ershowsky Deli
Gaiety East
Hyde Park Restaurant
Katz's Delicatessen
Lindy's
Max's Restaurant
Morgen's Restaurant
Paprika
Parkway East
Phil Gluckstern's
Ratner's
Reuben's
Smokehouse, The
Solowey's
Stage Delicatessen
Steinberg's
Tip Toe Inn

Near and Middle East

Athena East
Athenian Restaurant, The
Balkan Armenian Restaurant
Beirut Restaurant
Cedars of Lebanon
Dardanelles Armenian Restaurant
Electra
Golden Horn
Harout's
Hellenic Pallas
Hye Oriental Food Shop
Jimmy's Greek-American Restaurant
Keneret
Molfetas Cafeteria
Near East Restaurant
Palace d'Orient
Palladium
Pantheon Restaurant
Paradise Inn
Piraeus, My Love
Sayat Nova
Sheik Restaurant, The
Son of the Sheik
Sultan's Table, The

Russian

Mirko
Russian Bear
Russian Tea Room

Scandinavian

Copenhagen
Nyborg and Nelson
Old Denmark
Scandia
Stockholm Restaurant
Three Crowns
Troll Smorebrod Shoppe

Seafood Houses

Blue Sea
Boat House, The
Captain's Table, The
Cavanagh's Restaurant
Christ Cella
Davy Jones Sea Food House
Emil's
Fin 'n Claw
Fisherman's Net
Gage and Tollner
Gloucester House
Grand Central Terminal
Harvey's Sea Food House
King of the Sea
Kippy's
Lobster, The
Nautilus, The
Oscar's Salt of the Sea
Pappas
Rick's Sea Food House
Sea-Fare of the Aegean
Sea-Fare Restaurant
Sea Hunt
Sloppy Louie's
Sweet's Restaurant
Vincent Petrosino
Vincent's Clam Bar
Vorst's Century Sea Grill
Wards Black Bass
White's Sea Food Restaurant
Whyte's
Whyte's Downtown

Spanish and Latin-American

Alamo Chile House, The
Brazilian Coffee Restaurant
Café Renaissance
Casa Brasil
Castilla Restaurant and Bar
El Charro
El Cortijo
El Faro
El Matador
El Parador Café
El Quijote
El Radiante
Fonda La Paloma
Fornos
Fundador
Good Table, The
Granados Restaurant
Hacienda La Paloma
Jai-Alai
La Cabana
La Concha
La Fonda del Sol
Liborio
Mañana
Mayan Room, The
Old Mexico Restaurant
Oviedo
Pablo's
Pancho Villa's
Sevilla
Spanish Pavilion, The
Toledo Restaurant
Tortilla Flat
Trini
Un Rincon Argentino
Victor's Café
Xochitl Mexican Restaurant

Steak Houses

Al and Dick's Steak House
Assembly Steak House
Benihana East
Benihana of Tokyo
Black Angus
Broadway Joe Steak House
Cattleman, The
Cavanagh's Restaurant
Christ Cella
Dan Dowd's Steak House
Danny's Hide-A-Way
Davy Jones Sea Food House
Frankie and Johnnie
Gage and Tollner
Gallagher's
Henry Stampler's Filet Mignon
Jack Delaney's Steak House
Jim Downey's
Johnny Johnston's Charcoal Room
Jumble Shop Steak House
Kenny's Steak Pub
Kippy's
Le Steak
Manero's Steak House
Manny Wolf's
Marsh's Steak Place
McCarthy's Famous Steak House
O. Henry's Steak House
Old Forge Steak House
Old Homestead
Palm Restaurant
Pen and Pencil, The
Peter Luger
Peter's Backyard
Steak Casino
Steak Joint, The
Steak Place, The
Walsh's Steak House
Ye Olde Chop House

The New York Times Guide to Dining Out in New York

CREDIT CARD INFORMATION

Many dining establishments honor various credit cards. For the convenience of patrons, reviews of these restaurants are followed by one or more of the following keys:

AE *American Express*

CB *Carte Blanche*

DC *Diners Club*

In the following listings, if no closing day is indicated, the restaurants are normally open seven days a week.

ABSINTHE HOUSE

130 West 48th Street CO *5-6571*

Perhaps it is wrong to judge this restaurant on the basis of its name, but there must be many people from New Orleans who come here in hope of finding such dishes as a splendid shrimp creole or oysters Bienville or trout Marguery. The menu has cartoons of a steamboat and Jean Lafitte and a streetcar named Desire. And the shutters out front are a little tattered. But any genuine resemblance more or less ends there. The shrimps rémoulade here are drenched in a Russian-mayonnaise-type thing whose only acquaintance with the New Orleans rémoulade is an overdose of mustard. The pecan pie on one visit was topped with whipped cream that had the taste of refrigerator storage, and the crust was both soggy and tough. The filling itself was tolerable. Otherwise, the foods are acceptable but not memorable. The Philadelphia mixed grill had very good broiled chicken but a thin, tough, overcooked piece of calves' liver. The beef à la mode was edible, but the potato pancake served with it wasn't. All dishes are à la carte with main courses at lunch from about $2.75 to $5.75; at dinner from about $3.95 to $6.75. *Cocktails, wines. Luncheon is not served on Saturday. Closed Sunday and all other holidays. Closed Saturday and Sunday during the summer.*

★★ ACT I

Allied Chemical Tower, Times Square *695-1880*
(15th and 16th floors)

This relatively new restaurant is far and away the best-looking restaurant in the vicinity of Times Square, an area of the city not generally known for elegance. Act I provides absorbing views of the city below: spires, hotels, water towers, commercial buildings, the Hudson and glimpses of Central Park's trees by day; the gaudy, flashy necklace of Broadway and Seventh Avenue by night. The view is particularly appealing when it rains and the drops ricochet from the restaurant windows. The mystery is why amid some fairly luxurious trappings and carpeted surroundings there is such an abundance of plastic flowers and plants. The menus are simple and well tailored, and the food can be excellent if rarely distinguished. At noon there are sandwiches and down-to-earth dishes like scrambled eggs and grilled meats. The cost is from about $2.75 to $7.25. In the evening there are à la carte grilled dishes and roast ribs of beef that cost from about $5.95 to $7.25. In the evening there is also a "Continental Dinner" priced at $6.75. Supper is served from 10 p.m. to midnight. *Cocktails, wines. Closed Sunday, New Year's Day, Memorial Day, July 4, Labor Day, Thanksgiving and Christmas.*

AE CB DC

★ ADANO

115 West 48th Street CO 5-9336

This is a long-established Neapolitan restaurant in the theater district. The food is prepared and seasoned with a somewhat heavy hand, but the restaurant is frequently crowded and noisy. With all its lack of subtlety, the Adano's kitchen turns out creditable hot or cold antipasto including stuffed green peppers, stuffed zucchini and mushrooms. The menu is by and large standard, with its various veal and poultry dishes. There are complete luncheons priced from about $1.80 to $5.75. The à la carte menu lists main courses from about $2.25 to $6. *Cocktails, wines. Luncheon is not served Saturday and Sunday.*

AE DC

★ AKI DINING ROOM

420 West 119th Street UN *4-5970*

The Aki is a long-time favorite with the faculty and students of Columbia University. It is one of the best Japanese restaurants uptown and has seating in the Western style. The menu is reasonably authentic, from sashimi (raw fish) to sunomono (salad), and the same menu is used for both lunch and dinner. Complete meals from $1.25 to $2.95. There is frequently a wait for tables in the evening. *Beer and Japanese wine. Closed Monday.*

★★ A LA FOURCHETTE

342 West 46th Street CI *5-9744*

This small, unpretentious French-style restaurant serves mostly provincial-style dishes. Daily specialties such as veal chipolata (veal balls and tiny sausages in wine sauce served with rice and vegetables), cassoulet Toulousain and brook trout amandine arc listed on a blackboard. Complete à la carte menus are also available at luncheon and dinner. Luncheon entrees from about $2.25; dinner main courses from about $3.50 to $6. *Cocktails, wines. Luncheon is not served Saturday. Closed Sunday and the month of August.*

★ ALAMO CHILE HOUSE, THE

142 West 44th Street CI *5-4288*

This is a small, crowded, noisy restaurant with a decor that is the antithesis of the "don't fence me in" school. The chile is hot, and the beer, whether domestic or Mexican, dark or light, is ice cold. For those who fancy such food, a bowl of chile without beans costs $1.10 and makes an excellent meal with a side dish of rice and a liberal sprinkling of raw onion. The most frequently ordered dish appears to be an enchilada and chile combination that costs $1.25, but it is not always as hot (from a temperature standpoint) as it might be. *Beers and soft drinks. Closed Sunday.*

AL AND DICK'S STEAK HOUSE

151 West 54th Street PL *7-0095*

It is a point in this steak house's favor that it is close to Broadway. The menu is à la carte throughout the day, with main luncheon courses from about $2.25 to $6.25; main dinner dishes from about $2.25 to $6.25. *Cocktails, wines. Luncheon is not served Saturday. Closed Sunday and, during July and August, Saturday also. Closed New Year's Day, Labor Day, Thanksgiving, Christmas and the first two weeks of July.*

AE CB DC

ALBERT

42 East 11th Street OR *3-3890*

This is a Greenwich Village restaurant with a pseudo-French atmosphere and a kitchen that is studiously middle-class. The specialty of the house is steaks of ordinary quality. There is one menu for luncheon and dinner and it lists complete meals at $3.25. *Cocktails, wines.*

★★ AL COOPER'S HERALD SQUARE RESTAURANT

130 West 36th Street CH *4-2828*

This is a neat and relatively expensive restaurant that admirably reflects the flavor of Manhattan. The service is prompt, the portions are generous and the food is generally first-rate. There are such specialties as prime beef tongue, Rumanian pastrami and boiled beef. Both luncheon and dinner are à la carte with main luncheon courses from $3.25 to $7.95; main dinner courses from about $4.75 to $8.50. *Cocktails, wines. Luncheon is not served Saturday. Closed Sunday, New Year's Day, Washington's Birthday, Memorial Day, July 4, Labor Day, Thanksgiving and Christmas.*

AE CB DC

★ ALDO AND EDDIE RAPALLO RESTAURANT

834 Second Avenue MU *3-1050 and* MU *4-8956*
(between 44th and 45th Streets)

If anyone wished to capture for a stage set the atmosphere and feeling of a small, well-received Italian restaurant, he need go no farther than the Rapallo. It has all the clichés, from minestrone to cannelloni to piped-in music and the graphic oils on the walls. The food is agreeable, however, and it is a friendly place. All the dishes are à la carte with main luncheon courses from about $2.25 for spaghetti with meat sauce to $4.50 for broiled minute steak; main dinner dishes from about $2.50 for manicotti to $6 for filet mignon. *Cocktails, wines. On Saturday the restaurant opens at 4 p.m. Closed Sunday, New Year's Day, Washington's Birthday, Memorial Day, July 4, Labor Day, Thanksgiving and Christmas.*
AE CB DC

★ ALFIE'S

1290 Third Avenue (at 74th Street) *628-6265*

This is a recently opened and popular place with a fairly steady beat from a jukebox. There is a neat decor with a birdcage and, over the bar, wooden nudes in bas-relief. The menu is more or less English pub, with its fish and chips, prime ribs of beef and so on. The quality of the food is good, but it should be better. For example, the shrimp in a cocktail were tender and freshly cooked but still warm from the kettle. The prime ribs of beef were admirably rare but tepid. A beef on skewers came off very well. The smoked trout recently listed on the menu was not available. All dishes are à la carte with main courses at midday from 95 cents for a cheese omelet to $2.95 for steak and eggs; in the evening from $1.50 for the fish and chips to $3.95 for the ribs of beef. *Cocktails, wines.*

★★ ALFREDO OF NEW YORK

240 West 56th Street JU *6-7975*

One of the pleasantest of North Italian restaurants, and at its best one of the finest. The homemade fettucine is extraordinary. The quality overall can vary. Complete luncheons from about $2.50 to $3.75. Dinners à la carte with entrees from about $2.50 to $6. *Cocktails, Italian wines. Luncheon is not served Saturday. Closed Sunday, New Year's Day, Labor Day and Christmas. Reservations recommended.*

AE DC

ALGONQUIN HOTEL

59 West 44th Street MU *7-4400*

The Algonquin has two of the most civilized dining rooms in the Times Square–Broadway area. They are the ★★**Oak Room**, with its masculine appeal, and the ★★**Rose Room**, which is more intimate. The surroundings are pleasant, the menu is well varied and the food, although it may not be illustrious, is nonetheless agreeable. Recommended in particular is the roast beef with Yorkshire pudding, available in the evening. Both luncheon and dinner menus are à la carte with main courses from about $2.10 for scrambled eggs to $7.85 for planked steak Algonquin. Supper is served from 10 p.m. to 1 a.m. *Cocktails, wines. Closed Sunday, New Year's Day, Washington's Birthday, Memorial Day, July 4, Thanksgiving and Christmas.*

AE DC

AL SCHACHT'S RESTAURANT

10 East 52nd Street PL *9-8570*

Al Schacht's moved last year to a new location and, if anything, it is a bit more elegant than before. It is still a gregarious, back-slapping place with a cigar-smoking clientele, oversize baseball photostats on the wall and colorful waiters with Brooklyn accents. In the evening there is a piano player with an agreeable jazz repertory, and the quality of the steaks is generally

excellent. The roquefort salad dressing has no special distinction, and the cole slaw was, on a recent visit, saltless. Worse, one order of sliced sirloin, although perfectly cooked, was brought to the table at room temperature. All dishes are à la carte. Main dishes at midday are from $2.95 to $4.75; in the evening from about $3.75 to $8. *Cocktails, wines. On Saturday and Sunday the restaurant opens at 5 p.m.*
AE DC

★ AMATO'S ITALIAN RESTAURANT

301 West 47th Street 245-9498

This is a most agreeable and inexpensive restaurant in the Broadway area. The restaurant incorporates such bad features as piped-in music, wine glasses that are too small and a brodo that smacks of bouillon cubes. But the food, otherwise, is generally excellent, and the restaurant is as much like a sidewalk café in Italy as you're apt to find in the city. The windows open onto the street and the traffic, there are corny Venetian murals, and the place deserves more patronage than it gets. Amato's is open for dinner only. The menu is à la carte with main courses from about $1.10 for spaghetti with tomato sauce to $3.75 for lobster fra diavolo. *Cocktails, wines. Closed Sunday.*
CB DC

★ ANGELINA'S

41 Greenwich Avenue CH 3-9650

A small, comfortable Italian restaurant with plain but palatable cuisine. The breaded pork chop is excellent and the tomato sauces are good. The same à la carte menu serves for both luncheon and dinner with main courses from about $1.30 to $4.50. There is a complete prix fixe dinner with main courses from about $2.60 to $5.35. *Cocktails, wines. Closed Tuesday.*
CB DC

★ ANNETTE'S LE PETIT VEAU

982 Second Avenue *355-8509*
(between 49th and 50th Streets)

There is much to recommend this restaurant, one of the most popular in the Beekman–Sutton Place area. If all the foods that appear at table were on a par with the main courses, all would be well. The main dishes, such as well-glazed duck à l'orange and veal à l'Annette, are prepared with considerable care. The hors d'oeuvres, on the other hand, are studiously pedestrian, and the kitchen serves sodden, water-logged green beans and overcooked, watery peas in typical New York bistro style. The menu will seem familiar to most hands with its omelets, sole amandine and so on. Annette's well-worn premises include tile floors, old-fashioned booths and crazily hung black-and-white photographs. The cost of a complete luncheon is from $2.95 to $4.35; of a complete dinner from about $5.50 to $8. *Cocktails, wines. Luncheon is not served Saturday. Closed Sunday.*

AE CB DC

★★ ANTICA ROMA

94 Baxter Street CA *6-9847*

There is an uncommonly decent neighborhood restaurant with an Italian kitchen. There is nothing fancy about the place, but the food is prepared with care and caution and it is reasonably priced. The tomato sauces are not distinguished, but they are palatable; the osso buco is very good and so is the mixed fried seafood. The vegetables are excellent. All dishes are à la carte with main courses at midday from about $1 for spaghetti marinara to $2.10 for the osso buco. In the evening prices range from about $1.40 for spaghetti to $4.95 for sirloin steak. *Cocktails, wines. Closed Sunday, New Year's Day, July 4, Labor Day, Thanksgiving and Christmas.*

★ ANTLERS

67 Wall Street HA *2-4393*

This is a well-known restaurant in New York's financial district. The menu is largely American, but there are international touches such as pig's knuckles, sauerkraut and curry. The food is hearty and good. All dishes are à la carte with main luncheon dishes from about $1.90 to $6.75; main dinner courses from about $2.45 to $6.75. *Cocktails, limited wine list. Closed Saturday, Sunday and holidays.*

AE DC

★ ANTOLOTTI'S

337 East 49th Street MU *8-9668 and* EL *5-9196*

A favorite and therefore frequently crowded North Italian restaurant. The menu is somewhat conventional, with its veal and pasta dishes, but all in all the foods are prepared with a good deal of finesse. The service too is above average. Luncheons are à la carte. Main luncheon dishes with spaghetti or salad from about $2 to $5.50. Dinners are both prix fixe and à la carte. Complete dinners from about $5 to $7.50; à la carte dishes from about $2.25 to $5.75. *Cocktails, wines. Luncheon is not served on Saturday and Sunday. Closed Christmas, New Year's and Easter.*

★★ ARIRANG HOUSE

30 West 56th Street LT *1-9698 and* LT *1-9699*

This is one of the most unusual and interesting restaurants in Manhattan. The food is Korean, well seasoned and a welcome change from that found in run-of-the-mill French and Italian restaurants in the city. There is a large, split-level dining room, and the waitresses wear traditional dresses without ostentation. The menu has numerous fish, poultry, pork and beef dishes, the best known of which must be the sin sul lo, in which various foods are simmered in a broth cooked over charcoal at the table. The main menu is principally à la

carte with entrees from $2.25 to $3.75. There is also a luncheon menu with complete luncheons at $2 and à la carte dishes from $1.30 to $1.60. Complete dinners cost from $4.50 to $5.50. *Cocktails, wines. Closed Sunday.*
DC

★ ARTIST AND WRITERS RESTAURANT

213 West 40th Street LO *3-2424*

This restaurant, with a comfortable, old-fashioned decor, is a favorite haunt of numerous people in the newspaper field. To many of them the restaurant is known affectionately as Bleeck's, after the original owner, Jack Bleeck, now deceased. The same menu serves for both lunch and dinner with main entrees from about $2.10 to $6.40. Supper is served from 10 p.m. to 1 a.m. *Cocktails, wines, draught beer. Closed Saturday, Sunday, New Year's Day, Washington's Birthday, Memorial Day, July 4, Labor Day, Thanksgiving and Christmas.*
AE CB DC

ASIAN PEARL

959 First Avenue (near 52nd Street) *421-2322*

This is another Chinese restaurant whose mediocrity is underscored because it is in a city with Chinese restaurants of general excellence. The soup sampled on one occasion was watery and the remainder of the menu so bland that there was a temptation to use soy sauce, a gesture that would offend the sensibilities of a first-class Chinese chef. There are complete luncheons from about 99 cents to $3.25. The à la carte menu lists entrees from about $2 for shredded pork with bean sprouts to $4.75 for lobster Cantonese. *Cocktails, wines. Luncheon is not served Saturday and Sunday.*

★★ ASSEMBLY STEAK HOUSE

207 East 43rd Street MU 2-4120

In an area famous for its steak houses, the Assembly ranks with the best for top-quality beef and lobster generally well prepared. A relatively small and popular restaurant, it tends to be noisy at peak periods. Complete luncheons from $2.95; à la carte entrees from $2.25. Dinner entrees from $3.95 for swordfish to $14.95 for sirloin steak or chateaubriand for two. *Cocktails, wines. Luncheon is not served Saturday, Sunday and holidays. Reservations suggested.*

AE CB DC

ASTI

13 East 12th Street AL 5-9773

Tourists and a host of New Yorkers seem fascinated with the opera-participation restaurant where guests join the waiters in renditions from Puccini, Verdi and others. The menu is, of course, Italian, and the cost of a complete dinner is from about $6.50 to $7.75. Luncheon is not served. There is an entertainment tax after 7:30 p.m. *Cocktails, wines. Closed Monday and July 1 through Labor Day.*

AE CB DC

★ ATHENA EAST

1230 Second Avenue LE 5-5548 *and* LE 5-5549
(between 64th and 65th Streets)

There is better Greek food in a few other restaurants in Manhattan, but this one is the largest and, for what it's worth, the most stylish. The Athena East has a certain noisy charm and should appeal to those who enjoy the restaurants of the Plaka section of Athens. There is music, music, music, very loud and to some ears no doubt festive. The kitchen is competent whether in making mezedakia (the Greek appetizers) or more substantial main courses such as baked striped bass or the baked macaroni dish called pastitsio. The Athena East is a trifle

expensive, with à la carte dishes in the evening from about $3.25 to $7.50. There is a complete dinner priced at $7.50. *Cocktails, wines. Open for dinner only. Reservations suggested.*
AE CB DC

★ ATHENIAN RESTAURANT, THE

709 Eighth Avenue LT *1-1667 and* CI *5-9966*
(between 44th and 45th Streets)

This is one of several restaurants with Greek cuisine that have opened in the Broadway area in recent years. The food is moderately priced and well prepared. The same à la carte menu serves for both luncheon and dinner, with main dishes from $1.25 to $6.25. In the evening there is Greek music which is, by some standards, fairly subdued. Supper is served from 9 p.m. to 3 a.m, *Cocktails, wines. Closed Monday.*
DC

★ AU CANARI D'OR

134 East 61st Street TE *8-7987*

The character of this place changes. Sometimes it seems like a tearoom for hungry shoppers; at other times it seems quite respectable. The trouble may be an exceedingly limited service staff, with only two or three people to get the food to tables on time. A recent crêpe Canari filled with chicken was good and well gratinéed, and a serving of mussels maison was excellent. Then the food varies from an ordinary chicken Marengo to a generous portion of well-seasoned cold salmon with an admirable sour cream and cucumber sauce and green mayonnaise. There are both prix fixe and à la carte menus. At midday à la carte items are priced from about $2.25 to $3; complete luncheons from about $3 to $4.25. In the evening à la carte items are priced from about $3.50 to $5.75; complete dinners from about $4.50 to $6.75. *Cocktails, wines. Closed Sunday and Monday.*

★ AU STEAK POMMES FRITES

22 West 56th Street CO *5-8743*

This is a conventional and popular bistro with a reasonably priced menu. The luncheon menu is French and Italian, the dinner menu primarily French. The food is generally good and very much like that in a dozen other restaurants of the same genre. There are complete luncheons from about $1.50 to $1.75; complete dinners from about $2.50 to $3.75. *Cocktails, wines. Closed New Year's Day, July 4, Thanksgiving and Christmas.*

BACCARÁ RESTAURANT

203 East 45th Street MU *2-4505*

This is a relatively small, unpretentious restaurant with a menu and kitchen that are generally undistinguished. The restaurant has à la carte menus at both luncheon and dinner, with main courses at luncheon from about $2.25 to $5.50 and at dinner from about $2.60 to $6.25. *Cocktails, wines. Luncheon is not served Saturday. Closed Sunday, Thanksgiving and Christmas.*

AE CB DC

★ BALKAN ARMENIAN RESTAURANT

129 East 27th Street MU *9-7925*

New York contains several Armenian restaurants, and this one has interesting food. Lamb, chicken, eggplant, and chick-peas occur frequently on the menu. The food is simple, somewhat heavily spiced, but good. Luncheons are à la carte with main courses from about $1.80 to $3. Dinners are both à la carte and prix fixe. Complete seven-course dinners from about $4.25 to $5.75; à la carte dishes in the evening from about $2.25 to $2.60. *Cocktails, wines. Dinner is served from noon on Saturday. Closed Sunday, New Year's Day, Memorial Day, Labor Day and Christmas. Reservations accepted.*

AE DC

★★ BALLATO RESTAURANT

55 East Houston Street CA *6-9683*

This is one of the best of Manhattan's small Italian restaurants. It is neat, the kitchen is above average and the pasta dishes and tomato sauces are excellent. The same à la carte menu serves all day, with main dishes from about $2.25 to $6.75. *Beer, wines. Closed Sunday, New Year's Day and Christmas. Reservations recommended.*

★★ BARBETTA RESTAURANT

321 West 46th Street CI *6-9171*

Barbetta, which has been in New York for several score years, may be the most elegantly decorated Italian restaurant in town. There are wall sconces, chairs with needlework upholstery and discreetly illuminated table lamps. The food may not always ravish the palate, but it is worthwhile nonetheless, particularly the chicken, veal and pasta dishes. The tortellini alla panna, or small meat-stuffed pasta, is good but would be better served in a pure cream-and-cheese sauce rather than one slightly thickened with flour. Complete luncheons from about $3.25 to $3.95. Dinners are à la carte with main courses from about $4.50 to $5.75. *Cocktails, wines. Closed Sunday.*

★★★ BAROQUE

14 East 53rd Street EL *5-4195*

Among the numerous French restaurants in Manhattan, a few have special eminence. Baroque is one of these. It is somewhat small and crowded at times, but the menu is excellent and the service well above par. If there is a fault to be found with the restaurant, it is that the tables are too close together and the portions of food are frequently gross. Luncheon entrees from about $3 to $6; dinner entrees from about $3.50 to $7.75. *Cocktails, fine wines. Luncheon is not served Saturday. Closed Sunday and major holidays. Reservations frequently essential.*

AE CB DC

★ BEAUJOLAIS

28 West 56th Street CI *5-0525*

This is a small French restaurant with a simple but pleasant decor. The relatively small staff offers friendly, albeit sometimes hurried, service. The menu follows the usual pattern for restaurants of this genre, but a few notable specialties of the house generally show care in preparation. The coquilles St. Jacques appetizer on the dinner menu and the main dishes quenelles de turbot Nantua and caneton au Calvados are recommended. Complete luncheons from $2.75 to $3.50; complete dinners from $4.75 for brook trout to $15 for chateaubriand for two. *Cocktails, wines. Luncheon is not served Sunday. Closed New Year's Day, Thanksgiving and Christmas.*

AE CB DC

BEEF AND BOURBON RESTAURANT

66 Park Avenue (at 38th Street) MU *3-0135*

This restaurant serves American cuisine. At luncheon the menu is à la carte with entrees from about $2.50. In the evening there is an à la carte menu which lists entrees from $2.95 and a prix fixe menu with complete meals from about $5.25. *Cocktails, wines. On Saturday the restaurant opens at 5:30 p.m. Closed Sunday.*

AE DC

★ BEIRUT RESTAURANT

43 West 32nd Street OX *5-9898*

This is the latest addition to the roster of New York's Middle East restaurants, and the food here, as in many another, is very good, particularly the appetizers. These would include the baba gannouj, or eggplant salad, hummus bi tahini, which is puréed chick-peas with sesame oil, and grape leaves. The restaurant's laban, or yogurt, is excellent. The lamb dishes are somewhat standard. The decor is a bit garish, and a noisy jukebox seems to be in constant use. There is a club luncheon, minus appetizer,

that costs $1.50. Complete dinners from $2.95 to $3.25; à la carte dishes from about 90 cents to $2.20. *Cocktails, wines.*
AE CB DC

★ **BELCREP**
47 West 44th Street 986-6678 and 687-9535
New York seems to become increasingly studded with variations of European pancake houses, and one of the most recent to open here is the Belcrep, which offers not only pancakes but waffles as well. The crêpes are large, thin wafers, generally stuffed with such fillings as crab meat or creamed chicken or vegetables, and they can be good. At times, however, the fillings may be only lukewarm, as on one occasion in the case of a crêpe stuffed with eggs, ham and spinach. The Belgian waffles, first introduced en masse at the recent New York World's Fair, are excellent, and the various accompaniments for the dessert include vanilla, coffee and chocolate ice cream or various fruits. The cost of dishes on the Belcrep menu is from 50 cents for an ungarnished crêpe to $2.50 for a crêpe filled with caviar or foie gras. There is also a limited luncheon and dinner menu with à la carte main courses at midday from $1.25 to $2.50; complete dinners at $3.25. The Belcrep is a long, "railroad"-shaped room, with checked cloths and pleasant service from the French-speaking service staff. *There is no bar. Closed Sunday.*

★★ **BENIHANA EAST**
120 East 56th Street LT *1-0930*
Like its counterpart, Benihana of Tokyo, this is an interesting Japanese steak house with very good food. The menu includes clear soup with scallions, salad, chicken and steaks. The meats are cooked on a smooth, heavy, flatiron slab in the center of each dining table. At noon à la carte dishes at the Benihana cost from about $2.50 to $4; special luncheons cost $4. In the evening the cost of a

dinner without dessert is from $5 to $6.75. There is also a special dinner that costs $10. *Cocktails, wines. Reservations are recommended. Closed Sunday.*
AE CB DC

★★ BENIHANA OF TOKYO

61 West 56th Street LT *1-0930*

This is a most agreeable Japanese steak house, perhaps the best of its kind in the city. The steak, vegetables and whatever are cooked at the tables, in which are solid metal slabs heated from below. The food is excellent and its appeal seems universal inasmuch as at meal hours there are frequent and lengthy waits for tables. Service is marked by the usual Japanese politesse. Luncheons are à la carte with main courses from $2.50 to $4; special luncheons cost $4. There are dinners without desserts from $5 to $6.75. There is also a special dinner that costs $10. *Cocktails, wines. Reservations are recommended. Open seven days a week. Luncheon is not served on Sunday.*
AE CB DC

★ BERNSTEIN-ON-ESSEX-STREET

135 Essex Street (at Rivington Street) GR *3-3900*

Bernstein's slogan is "Where kashruth is king and quality reigns." This is conceivably the only Jewish-Chinese restaurant in the city. There is chow mein Bernstein and lo mein Bernstein, and the food is not bad at all. There is also an elaborate Jewish menu with such specialties as stuffed cabbage, Rumanian pastrami and chopped chicken liver sandwiches. The menu for lunch and dinner is both prix fixe and à la carte with complete meals from $2.90. The Chinese dishes cost from about $2.25 to $6. *Beers and kosher wines. Closed from Friday evening to Saturday at sundown and on Jewish holidays.*

BIANCHI AND MARGHERITA

186 West 4th Street CH *2-2756*
(between Avenue of the Americas and Seventh Avenue)

Here there is music in generous supply. This is one of those restaurants that encourage all hands to join in or listen to operatic arias, and, like the food, the voices could be better. Those who enjoy such impromptu entertainment, however, rate Bianchi and Margherita as A No. 1. The cuisine is, of course, Italian, and the dinner menu is both prix fixe and à la carte. Complete four-course dinners from about $5.25 to $6.75. *Cocktails, wines. Open for dinner only. Closed Sunday.*

AE CB DC

BILL HONG'S

133 West 52nd Street LT *1-6730*

Chinese cuisine that is good but not distinguished is served here. Complete luncheons are from about $1.85 to $3.20. Dinners are à la carte, and the à la carte menu is available at all times. As in most Chinese restaurants, the food on the à la carte bill of fare is far more interesting than the prix fixe items. A la carte dishes cost from about $2 to $6.50. *Cocktails, wines. On Sunday the restaurant opens at 3 p.m. Closed Thanksgiving.*

AE DC

BILLY GWON'S

28 West 58th Street MU *8-0670*

A long-established and popular Chinese restaurant with dim lighting and oddments of decoration that include smoked mirrors, wood paneling and gilt strips. The trouble with all the dishes sampled at Gwon's is that they are too bland to be of real interest. The won ton soup with its spinach, mushrooms and pork is very good, but that too needed salt for salvation. There are complete luncheons priced from $1.50 to $3.25. A la carte dishes from about $3 to $5.75. *Cocktails, wines. Open seven days a week.*

★★ BILLY'S

948 First Avenue (near 52nd Street) 355-8920

The wrecker's ball wrecked Billy's, the wonderful Sutton Place landmark, in 1966, and now it has reopened at a new location with many of the sentimentally remembered trappings intact. The same antique paneling, gaslight fixtures, red-checked tablecloths and turn-of-the-century bar are there. The present establishment seems smaller, cleaner, more polished, more civilized, lower ceilinged, less personal. In the move Billy's has lost a good deal of its patina and original charm, but it is still worthwhile and tables are at a premium. At times people stand two deep at the bar waiting their turn. The kitchen, with two exceptions, seems to have maintained its standards. The exceptions are the shrimp, which seem smaller, and the cole slaw, which doesn't seem quite as tasty. The steaks, chops and chicken are excellent. All dishes are à la carte and the cost is from $2.75 for Billy's well-known large hamburger to $6.50 for sirloin. *Cocktails, beer. Open for dinner only.*

AE CB DC

★ BLACK ANGUS

148 East 50th Street PL *9-7454*

Count steaks and chops among the favorite fare of New Yorkers. Here they are served in a typical, if somewhat labyrinthine, setting. Luncheons are both prix fixe and à la carte. Complete luncheons cost approximately $2.85; main courses from about $2.50 to $4.95. Dinners are à la carte with main dishes from about $4.25 to $7.50. *Cocktails, wines. Luncheon is not served Saturday and Sunday.*

AE DC

★ BLAUE DONAU

1623 Second Avenue RH *4-9841*
(between 84th and 85th Streets)

The Blaue Donau, or Blue Danube, is another friendly restaurant where the food is reasonably priced and well cooked in a manner that many refer to as "home style." The restaurant has an excellent suelze, or jellied calf's head, as a first course and very good main dishes that include braised veal shanks and roast duckling. There are luncheons with soup and main course priced from $1.45 to $1.65, and à la carte dinner entrees from $1.55 to $4.95. *Cocktails, wines. Dinner is served Sunday from noon.*

BLUE MILL TAVERN

50 Commerce Street CH *3-7114*

The commendable things about this Greenwich Village restaurant are the neighborhood, which is colorful, the service, which is generally good, and the modest prices of the food, which is undistinguished but palatable. The restaurant is neat and is near the Cherry Lane Theater. The menu is plain and à la carte, with main courses from $1.40 to $4.25. *Cocktails, Italian and Portuguese wines. On Saturday the restaurant opens at 5 p.m. Closed Sunday, New Year's Day, Memorial Day, Labor Day, Thanksgiving, Christmas and two or three weeks in August. Reservations accepted.*

BLUE RIBBON

145 West 44th Street JU *2-4898*

This restaurant has a German-American menu and rather heavy surroundings. The odor of sauerkraut seems omnipresent, but the restaurant is convenient to several Broadway theaters. All dishes are à la carte with main luncheon dishes from about $2 to $5.75; dinner entrees from about $2.50 to $5.75. Supper is served from 9 p.m. to 12:30 a.m. *Cocktails, wines. Closed Sunday, July 4 and Christmas.*

★ **BLUE SEA**

135 Third Avenue SP *7-2948 and* OR *4-9882*
(near 15th Street)

There is a dearth of good seafood restaurants between midtown Manhattan and Fulton Street, and this may be the best in that area. A point strongly in its favor is that the fish seems to be of the freshest quality. The whole flounder stuffed with crab meat is cordially recommended. On the other hand, the restaurant is overly bright and overdecorated. There are special luncheons from about $1.65 to $3.50. The à la carte menu lists dishes from about $2.95 to $6.25. *Cocktails, wines. Only à la carte items are available on Sunday, from 11 a.m.*

AE DC

BOAT HOUSE, THE

161 East 54th Street *752-3091*

One thing that the Boat House has in abundance is atmosphere in the dining room. The kitchen is commonplace. There is an oyster-bar-cum-buffet atop a long boat, and most of the dishes look a little fatigued except for the clams on the half shell. Some of the broiled dishes, including red snapper when available, are respectably cooked and a New England clam chowder sampled on one visit was edible if a bit pasty. Salads, desserts and service are all on a par and the less said the better. For both lunch and dinner, à la carte dishes cost from about $2.60 for filet of grey sole to $8.25 for a large lobster. *Cocktails, wines. Closed Sunday during the summer.*

AE CB DC

★★★ **BO BO**

20½ Pell Street WO *2-9458*

The trouble with Bo Bo's, which has food made with a fine Chinese hand, is its extreme popularity. It is a small place, notably not elegant, and at times it is next to impossible to obtain a table. However, the fare is worth waiting for. There is no written menu, and the cost of main dishes at both lunch and dinner is about $2.50. *No alcoholic beverages. Closed for the Chinese New Year.*

★★ BRASSERIE

100 East 53rd Street PL *1-4840*

One of New York's plainest yet most sophisticated restaurants, the Brasserie also has one of the most interesting menus. It is international in scope, and the choucroute garnie may be the best in town. Luncheon and dinner are both prix fixe and à la carte. Complete luncheons from $2.55; complete dinners from $5.25. The Brasserie is open for sandwiches, omelets and the like around the clock, and the restaurant is frequently crowded. *Imported beers; wines by the carafe, cocktails. Reservations are accepted for dinner.*

AE CB DC

BRASS RAIL, THE

100 Park Avenue (at 40th Street) LE *2-1210*
521 Fifth Avenue (at 43rd Street) MU *7-5880*
745 Seventh Avenue (at 49th Street) PL *7-6070*

The menus of The Brass Rail are quite plain and somewhat conventional, with such dishes as spaghetti and potted meat balls, steak sandwiches and grilled meats. The menus are both prix fixe and à la carte with complete luncheons from about $1.95; à la carte main dishes from about $2. Complete dinners from about $3.75; à la carte entrees from about $2.50. *Cocktails, wines. The restaurant on Park Avenue is closed Saturday and Sunday; the one on Fifth Avenue is closed Sunday.*

AE CB DC

★★ BRAZILIAN COFFEE RESTAURANT

70 West 46th Street PL *7-9352*

For anyone with an interest in foreign foods this is an uncommonly rewarding restaurant. It is a simple, raffish place with a jukebox, but the food is on a par with that of the best native restaurants in Rio de Janeiro. Feijoada, the national dish of Brazil, is available Monday, Wednesday and Saturday. The dish is a fascinating mélange of meats and sausage cooked with beans and served with rice, greens and fresh orange sections. Other specialties include shrimp Bahia style with tomatoes and onions, and picadinho, the traditional savory stew served with fried eggs, rice and beans. The same menu serves throughout the day and it is à la carte. The cost of main dishes is about $2 to $3.85. *Beers and wines. Closed Sunday and Christmas.*

DC

★ BRITTANY DU SOIR

800 Ninth Avenue (at 53rd Street) CI *5-9484*

This restaurant is bistro style and has very good French food at modest prices. All dishes are à la carte with main luncheon courses from about $1.95 to $4; dinner entrees from about $2.75 to $5.25. *Cocktails, wines. Closed Sunday, holidays and the last two weeks in July and the first week in August.*

★★ BROADWAY JOE STEAK HOUSE

315 West 46th Street CI *6-6513*

Some of the best-known restaurants in the theater district are packed to capacity before the show only to become mausoleums five minutes before curtain time. This isn't true of Broadway Joe. It is crowded after the overture for a very good reason: it is one of the best steak houses in Manhattan. It is a congenial, unpretentious place with wood-paneled and whitewashed walls, and the service is friendly. More important, however, the sirloin steaks are first-rate and cooked to perfection. The restaurant opens at 4:30 p.m., and there is no menu. In addition to the steak there is a choice of three grilled entrees—chicken, lamb chops or chopped sirloin—served with baked potatoes and salad. The cost is from $4 to $7. First courses include shrimp cocktail ($1.75), marinated herring ($1), onion soup ($1) or pâté ($1). The large shrimp taste overcooked and bland, and the garlic in the salad dressing tastes more like powdered, day-old garlic rather than freshly chopped. *Cocktails, wines. Closed Sunday.*

★ BRONCO RESTAURANT

165 West 72nd Street *874-1540*

Anyone who hankers for well-spiced chili and barbecue related to that found in numerous villages of the Southwest will probably enjoy the Bronco. The food will not beguile the most fastidious of palates, but it has a definite regional appeal. The best dishes are the spareribs, which are tender and well seasoned, and the barbecued pork. The barbecued chicken tends to be dry and smacks too strongly of smoke. The chili has an authentic flavor; it is a trifle oily, and that is authentic too. The fried fruit pies are crisp and good; the coffee unspeakably weak. The cost of food is from about 45 cents for a sandwich to $4.50 for barbecued spareribs with potatoes, onion rings and salad. *There is no bar, but beers are available. Closed Sunday, New Year's Day, July 4, Labor Day, Thanksgiving and Christmas.*

BROWNIES

21 East 16th Street AL *5-2838*

This is certainly no place to flock to for the sheer joy of eating, but Brownies has a following that almost any restaurant might envy. Those who admire the restaurant are legion. They are principally those who have a weight or diet problem and those who have a yen for "natural food specialties." It is a good source, for example, for whole-grain breads, shredded carrots, vegetarian chicken liver and green soy beans with dill. Fish is frequently recommended by constant customers, but a recent serving, covered with a bland tomato sauce, was saltless. It was served with squash in another tomato sauce. A lentil soup sampled was creditable. No meat dishes are available, but the menu lists such dishes as eggplant steak. The luncheon menu is both à la carte and prix fixe. Complete luncheons cost about $1.40. A la carte dishes cost from about 65 cents for a salad to $1.49. Complete dinners cost from about $2.50 to $4.25. *Closed Saturday and Sunday.*

BRUNO'S ITALIAN RESTAURANT

161 West 4th Street CH *3-9365*

There are several people in Greenwich Village who rave about Bruno's, a small restaurant with wall-to-wall Italian art, paper place mats and candlelight. Guests hang their coats on a public hanger. The food is very good, of the sort that some people call "home style." The tomato sauces are tasty, and there are a few interesting dishes like chicken à la Bruno with mushrooms and peppers. The pasta dishes are good but not exceptional. All dishes are à la carte with main courses from $1.25 to $5. Bruno's does not yet have a liquor license, but they expect it soon. *Open for dinner only.*

★★ BRUSSELS RESTAURANT

115 East 54th Street PL *8-0457*

In its day the Brussels has been one of the city's most laudable restaurants. The atmosphere is still distinguished and the cuisine can be exceptionally good. The kitchen can serve ordinary dishes, however, including tough aspic on smoked trout and a mediocre preparation of sweetbreads financière, and the portions served are frequently excessive for good taste. The Brussels boasts a fine wine list and Victor, one of the city's finest wine stewards. All dishes are à la carte with main luncheon entrees from $2.75 to $8; main dinner dishes from $4.50 to $8. *Cocktails, wines. Closed Saturday, Sunday and almost the full month of July.*

★ BUDAPEST HUNGARIAN RESTAURANT

1481 Second Avenue (at 77th Street) UN *1-3600*

There are several small ethnic restaurants in New York offering the public excellent food that is frequently referred to as "home style." The Budapest is one of them. The service is friendly and the portions are generous and relatively inexpensive. The specialties of the house are, of course, goulash and paprika dishes. When available, the dishes made with kolbas, or Hungarian sausage, are excellent. There are complete luncheons for $1.75. Complete dinners are $2.95 to $4.80; à la carte entrees from $2.25 to $4. *Cocktails, wines. Dinner is served from noon Saturday and Sunday.*

★ CA D'ORO

59 West 56th Street CO *5-8518 and* CO *5-8519*

The menu at the Ca d'Oro shows more imagination than that of many of its counterparts. It lists at times an excellent fritto misto, or "mixed fry," of shrimp and squid, risotto with shrimp, pot roast with polenta and cod in wine sauce. During the warm weather there is open-air dining on a sidewalk terrace. Luncheon is à la carte with main courses from about $2.25 to $4.75. Complete dinners from $3.50 to $8; à la carte entrees from $2.50 to $7. *Cocktails, wines. Closed Sunday, New Year's Day, Christmas and from July 1 to July 15.*

AE CB DC

★★ CAFÉ ARGENTEUIL

253 East 52nd Street (at Second Avenue) PL *3-9273*

This is a French restaurant with a good deal of physical charm. If the Argenteuil maintained the excellence it sometimes achieves, it would be one of the prizes of the city. Unfortunately the kitchen wavers at times, and the service is occasionally slipshod. It is a favorite restaurant of publishing circles. There are complete luncheons from about $3.35 to $5.35. Dinners are à la carte with main courses from about $4.70 to $6.90. *Cocktails, wines. Luncheon is not served Saturday. Closed Sunday, New Year's Day, Thanksgiving, Christmas and from the middle of August through Labor Day.*

★★ CAFÉ BRITTANY

807 Ninth Avenue (at 53rd Street) CI *7-9566*

There is an authentic French bistro-style atmosphere about the Café Brittany, and the restaurant's popularity is well deserved. The food is plain but excellent, whether it be an appetizer or main course. For those who fancy such, the tripe is first-rate. A la carte luncheon dishes from about $1.50; à la carte dinner entrees from about $2. *Cocktails; wines by the bottle and by the glass. Luncheon is not served Saturday and Sunday. Reservations for parties of six or more.*

★★★ CAFÉ CHAUVERON

139 East 53rd Street PL *1-6480*

The Chauveron is scarcely more than ten years old, but it has an old-guard patina. The decor may seem a trifle dowdy, but the kitchen is meritoriously old-fashioned and classic. Complete luncheons from $5 to $9.50; à la carte main courses from $3 to $8. Dinners are à la carte from $4.50 to $10. *Cocktails, wines. Closed Sunday and, during August, Saturday also. Closed New Year's Day, Memorial Day, Labor Day, Thanksgiving, Christmas and the month of July.*

AE CB DC

★★ CAFÉ DE FRANCE

330 West 46th Street CO *5-8927*

The Café de France is one of several relatively small, inexpensive French restaurants on New York's West Side, generally crowded—particularly at midday—with a knowledgeable clientele that enjoys bourgeois cooking. The service, mostly by French-speaking waitresses, is offhand and friendly. The food is substantially good, but there is more stress on the flavor of the sauces than on the prime quality of the kitchen's raw materials. The menus are à la carte with luncheon entrees from $2, dinner entrees from $2.65. *Cocktails, wines. Closed Sunday.*

CAFÉ DES ARTISTES

1 West 67th Street EN *2-6700 and* TR *7-3343*

The most compelling feature of this restaurant is the murals by Howard Chandler Christy. The menu is mostly American with French overtones, and the food is relatively plain. Club luncheons, without appetizer, are $2.60; à la carte main courses from about $2 to $4.25. Dinners, without appetizer, are $4.70; à la carte entrees from about $3.50 to $6. *Cocktails, wines. Luncheon is not served Saturday. Closed Sunday, New Year's Day, Memorial Day, Christmas and the months of July and August.*

AE CB DC

CAFÉ DES SPORTS

329 West 51st Street CI *7-9281*

A small, inexpensive French restaurant tucked away in back of a well-populated bar. It is short on atmosphere and long on menu predictability, but many of the patrons appear to be French. There are four daily "spécial du chef" dishes and these on one visit included a commendable boeuf bourguignon. But the veal kidneys during the same visit were remarkable only in quantity. All dishes are à la carte with luncheon entrees from about $1.30 and dinner entrees from about $1.90. *Cocktails, wines. On Sunday the restaurant opens at 5 p.m.*

CAFÉ DU SOIR

322 East 86 Street AT *9-9996*

Café du Soir is a most agreeable little bistro with French cuisine. The menu, with its coq au vin and boeuf bourguignon, is somewhat standard, but the food is good. Complete luncheons from $2.25 to $3.75; à la carte main dishes from $1.75 to $3. Complete dinners from $2.75 to $5.25; à la carte entrees from $4.10 to $6.40. *Cocktails; wines by the bottle and by the glass.*

★ CAFÉ EUROPA

220 East 53rd Street PL *5-0160*

This restaurant, formerly known as Peter's Café Europa, has a sleek new decor at a new address. It is physically appealing with its iron grillwork and small, compartmented rooms hung with art. Some of the dishes are good, including the quiche Lorraine and mussels marinière, both of which appear frequently on the menu. The soups are generally excellent, and the duck à l'orange sampled on one occasion was creditable. The sauce for a carbonnade of beef, on the other hand, tasted pasty with flour, and the bananas au rhum were bitter and in a sauce slightly curdled. One four-course menu with a two-choice entree serves throughout each week and the cost is $6. *There is no bar, but guests may bring their own wines and spirits. Open for dinner only. Closed Sunday.*

★ CAFÉ FRANÇAIS

Lower Plaza, Rockefeller Plaza CI *6-5800*

In a physical sense, particularly during the winter season, this is one of the most agreeable places in New York to dine. The panoramic view of the skating rink is a delight, and the service at the Café Français is generally excellent. The kitchen is something else again. The menu is interesting, but although the food may be palatable, it smacks of being overcooked or cooked too long in advance —the broiled striped bass, for example. In other details too, such as machine-sliced smoked salmon, it lacks finesse. The luncheon menu is à la carte with main courses from about $2.50 to $5.95. There are complete dinners from

about $4.50 to $6.50; à la carte dishes in the evening from about $3.25 to $6.75. *Cocktails, wines.*
AE CB DC

CAFÉ GEIGER

206 East 86th Street RE *4-4428*

German-American cuisine in an undistinguished atmosphere but from a reasonably good kitchen. Menus are prix fixe and à la carte. Complete luncheons from about $1.95; complete dinners from about $2.70. A la carte main courses at luncheon from about $1.10; at dinner from $1.30. *Cocktails, wines. Open until midnight.*
AE DC

CAFÉ HINDENBURG

220 East 86th Street RH *4-9754*

German cuisine. The menu is à la carte at luncheon and dinner and lists entrees from about $1.75. *Cocktails, wines.*

CAFÉ LUCCA

143 West 44th Street CI *6-6400*

A conventional Italian restaurant in the Broadway area. Some dishes, such as the boiled beef when it is available, can be excellent, but the pasta is generally overcooked and the tomato sauces are pedestrian. There are complete luncheons from about $1.60 to $2.95; complete dinners from about $2.40 to $3.85. *Cocktails, wines. Closed Saturday and Sunday during the summer. Closed Sunday only during the winter.*
AE CB DC

★★ CAFÉ NICHOLSON

323 East 58th Street EL *5-6769*

This is one of New York's most fascinating restaurants and it opened recently in a new location. The atmosphere is rather Alice in Wonderland with such far-out furnishings as giant marble slabs in the center of the main dining room, a ceramic stove, a china dog, a Tiffany lamp, an antique clock, potted palms, ceiling fans and decorative tiles wall to wall. With one extraordinary exception, the food is merely interesting. The meats are of first-class quality, but the lamb chops, for example, are served with an odd but edible orange marmalade sauce; the steak with a flour-based béarnaise, a sauce that the French call bâtarde. The exception is a formidably good chocolate soufflé (really a pudding) served with a chocolate sauce and whipped cream. Dining at Nicholson's is almost a theatrical entertainment, and the cost of such a four-course diversion, including a bottle of very good Spanish wine, is $13.50. The tip is included in the bill. *Cocktails, wines. The restaurant is open evenings only except on Wednesday, when luncheon is served. Closed Sunday.*

AE CB DC

★ CAFÉ RENAISSANCE

338 East 49th Street PL *1-3160*

This restaurant, heavy with plush and rococo atmosphere, serves Spanish and Italian food. Paella, served Sunday, is a specialty. Luncheons are à la carte with entrees from about $2.75 to $3.50; à la carte dinner entrees from about $4.75 to $6.75. *Cocktails, wines. Luncheon is not served Saturday and Sunday. Closed Easter, Memorial Day, July 4, Labor Day, Thanksgiving and Christmas. Dinner reservations recommended.*

AE CB DC

★★ CAFÉ SAINT DENIS

11 East 53rd Street *755-1795 and 355-8032*

This is a French restaurant of some distinction with a menu that is interesting and reasonably priced. The restaurant's bouillabaisse can be exceptional. Both luncheon and dinner are prix fixe with complete luncheons from about $3.25 to $5.15; complete dinners from about

$4.50 to $8. *Cocktails, wines. Closed Sunday, New Year's Day, Memorial Day, July 4, Labor Day, Columbus Day, Thanksgiving and Christmas.*
AE CB DC

★★ CAMILLO

5 Mitchell Place (49th Street and First Avenue) 755-4388

The Beekman Place area is not notably burdened with good restaurants, and the recently opened Camillo is a welcome addition. It has a pleasant decor, the main dining room is square-shaped and separated from the bar by an arch. The management is the same as that of the former Camillo restaurant on East 48th Street, a place remembered for very good pasta. The pasta is excellent at the present address, and other main dishes are prepared with care and imagination. Complete luncheons cost from $3 to $5. Dinner is à la carte with main dishes from $3 to $7. *Cocktails, wines. On Saturday the restaurant opens at 5 p.m. Closed Sunday, New Year's Day, July 4, Labor Day, Thanksgiving and Christmas.*

★ CANTON RESTAURANT

6 Mott Street BE 3-9512

This is another addition to the seemingly endless roster of small but commendable restaurants in Chinatown. The dishes on the luncheon menu are commonplace, but the à la carte menu has several admirable prepared dishes including the steamed fish with ginger and scallions and the lo mein, or soft-noodle dishes. There are complete luncheons from about 80 cents for chow mein to $2.95 for lobster Cantonese; à la carte dishes from about 95 cents to $4.50. *There is no bar. Only à la carte items are available Saturday and Sunday. Closed Monday.*

CANTON VILLAGE

163 West 49th Street CI *7-2076*

This was at one time one of the best Chinese restaurants in New York. There were some major changes in the staff some time ago, and the result is noticeable. The food is still palatable but hardly distinguished. There are complete luncheons from about $1.10 to $3; complete dinners from about $2 to $3.25. A la carte dishes range from about $1.95 to $5.50. *Cocktails, wines.*

AE

★★ CAPRI RESTAURANT

233 West 52nd Street CO *5-9654*

Credit the Capri with a menu that is more interesting and varied than those in most of the city's Italian restaurants. There are very good soups—such as lentil with spinach—fine fish stews and pork chops with imported peppers. The homemade antipasto is far too oily and the food in general robustly spiced, but the chef has imagination. At midday in particular the Capri is crowded. The same menu serves throughout the day, with main courses from about $1.60 to $5.50. *Cocktails, wines. Closed Thanksgiving, Christmas and New Year's Day.*

★ CAPTAIN'S TABLE, THE

410 Avenue of the Americas (near 8th Street) AL *4-6825*

A pleasant enough fish and seafood restaurant in Greenwich Village. The bill of fare is run of the mill, but the broiled fish dishes, in particular, can be good. There are complete luncheons from $1.65 to $3. The à la carte menu, available for both luncheon and dinner, lists entrees from about $2.10 to $6.25. *Cocktails, wines.*

AE DC

CARACALLA

168 Amsterdam Avenue (at 68th Street) 799-4600

One of the best things to be said about this relatively new restaurant is that it is in the vicinity of Lincoln Center. This may be a minority voice of one, because several customers have reported excellence both in service and food. This visitor found both the surroundings and the menu of the restaurant interesting but the food ordinary, from the scampi to the vitella Conti, or veal with mushrooms, anchovies and Marsala. The simple tomato sauces are palatable, but the pasta dishes are served in mean little dishes about the size of cereal bowls. The food at the Caracalla is preferable to the service. Of the wines, the less said the better. Luncheon dishes are à la carte with main courses from about $1.50 to $2.10. In the evening there are complete dinners from about $4.50 to $6.25; à la carte dishes from about $2 to $5.95. *Cocktails, wines. The restaurant opens at 4 p.m. Saturday and at 3 p.m. Sunday. Closed New Year's Day, Thanksgiving and Christmas.*

AE DC

★ CARNEGIE DELICATESSEN AND RESTAURANT

854 Seventh Avenue (near 55th Street) PL 7-2245

The Carnegie continues to be a favorite of the Broadway set, along with many others who appreciate man-sized sandwiches. One of the most popular, Max's special, is a three-decker combination of turkey, corned beef and tongue with cole slaw and Russian dressing, at $1.45. The menu is à la carte with sandwiches priced from about 85 cents; main entrees from about $1.50. *Soft drinks, beer.*

★ CAROLINA

1409 Mermaid Avenue, Brooklyn CO *6-8311*
(between 14th and 15th Streets)

This is a very plain Italian restaurant that is widely admired in its neighborhood. The menu is well varied and some of the dishes are a bit robust, bathed in tomato and garlic sauces. The fritto misto, or Italian "mixed fry," with various vegetables, meats and cheeses, is interesting. One menu serves throughout the day, and à la carte items range in cost from about 80 cents for spaghetti with tomato sauce to $4.75 for steak. *There is no bar, but wines and beer are available.*

★★★ CASA BRASIL

440 East 86th Street BU *8-5284*

The intricate charm of New York, ever since the original sale of Manhattan, has involved a few surprises. Things range from the mammoth to the smallest smidgen. In the latter category is the Casa Brasil. It is a most agreeable and relatively new restaurant with a seating capacity for scarcely more than 20 guests. There is no written menu and the food includes such dishes as quiche Lorraine, roast lamb, beef Stroganoff and filet mignon with mushrooms. On Wednesday nights there is feijoada, the national dish of Brazil, composed of black beans, roast pork, rice, sausage, tongue, orange sections and a sprinkling of farinha de mandioca, a flour made from a tuberous South American plant. The cost of an extensive meal, first course to last, is $8. *There is no bar, but guests may order wine from a nearby store or bring their own. Reservations recommended. Closed Sunday.*

★ CASA DI PRE

89 Greenwich Avenue CH *2-9255*

This is a small, frequently crowded Italian restaurant in Greenwich Village. The menu is well varied, the sauces are basic and good and the cost of dining is relatively low. All dishes are à la carte with main luncheon courses from about $1.35 (homemade lasagne) to $2.50 (combination seafood plate); main dinner entrees from about $2.60 (spaghetti) to $4 (filet mignon). *Cocktails, wines. Closed Sunday.*

CASA JOHNNY

135 West 15th Street CH *2-9520*

This is a small hideaway in an old brownstone, and the kitchen, which is Italian, can be above average. The attitude of both the management and service staff, however, is frequently lackadaisical or of the take-it-or-leave-it school. The cost of a complete luncheon is from about $2.10 to $3; of a complete dinner from $3.50 to $5.50. In the evening there is also an à la carte menu with main dishes from about $3 to $5.75. *Cocktails, wines. Luncheon is not served Saturday. Closed Sunday, New Year's Day, Thanksgiving and Christmas.*

★★ CASA MARIO

136 West 55th Street CI *6-6262*

This is a notably agreeable restaurant. The dishes on the menu are prepared with care, and the management pays attention to the detail in the dining room. The fettucine Alfredo is excellent. There are complete luncheons from about $2.75 to $5.50. The dinner is à la carte with entrees from about $2.50 to $7. *Cocktails, wines. Luncheon is not served Saturday. Closed Sunday, Labor Day and Christmas.*

AE DC

CASTILLA RESTAURANT AND BAR

35 Madison Street BE *3-9492*

This is a small, offbeat restaurant that should appeal to anyone with a sense of adventure who enjoys good food no matter what the ambiance. The food at the Castilla is Spanish and could be called "home style."

Don't be misled by the menu that emphasizes, on the one hand, sirloin steak, veal cutlet, pork chops and hamburger. Do insist on the Spanish dishes, which might include a delicious caldo gallego, or bean soup; cocido, the Spanish boiled dinner; chorizos (Spanish sausage) and rice; bacalao (cod) dishes; and paella. The Spanish boiled dinner is available on Sunday and on special order. It is generally necessary to order a paella two hours in advance. The cost of main courses throughout the day and evening is from $1.75 to $3.50. The restaurant is frequently crowded on Sunday with a Spanish-speaking clientele. Both the bar and dining room are unpretentious and inelegant. *Cocktails, wines.*

★★ CATTLEMAN, THE

5 East 45th Street MO *1-1200*

The average New Yorker is a pushover for showmanship, and among the town's restaurants it is nowhere better evidenced than at this many-roomed, gas-lit and unabashedly contrived dining establishment. Customers flock here for such dishes as steaks, baked potatoes Laramie and Cow Town sandwiches. The steaks and prime ribs of beef are excellent, the mixed Western barbecue undistinguished. The menus offer all à la carte dishes. The cost of main courses at midday is from about $2.25 to $6.95; in the evening from $4.25 to $7.25; at supper (11 p.m. to 2 a.m. except Sunday) from $1.85 to $7.25. Brunch is served Sunday from 11:30 a.m. to 3:30 p.m., with entrees from $2.55. *Cocktails, wines.*
AE CB DC

CAVANAGH'S RESTAURANT

260 West 23rd Street AL *5-1100*

This is one of the city's oldest steak and seafood houses and it has a pleasant, old-fashioned decor. The kitchen is not distinguished. In addition to steak there are many entrees on the menu, such as roast turkey, broiled

red snapper and boiled beef with horseradish sauce. Luncheon and dinner are both prix fixe and à la carte. Complete luncheons at $2.75; à la carte main courses from about $1.95 to $5.95. Complete dinners are $4.75 to $6; à la carte entrees from $3.50 to $6.75. *Cocktails, wines. On Saturday the restaurant opens at 5 p.m.*
AE DC

★★ CEDARS OF LEBANON

39 East 30th Street MU *6-9634 and* OR *9-6755*

This is a Middle Eastern restaurant with a strictly utilitarian aspect. It should appeal to people with a taste for interesting lamb dishes, excellent appetizers flavored with sesame oil, and budget prices. The appetizers, such as the mashed chick-peas with sesame oil (50 cents) and a similar eggplant mixture (50 cents), are particularly outstanding. Main courses include a generally good shish kebab ($1.90) and kafta kebab, or chopped lamb on a skewer ($1.30). A complete luncheon (entree, dessert and coffee) costs $1.50; complete dinners, including a sampling of four appetizers, from $2.95 to $3.25. A la carte dishes from about $1.30 to $2.20. *Cocktails, wines. Closed New Year's Day, Easter, July 4, Labor Day and Christmas.*
AE DC

★ CEYLON INDIA INN

148 West 49th Street CO *5-9822*

This is reputedly the oldest Indian restaurant in the United States, and the atmosphere is exotic. The dishes are interesting, but the ventilation could be improved. At noon the menu is à la carte with entrees from about $1.20 to $1.50. There are complete dinners from $2.75 to $5.95; à la carte main courses from $1.85 to $3.75. *Beers and wines. Luncheon is not served Saturday and Sunday.*
AE

★ CHALET SUISSE

6 East 48th Street *355-0855*

This is one of the few Swiss restaurants in New York, and it is now in a new location with neat white walls and silhouetted iron grillwork. It is conceivably the best of the Swiss restaurants, and it should be a good deal better than it is. There are some admirable dishes including the bundnerfleisch, a dried beef, thinly sliced, from the Grisons; the Swiss potatoes; the museau de boeuf, or ox-snout salad; and a veal à la Suisse, which is cooked in cream. But the veal cordon bleu was a disappointment; the cheese was not properly sealed in the thin slice of veal before cooking. And the vichyssoise tasted as if it were made with smoked ham. However, the really regrettable thing about the Chalet Suisse is the ventilation. One of the restaurant's specialties is the fondue bourguignonne in which meats are cooked in oil at the table, and as a consequence the smell of cooking fat permeates the dining room. A recent meal was accompanied, incidentally, by a very good and interesting bottle of Dole de Sion, one of the best and best-known Swiss wines. It travels very well. There are complete luncheons from about $3 to $4.50; complete dinners at $6.95, with à la carte dishes from about $4 for Swiss fondue to $7.50 for steak. *Cocktails, wines. Luncheon is not served on Saturday. Closed Sunday.*
AE DC

★★ CHAMPLAIN RESTAURANT

115 West 49th Street CI *7-9274*

This restaurant conceivably offers the finest dining value in Manhattan. A club luncheon with main course and dessert is $1.60 and a regular luncheon is $1.80. A club dinner is $3.25 and a regular dinner is $3.50. There is an admirable selection of more than 20 main courses, and for bourgeois cuisine the food is generally excellent. The Champlain is a large French bistro, and it is, reasonably enough, generally crowded. The service is friendly and excellent. *Cocktails, wines. Closed Sunday.*

★ CHANDLER'S

49 East 49th Street PL *1-1960*

A large, popular and somewhat flashy restaurant that is best known for its steaks and generous portions. There are fish dishes too and such specialties as chicken in the pot and boiled beef in the pot. All dishes are à la carte with main courses at midday from about $2.60 for a Western omelet to $6.95 for sirloin steak. In the evening the prices range from about $4.25 for broiled chicken to $7.25 for filet mignon. *Cocktails, wines. On Saturday the restaurant opens at 4 p.m., on Sunday at 3 p.m.*

AE CB DC

CHARDAS

307 East 79th Street RH *4-9382*

This is an enormously festive Hungarian restaurant with Gypsy music and dancing. It is A-1 for some tastes but too noisy for others. Complete dinners cost from about $6.50 to $7.75. The specialties of the house include such dishes as veal or pork goulash and roast duckling. *Cocktails, wines. Open for dinner only. Closed Monday and July 1 through Labor Day.*

AE DC

★ CHARLES À LA POMME SOUFFLÉ

157 East 55th Street EL *5-8280*

This is a small and popular French restaurant where, on at least one occasion, one has seen members of the Kennedy family with young children in tow. There is no menu, but the names of the available dishes are recited by the maître d'hôtel or whoever. They do not seem to change appreciably throughout the year. Among the appetizers the batter-dipped and fried shrimp are good. The stuffed clams are too breaded and lacking in flavor. One

order of roast lamb was generous, pink and tender. A quiche was too salty, but the custard was delicate. There are, of course, souffléed, or puffed, potatoes. And canned peas. The cost of a complete luncheon is $3.25. Dinners cost from $6.75 to $7.00. *Cocktails, wines. Open seven days. Luncheon is not served on Sunday.*
AE DC

CHARLES V

34 West 53rd Street JU *6-1160*

A pleasantly appointed, somewhat crowded French restaurant with a nonexceptional kitchen. There is a table d'hôte menu at luncheon and dinner. Complete luncheons from about $3.30 to $5.95; complete dinners from about $6.50 to $9. *Cocktails, wines. Closed Sunday and, during the summer months, Saturday also.*
AE CB DC

★ CHARLES FRENCH RESTAURANT

452 Avenue of the Americas GR *7-3300*
(between 10th and 11th Streets)

Charles is a long-established restaurant in the Greenwich Village area, one of the few with pretensions to a French and international cuisine, and there is always the feeling that the kitchen should be a good deal better than it is. The smoked salmon is served with a large and unsightly leaf of iceberg lettuce, and the cheese assortment is a disaster. A waiter explains that very few people here order cheese and there is small wonder. One of the specialties of the house is the boiled beef, which is acceptable. The flavor of the double lamb chop on one occasion was excellent, although it was accompanied by oil-soaked deep-fried potatoes. The decor of Charles is theatrical but pleasant. The restaurant's Chassagne-Montrachet wine, 1961, costs $5.50, and it is special. Luncheons are à la carte with main dishes from about $2.50 to $6.25. There are complete dinners from about $5 to $6.50. A la carte

items range from about $3.50 to $7.75. *Cocktails, wines. On Saturday and Sunday the restaurant opens at 4 p.m.*
AE CB DC

★★★ CHARLEY O'S BAR AND GRILL

Rockefeller Center, 33 West 48th Street *582-7141*

This is one of the most joyous, colorful and smartly contrived restaurants ever to open in New York. At noon the restaurant has an elbow-to-elbow ambiance, pretends to be an Irish saloon (which it isn't) and has the best shrimp on ice, herring in cream, corned beef sandwiches and foaming, old, delicious draught beer. Charley O's is a largish restaurant with a long, handsome and sturdy bar for beer and spirits and another equally sturdy bar where the sandwiches, including tartar steak, shrimp and so forth, are dispensed. Guests help themselves to forks, knives and napery. The food in the main dining room is less festive, but at its best it is excellent. There is such interesting fare as pigs' knuckles with a vinaigrette sauce, soused shrimp and such main dishes (they vary every day) as boiled ham and cabbage, braised brisket of beef with egg barley and roast ribs of beef with boxty pudding, made with potatoes. It must be noted that the pudding recently was tough, but the roast beef was first-rank. All dishes on the menu are à la carte with main courses from about $2.85 to $6.25. The sandwiches at the bar cost from about $1.50 to $1.65. In addition to sandwiches at the bar there is also soup and one main course each day. Supper is served from 11 p.m. to 1 a.m. Brunch is served on Sunday from noon to 4 p.m. *Cocktails, wines.*
AE CB DC

★ CHARLIE BROWN'S

Main floor of Pan Am Building MO *1-2520*

An extremely popular and handsome place. At midday there is almost always a line of people waiting for tables, and the noise level is high. The service is confused.

Two waiters at times seem to share responsibility for a table, with one not knowing what the other is up to. When a busboy on one occasion started to remove appetizers, bread, etc., a waiter yelled across the table, "Hey, you crazy or something? They ain't finished yet!" Seafood dishes, chops, steaks, curries and stews are predominant on the menu. The menus are à la carte with main courses at midday from about $2.95 to $5.95. In the evening main courses cost from about $3.50 to $6.85. *Cocktails, wines. Closed Sunday.*
AE DC

★ CHATEAUBRIAND

131 East 54th Street *755-5260*

A handsome enough restaurant that is spacious and airy and, compared with many other restaurants in the city, quiet. There are red banquettes and a window opening onto the kitchen with its hanging copper pots and pans. There is an interesting cold table, and among the dishes that came off rather well at one visit were a duck pâté with pistachios and brains with black butter sauce. Crêpes filled with crab were creditable. A first course of coquilles St. Jacques was edible but not distinguished and the portion was far too large for an appetizer. One of the nicest dishes was a vanilla custard sauce flavored with Grand Marnier and served with strawberries. All dishes at midday are à la carte with main courses from about $3 to $8; complete four-course dinners from $7.25 to $12. *Cocktails, wines. Closed Saturday and Sunday during the summer. Closed Sunday only during the winter.*
AE CB DC

CHÂTEAU HENRI IV

37 East 64th Street RE *7-8818*

French cooking from a kitchen not overly distinguished for its finesse. Complete luncheons from about

$2.25 to $4.50; complete dinners from about $4.75 to $8.75. *Cocktails, wines. On Sunday the restaurant opens at 5 p.m.*
AE CB DC

★★ CHESHIRE CHEESE RESTAURANT

319 West 51st Street *765-0610*

A spate of so-called English restaurants and pubs has opened in New York in the last three years, and the Cheshire Cheese may well be the most impressive of the lot. It is an agreeable place on the West Side, fairly close to Broadway theaters, and both the food and service are above average. The menu is along the lines of steak and kidney pie, steak and mushroom pie and sausages and chips. There are very good homemade soups. All dishes are à la carte with main courses at noon from about $1.95 to $5.25; in the evening from about $4.95 to $9. *Cocktails, wines. On Saturday the restaurant opens at 5 p.m. Closed Sunday and August 1 through Labor Day.*
AE

★★ CHEZ CARDINALE

347 West 46th Street CI *5-9732*

This is a most agreeable restaurant in the Broadway area with a French and Italian menu. From the antipasto Italienne to the mousse au chocolat, the menu doesn't offer many surprises, but the food is well prepared. There is a pre-theater dinner that has an appetizing assortment of hors d'oeuvres including shrimp with mayonnaise cocktail sauce, pâté maison and eggs à la russe. The cost of the pre-theater dinner ranges from $4.25 to $5.50. Dinners are otherwise à la carte with main dishes from $2.95 to $5.75. Complete luncheons cost from about $2.25 to $3.95. *Cocktails, wines. Closed Sunday.*
AE CB DC

★ **CHEZ NAPOLEON**

365 West 50th Street CO *5-6980*

This small French bistro might not be to the emperor's taste, but it is a pleasant place to dine before the theater. The lamb is particularly good; the boeuf bourguignon, made solidly of meat, is a little heavy going. There is the usual list of appetizers and desserts, and prices are reasonable. Complete luncheons cost from $1.95 to $4.25; à la carte main courses from $1.25 to $3. Dinner is à la carte with entrees from about $2 to $4.25. *Cocktails, wines. On Saturday the restaurant opens at 5 p.m. Closed Sunday, New Year's Day, Memorial Day, July 4, Thanksgiving, Christmas and August 1 through Labor Day.*

★★ **CHEZ RENÉE**

248 East 49th Street EL *5-1810*

This is a fairly engaging restaurant, and if all the bistros in town had equal charm and food of equal merit, New York might be a pleasanter place to live in. During the summer months there is a garden where guests may sit under an ailanthus tree and dine on coq au Riesling or trout grenobloise. Dishes remembered from summer or winter at the restaurant include a fine-grained pâté maison, a soupe MacIlwane (vaguely resembling a cold vichyssoise but containing bits of tomato and chopped scallion) and a filet of sole Orly (batter-fried). At one meal the establishment's sweetbreads came off poorly and seemed a bit spongy. The kitchen at Chez Renée is small, and when the dining room is crowded the service may tend to be maddeningly slow. It is a rather expensive restaurant. Complete luncheons range from about $3 for an omelet to $6.25 for mignonettes of beef bordelaise; complete dinners from about $6 for sole meunière to $9.50 for steak au poivre. *Cocktails, wines. Luncheon is not served Saturday. Closed Sunday.*

AE

★ CHEZ VOUS

78 Carmine Street CH *2-2676*

Despite the name, this relatively small, impeccably neat restaurant in Greenwich Village offers South Italian cuisine. Luncheon and dinner are à la carte with main courses at midday for about $1.50 to $3.50 and in the evening from about $1.50 to $4. There is a 50-cent cover charge at each meal. *Cocktails, wines. Luncheon is not served Saturday. Closed Sunday, New Year's Day, Thanksgiving and Christmas. Reservations frequently essential.*

★ CHEZ YVONNE L'ESCARGOT

54 Stone Street *944-9887*

This rather large bistro in the city's financial district boasts a very plain menu with well-prepared French cuisine. Those who fancy rare lamb will find it here on request, and the snails, stuffed with shallot butter, are notable. The menu, which is à la carte, is the same for luncheon and dinner. Main courses range from about $2.15 for an omelet to $4.75 for steak with maître d'hôtel butter. The snails, served as an appetizer, are somewhat expensive but worth the price at $1.75 a half dozen. Like many restaurants in the neighborhood, Chez Yvonne is open only until 7 p.m. *Cocktails, wines. Closed Saturday, Sunday and all major holidays.*

★ CHINA BOWL, THE

152 West 44th Street JU *2-3358*

This is a crowded, compact Chinese restaurant in the theater district. The menu may have too much of chow mein and chop suey for old China hands, but the food is generally well prepared. The restaurant is, by the way, a place where you will see on occasion a Broadway personality. There are complete luncheons from $1.75 to $2.45. The à la carte menu lists main dishes from about $1.70 to $5.20.*Cocktails, wines. Only à la carte items are available on Sunday, from 12:30 p.m.*

★ CHINESE RATHSKELLER

45 Mott Street WO *2-8943*

This downstairs establishment on a main street in Chinatown is a favorite with tourists and many Chinese. The quality and the flavor of the food varies, and it is best to order from the à la carte menu. The lobster with chicken livers is an unusual combination and can be delicious. Complete luncheons from about $1.15 to $4. A la carte dishes are available at all times, with main courses from about $1.50 to $8.50. Complete dinners are priced from $1.95 to $4.25. *Cocktails, wines. Luncheon is not served Sunday.*

AE CB DC

★ CHOCK FULL O'NUTS

There are about fifty of these first-class establishments in the metropolitan New York area. They are clean as a whistle, and the sandwiches and pastries are of a high order. The doughnuts and coffee cake are particularly good. Counter service only. Freshly squeezed orange juice, available in the morning, costs 15 cents and 30 cents. Sandwiches, whether lobster salad or chopped liver and egg, cost about 35 cents. *No alcoholic beverages. Closing hours at the various locations differ. Most of the restaurants are closed Sunday.*

★★★ CHRIST CELLA

160 East 46th Street OX *7-2479*

Although by most standards it is relatively obscure, this small, immaculate establishment has an international reputation. As to the cost, it is on a par with many of the city's most expensive restaurants. The steaks and lobsters are superb, and some of the less lordly dishes are good too. There is no menu. The cost of an average luncheon is in the vicinity of $5; the average dinner about $12. *Cocktails, wines. Luncheon is not served Saturday. Closed Sunday and, during*

July and August, Saturday also. Closed major holidays. Reservations recommended.

AE

★★ CHRISTO'S

143 East 49th Street EL *5-6531*

This is a pleasant, comfortable, neat and frequently crowded steak house, and what's more, the food is good. Although the emphasis is on steaks and chops, the evening menu has Italian entrees; at luncheon there are several American dishes, such as shirred eggs with country sausage. Both menus are à la carte with main courses at midday from about $2.25 for a Western omelet to $4.50 for a small prime sirloin steak. In the evening the prices range from about $3.75 for chicken in pot to $6.95 for filet mignon. *Cocktails, wines. On Saturday and Sunday the restaurant opens at about 4:30 p.m.*

AE CB DC

★★ CHUAN HONG RESTAURANT

2748 Broadway (between 105th and 106th Streets) 866-5960

Upper Broadway is becoming more and more a center for out-of-the-ordinary Chinese restaurants, and this is one of the latest on the roster. The food is prepared with great skill and variety whether it is sautéed shredded chicken, sweet and sour fish, a dumpling or various Szechuan dishes, which are uncommonly good for those who relish highly spiced foods. The Chuan Hong is a small, inexpensive restaurant, with, apparently, only one waiter. As always, it is best to order from the à la carte menu. There are complete luncheons from about 95 cents to $2; complete dinners from about $1.75 to $3.50. A la carte dishes from about $1.50 to $3.25. *There is no bar. Open seven days a week.*

★★ CLOS NORMAND

42 East 52nd Street PL 3-3348

This is physically a most agreeable French restaurant. There are original tiles by Jean Pagès and the over-all atmosphere has the warmth of a Normandy village. Many of the dishes come off very well. Remembered in particular are a cream of lettuce soup and a cream of mussel soup. One also recalls with special favor a tender, admirably cooked dish of thin white slices of veal and a roast chicken with a tarragon cream sauce. The quiche, made with Alaska king crab meat and other sea food, is very good and far superior to an all but inedible dish of braised sweetbreads that were undercooked and spongy. The luncheon menu is à la carte with main courses from about $2.95 to $4.50. The dinner menu is prix fixe. The cost of a complete meal in the evening is $6.95. *Cocktails, wines. Closed Sunday.*

AE CB DC

★★★ COACH HOUSE, THE

110 Waverly Place SP 7-0303

The Coach House is the finest restaurant in the Greenwich Village area and one of the best in the city. It is a handsome, conservatively styled place with a management that has a dedicated interest in its profession. The kitchen is largely American, and specialties of the house include black bean soup, excellent steaks, charcoal-grilled giant lamb chops and pecan pie. When available there is also an extraordinarily good French dessert called dacquoise. There are complete luncheons from about $2.80 to $3.30 and à la carte entrees at midday from about $2.50 to $6.50. There are complete dinners from about $7.50 to $8.50 and à la carte main courses in the evening from about $4.25 to $8.50. *Cocktails, wines. On Saturday the restaurant opens at 5:30 p.m. Dinners are served Sunday from 1 p.m. Closed Monday, New Year's Day, Christmas, the last week of July and the first week of August. Reservations recommended.*

AE CB DC

COACHMAN RESTAURANT, THE

13 William Street WH *4-3595*

American cuisine. The à la carte menu, available all the time, lists entrees from about $3.95 to $6.95. Complete luncheons from $4; complete dinners from $4.95. *Cocktails, wines. Dinner served until 8:45 p.m. Closed Saturday and Sunday.*

CB

★★★ COLONY, THE

30 East 61st Street TE *8-6660*

When most luxury restaurants decline in one way or another, it is generally because of a change in quality or talent in the kitchen. In the case of The Colony, the change has been in the dining room. The menu, once written by hand, is now composed by machine; the long-stemmed red roses that once abounded in the main dining room are now artificial and the flowers on the table are commonplace. The handsome rolling silver "wagon," where roasts and other specialties of the day were carved, has been dispensed with. On the other hand, the kitchen has been restaffed with an excellent chef, and the food is for the most part admirable. There is a commendable canapé Colony with crab meat, smoked trout with horse-radish and first-rate main dishes. And it is still a haven for the wealthy and famous. All dishes are à la carte with main courses at midday from about $4.25 to $5.75; in the evening from about $5.50 to $8.95. *Cocktails, wines. Closed Sunday and for certain weeks during the summer.*

AE CB DC

COOKERY LAFAYETTE, THE

21 University Place OR *4-4450*

The menu at the Cookery in Greenwich Village is international and ranges from the all-American hamburger to a Basque omelet called piperade. The quality of the food is generally mediocre. There are many kinds of sandwiches ranging in price from about 75 cents to $1.75, and other à la carte dishes from about $1.25 to $1.95. Sunday brunch, served from 11 a.m. to 4 p.m., is $1.95 and $2.50. The restaurant has a large and pleasant outdoor terrace. *No alcoholic beverages. Closed New Year's Day, Thanksgiving and Christmas.*

COPAIN

891 First Avenue (at 50th Street) PL *8-0554*

The menu at the Copain is French, but the cuisine for the most part is not distinguished by its finesse. Both luncheon and dinner are table d'hôte. Complete luncheons from $2.50 to $3.50; complete dinners from $5.75 to $7.95. Sunday brunch, served from 1 p.m. to 3:30 p.m., is $3. *Cocktails, wines.*

AE CB DC

★★★ COPENHAGEN

68 West 58th Street MU *8-3690*

For a herring fancier there should be nothing but unreserved enthusiasm for the Copenhagen's remarkable assortment. There is herring with mustard, herring with curry, herring with horseradish, plus six or seven more, and all of them are a joy. The remainder of the Copenhagen's food is not on a par with the best that Denmark has to offer, but it is palatable nonetheless and will cosset the appetite. Both the luncheon and dinner menus are à la carte. The cost of the abundant Danish cold table at midday is $3.95; in the evening $6.50. Main course dishes at midday cost from $3 to $4.50; in the evening from about $3.75 to $6.50. Also, Danish open-faced sandwiches, ranging in price from $1.10 to $3.75, are served all day. *Cocktails, wines. Closed Sunday, New Year's Day, July 4, Thanksgiving and Christmas.*

AE CB DC

★★ **COPTER CLUB**

Heliport Lounge of the Pan Am Building *973-2100*

From a certain height the views of Manhattan on a clear day or cloudless night are breath-taking. Considering that, it is astonishing how few restaurants in town celebrate the fact. One of the most recent to open here and one of the best is the Copter Club. The view from the windows on the fifty-eighth floor is, of course, spectacular. What is equally interesting is the menu. For the fixed price of $3.50 a guest may dine on roast beef with salad, dessert and coffee. The only exception is on Friday, when a blend of seafood in wine sauce is also available. That is the menu Q.E.D. and it is a refreshing change from those wind-blown, pompous and overly ambitious bills of fare that have been with us late and soon for several years. It should also be mentioned that the interior of the Club is handsome. There is fault to be found with the salad, which contains iceberg lettuce, the least distinguished of salad greens. At one visit the restaurant was also serving something awful called "instant" espresso. *Cocktails, wines and beers; with or without dining, the lounge is open to the public. Luncheon is served from 12:15 p.m. to 2:15 p.m. Monday through Friday. Reservations are essential. Dinner is not served.*

AE

★ **COQ AU VIN**

939 Eighth Avenue (near 56th Street) CI *5-9557*

A small French bistro-type café with a conventional menu and bourgeois cooking. All dishes are à la carte with main luncheon dishes from about $1.60 to $5; main dinner courses from about $1.90 to $5. *Cocktails, wines. Luncheon not served on Saturday and Sunday.*

★ **CORNER AT MARGARET'S**

502 Third Avenue (near 34th Street) *686-1502*

There are several good things about the Corner at Margaret's, a place of plastic flower bowers. Several of the dishes are well made and appetizing, and these include the head cheese and the sautéed chicken livers served as appetizers, the wiener schnitzel (breaded veal) served with excellent home-fried potatoes and the rindsroulade (beef rolls) with vegetable stuffing. No great cooking, but good. On the other hand, the small plate of vegetable appetizers offered gratis is dull, the liver dumpling soup sampled recently was overly bland and almost all the portions are gross. There is a warm reception by the owner of the establishment, but the welcome after a while begins to seem a trifle intrusive. And it should be pointed out that wine glasses should not be filled so amply as they are at Margaret's. The à la carte menu available throughout the day has main courses priced from $2.80 to $4.20. Complete dinners cost from $4 to $5.20. *There is no bar, but wines are available. Luncheon is not served Saturday and Sunday.* *AE DC*

★★ CRÊPES SUZETTE

313 West 46th Street 265-9510

This is a very good, small and inexpensive restaurant in the Broadway–Times Square area. There is nothing pretentious about the surroundings or the neighborhood, but it is a pleasant place to dine with a modest purse. All the dishes are à la carte with main courses at midday from about $1.50 to $3 and in the evening from about $2.50 to $5.50. *Cocktails, wines. Luncheon is not served Saturday. Closed Sunday, New Year's Day, Memorial Day, July 4, Labor Day, Thanksgiving and Christmas.*

CYRANO

11 West 56th Street CO *5-8733*

A restaurant with a pleasant atmosphere and a menu that is both French and Italian. Both luncheon and dinner are prix fixe and à la carte. Complete luncheons from about $3.25 to $6; à la carte main dishes from about $2.50 to $5.50. Complete dinners from about $5 to $7.25;

à la carte entrees from about $2.75 to $6.50. There is also a prix fixe pre-theater dinner at $4.75. *Cocktails, wines. Closed Saturday.*
AE CB DC

★★ CZECHOSLOVAK PRAHA

1358 First Avenue (at 73rd Street) YU *8-3505 and* RH *4-9787*

At midday, in particular, the food of the Czechoslovak Praha is one of the best bargains in Manhattan. One can dine reasonably well on main courses that cost from $1 for Czechoslovak sausages with potato and sauerkraut to $1.25 for excellent roast sirloin of pork with dumpling and sauerkraut. The sliced dumplings are light and outstanding. There are complete dinners that range in cost from $2.90 for a goulash to $5 for filet mignon. The decor of the restaurant is simple and there is noise at times from an all too persistent jukebox. *Cocktails, wines. Dinner is served from noon on Sunday.*

★ DALY'S DANDELION

1029 Third Avenue (at 61st Street) 838-0780

One of the oldest saloons in Manhattan, formerly called Daly's, was acquired recently by Skitch and Ruth Henderson, George Cothran and Dr. John Parenti. Its surroundings are very pleasant, and its service friendly and polite. The walls are neatly papered with a dandelion pattern, but its old-fashioned bar, white tile floor and stained glass have been retained. Best of all, the hamburgers are excellent and the brews on draft are cold and good. A thin, chilled vichyssoise is also good. The restaurant's mint-flavored gazpacho leaves much to be desired; it is a crude version of the Spanish soup, a far too thick dish of coarsely puréed or chopped vegetables. The cumin-flavored chili con carne is also amateurish. The menu, on a cedar shingle, lists prices from about $1.50 for sandwiches to $5.50 for shell steak. *Cocktails, beer and ale. Open seven days a week.*

★ DAMON'S

153 West 36th Street LO *4-3636*

The kitchen at Damon's is much like that of several other reasonably good Italian restaurants in New York. This restaurant is in the garment district and is, particularly at midday, a crowded rendezvous for members of the dress industry. Among the best dishes are breast of chicken parmigiana with cheese and tomato and chicken Gismonde with spinach. The portions, of whatever category, are mammoth. All dishes at Damon's are à la carte with main courses at midday from about $3.25 to $5.95 and in the evening from $3.25 to $6.95. *Cocktails, wines. Open for luncheon only on Saturday. Closed Sunday.*

AE CB DC

★★ DAN DOWD'S STEAK HOUSE

153 West 49th Street JU *2-6116*

Don't be put off by the sleek decor of Dan Dowd's Steak House. Behind those très moderne trappings is a kitchen that turns out excellent grilled steaks and chops. It is, in fact, one of the best steak houses in the Broadway area. The restaurant is large and the tables are, perhaps, too close together for comfort. Dowd's double English lamb chop with bacon strips and kidney is particularly good. At midday the restaurant is crowded. There are complete luncheons from $1.75 to $2.95; complete dinners from $3.75 to $5.95. A la carte dishes from $1.75 to $5.50. *Cocktails, wines. Closed Sunday.*

AE CB DC

D'ANGELO'S

252 West 55th Street CI *7-9855*

This is a neat Italian restaurant near the New York City Center. The menu is stereotyped, but there is something to be said for the stuffed artichokes and the lobster fra diavolo. All dishes are à la carte with main courses from about $1.35 for ziti to $2.95 for veal dishes. Two

exceptions are the lobster, which costs about $5.50, and the sirloin steak, which is priced at $5.50. *Cocktails, wines. Closed Sunday.*
AE CB DC

★★ DANNY'S HIDE-A-WAY

151 East 45th Street YU *6-5399*

Danny's is one of New York's best-known steak houses, and it certainly fits the town's classic pattern for steak houses. It is a large restaurant, and food is served on several levels. As to decor, there is a somewhat circuslike mélange of wall hangings, cartoons, photographs, paintings, Western saddles, hammered brass plaques, plaster masks and swords. The steaks and chops are excellent at Danny's, and the kitchen standards are reasonably high in other areas as well. All dishes are à la carte with main courses at midday from about $2.70 for deep-fried scallops to $4.25 for seafood salad. There is no printed menu in the evening, and the food is expensive. The cost of a cup of minestrone, for example, is $1. Grilled lamb chops cost $6.75; grilled sirloin steak $7.50. Danny's Hide-A-Way has on each table some of the most uninteresting-looking bread in town. *Cocktails, wines. On Sunday the restaurant opens at 4 p.m. Closed New Year's Day, Memorial Day, July 4, Labor Day and Christmas.*
AE CB DC

★★ DARDANELLES ARMENIAN RESTAURANT

86 University Place CH *2-8990*

This is probably the most elegant of New York's Middle Eastern restaurants, and the food, particularly such appetizers as chick-pea spread and cheese burreck, are both interesting and good. There are complete luncheons from about $2.35 to $2.90; complete dinners from about $4.25 to $6.95. A la carte dishes cost from about $1.75 at midday, from $2.45 in the evening. *Cock-*

tails, wines. Luncheon is not served Saturday and Sunday. Closed Christmas and Sundays during July and August.
AE CB DC

DAVY JONES SEA FOOD HOUSE

103 West 49th Street JU *6-2936*

One of New York's least distinguished seafood places, where both the piped-in music and decor are "early diner." The broiled fish dishes are smothered in paprika to make up for improper grilling. A waiter denied that the sticky orange stuff over the salad greens was patented glue, while at another table one of his colleagues was explaining to a couple that he didn't know whether the fish was fresh or not and offhand he couldn't think of anyone who might know. The cheesecake is not bad. A la carte main courses from about $2.25 for kippers to $7.50 for lobster stuffed with crab. *Cocktails, wines. Open seven days.*
AE CB DC

★ DAWSON'S HA-PENNY BAR

159 East 53rd Street PL *2-1387*

This is a fascinating and frequently crowded restaurant offering what may be the most copious hot and cold luncheon buffet in town. It has such items as deviled beef bones, pickled eggs, Scotch eggs, cold meats and salads. The food is good but not consistently special. There is a large variety of main courses available for both luncheon and dinner. The free-wheeling "pub" lunch costs $2.75. In the evening the main courses cost from about $3.25 to $7. There is a $5.95 prix fixe dinner served on Sunday. *Cocktails, wines. On Saturday and Sunday the restaurant opens at 5 p.m.*
AE CB DC

DELFINO

68 Fifth Avenue (at 13th Street) OR *5-7379*

The menu at Delfino's is quite varied. It is also more interesting than the cuisine. The food is not generally outstanding, but it can be quite palatable. The restaurant has complete luncheons from about $2.25 to $4. Dinner is à la carte with main courses from about $2.25 to $5.50. *Cocktails, wines. On Saturday the restaurant opens at 5:30 p.m. Closed Sunday.*

AE DC

★ DEL PEZZO

33 West 47th Street CO *5-8744 and* JU *6-9705*

The Del Pezzo is a most agreeable and unpretentious Italian restaurant and it is also one of the city's oldest. The veal dishes in particular are recommended, including the osso buco (braised veal knuckle) and stuffed breast of veal. Luncheons and dinners are both prix fixe and à la carte. Luncheons with salad and coffee from about $1.50 to $2.75; complete dinners $3.50. A la carte main courses from $1.60 to $5. *Cocktails, wines. Closed Sunday, New Year's Day, July 4, Labor Day, Christmas and usually one week in July.*

AE DC

★ DELSOMMA

266 West 47th Street CO *5-9294,* PL *7-9079 and* PL *7-9234*

The Delsomma is an Italian restaurant with a kitchen that is notably like that of a dozen other just-satisfactory Italian restaurants in the theater district. The menu, with its eggplant parmigiana, baked ziti Sicilian-style and linguine with white or red clam sauce, is thoroughly familiar. The food is good and, its most commendable aspect, inexpensive. There are complete three-course luncheons priced from about $2.25 to $2.95. The evening menu is à la carte with entrees from about $1.70 for spaghetti with tomato sauce to $6.25 for sirloin steak

pizzaiola. *Cocktails, wines. Dinner is served Saturday from noon. Closed Sunday and Christmas.*
AE

★★★ DINTY MOORE'S

216 West 46th Street JU *2-9820*

If Moore's is not the best restaurant in the Broadway area, it is certainly a contender for the title. The menu is plain and scarcely varies from day to day, but the food is more often than not first-rate. The specialties include corned beef and cabbage, outstanding calves liver with bacon and excellent fish dishes. All dishes are à la carte with main luncheon courses from about $2.75 to $4; main dinner entrees from about $4 to $7. *Cocktails, wines. Closed Sunday.*

DRAGON GATE

146 East 53rd Street *752-5190*

This is a place of dull delights, but it is enormously popular with many whose palates are ravished by the likes of egg rolls, chow mein and barbecued spareribs. The Chinese menu is conventional, and the food is palatable but uninspired in its seasoning; not even chopped scallions to relieve the monotony. If any dish sampled recently seemed above average, it was the lobster roll. There are complete luncheons from $1.50 to $3. The à la carte menu has main courses from about $3.25 to $7.50. *Cocktails, wines. Luncheon is not served Sunday. Closed July 4 and Thanksgiving.*
AE CB DC

★ DRESNER'S

1479 York Avenue (near 78th Street) RE *4-9105*

The first thing to consider about Dresner's is the cost of dining there. It may not have the most distinguished kitchen in town, but the menu is well varied and the food is agreeably prepared. The menu runs along the lines of broiled chicken livers, broiled shrimp, broiled chicken and chops, and all dishes are à la carte. At midday the cost is from about $1 for sandwiches to $1.75 for main courses. Entrees in the evening cost from about $1.85 for the chicken to $2.95 for the shrimp. *Cocktails, wines.*

★ DUE MONDI

120 East 40th Street YU *6-6434*

The Due Mondi has a thoroughly competent kitchen and produces food that is, if not distinguished, very well seasoned. There is an excellent hot mushroom appetizer, and main dishes include the usual veal and chicken dishes parmigiana, ravioli, cannelloni and manicotti. A slice of rum cake sampled on one occasion had the flavor of the refrigerator. The Due Mondi is a large restaurant and is crowded at noon. Luncheons are à la carte with main courses from $2.65 to $4.50. There are complete dinners from $4.15 to $7.75. *Cocktails, wines. On Saturday the restaurant opens at 5 p.m. Closed Sunday.*

AE CB DC

★★ DU MIDI

311 West 48th Street CO *5-9395*

Among the many small bistros of Manhattan, East Side or West Side, Du Midi is one of the best. The dishes are French provincial, prepared with admirable care and reasonably priced. Luncheons are à la carte with main courses from about $1.60 to $3.75. There are complete dinners from about $3.95 to $5.20. Du Midi is close to many Broadway theaters, and dinner is served until midnight. *Cocktails, wines. Dinner is served from noon on Saturday and from 1 p.m. on Sunday.*

★ DUMPLING HOUSE

3 East Broadway *233-3336*

This is a relatively new restaurant near Chatham Square in Chinatown that has already achieved a certain word-of-mouth fame. The owners are brothers who all but bubble with enthusiasm, and their food is very good, the portions large. They may recommend a hearty won ton soup whose broth has more body than one is accustomed to, or their moo sui pork, shredded pork and egg with pancakes, which, although appetizing, seems less delicate than in other restaurants where it is a specialty. The food at the Dumpling House is reasonably priced with lunch and dinner main courses from $1 to $3. *No alcoholic beverages.*

★ EATING HO

23 Chatham Square *964-5452*

This is a curious restaurant in that the potential seems greater than the realization. For example, the seasonings in the hot and sour soup had to be rectified at the table. A little soy sauce here, a little hot sauce there, and it becomes palatable. Are they afraid to offend the non-Chinese audience? There are excellent and unusual "house dem sem," made with shrimp-stuffed mushrooms and Chinese ham, and very good steamed chicken with soy. The place is worth a visit even by subway because the food there is interesting. There is, or was recently, very l-o-u-d music from the restaurant's radio, but most of the guests seemed oblivious to it. The menu, the same for lunch and dinner, is à la carte with main dishes from 85 cents for roast pork lo mein to $4 for fried squabs in oyster sauce. *No alcoholic beverages.*

EBERLIN'S

45 New Street DI *4-6237*

A cavernous, many-tabled restaurant in the Wall Street area that seems nearly as active during the luncheon period as the Stock Exchange at the peak trading hour. The menu is as conventional as a Western omelet, and so is the kitchen. The table service is lackadaisical. Tripe fanciers point out that tripe is available cooked in many ways at Eberlin's, two of the most popular ways being in a cream sauce and broiled. The same à la carte menu serves throughout the day. The cost of main dishes is from about $1.50 for stuffed pepper to $4.50 for sirloin steak. *Cocktails, wines. Dinner is served only until 7:30 p.m. Closed Saturday and Sunday.*

★★ EDUARDO'S

1140 Second Avenue (at 60th Street) MU *8-7390*

This is a happy and festive place that is alive with young people who come there precisely for pizza. The menu is fairly extensive, however, and the food is good and reasonably priced. The à la carte menu, available both day and night, has dishes from about $1.40 for spaghetti with garlic and oil to $4.95 for sirloin. *Cocktails, wines. Closed Thanksgiving and Christmas.*

86th STREET BRAUHAUS

249 East 86th Street LE *4-9840*

German-American cuisine. Menus are prix fixe and à la carte. Complete luncheons from about $2.25; complete dinners from about $3.25. A la carte main courses at luncheon from $1.50; at dinner from about $2.25. *Cocktails, wines.*

★ EL CHARRO

4 Charles Street (near Greenwich Avenue) CH *2-9547*

El Charro bills itself as "A bit of Mexico in Greenwich Village," and it is a worthwhile place for those with a palate for well-spiced foods. It is a small restaurant with a lusty but neat decor, and the service is excellent. There are very good combination plates with tostadas, tacos and enchiladas. A specialty of the house is a fiery but appetizing chicken Mexican style. The menu is à la carte with main courses from about $3 to $4.50. *Cocktails, wines. Open for dinner only. Closed Sunday.*

EL CORTIJO

128 West Houston Street OR *4-4080 and 473-9095*

This restaurant is offbeat, small and part and parcel of a neighborhood bar. The food is Spanish and sometimes notable, particularly the clams and green sauce, the seafood (zarzuela de mariscada) in egg sauce and the paella. There are also Italian dishes. Luncheons are à la carte with main dishes from about $1.30 to $3. A la carte main dinner courses from about $2.25 to $4. *Cocktails, wines. Dinner is served Saturday from noon and Sunday from 2 p.m. Reservations accepted.*

★ **ELECTRA**

949 Second Avenue *421-8425*
(between 50th and 51st Streets)

If the sum of this restaurant were equal to some of its parts it would be most agreeable indeed. The entrees, including the moussaka, the pastitsio (a blend of cinnamon-scented ground lamb, macaroni and custard) and the baked lamb, are excellent. The plate of assorted Greek appetizers lacks the style and imagination found in several of the city's restaurants of similar genre. The decor is nondescript modern. The luncheon menu lists à la carte entrees from about $1.10 to $1.55; complete meals from about $1.95 to $2.35. A la carte dinner dishes are from about $1.85 to $4.25; complete meals from about $2.85 to $5.25. *Wines, beer.*

★★★ **EL FARO**

823 Greenwich Street (corner Horatio Street) WA *9-8210*

This is an extraordinary restaurant with an excellent Spanish kitchen and a decor that has as much the feel of a small European restaurant as any restaurant in Manhattan. The menu encompasses such dishes as three kinds of paella and lobster with green sauce, and the preparation of all of them is admirable. El Faro has its crude aspects including bare, Formica tables, but it enjoys a well-deserved popularity and reservations are recommended. All dishes are à la carte with main luncheon dishes from about $1.50 to $4 and main dinner entrees from about $3 to $4. *Cocktails, wines. Dinner is served from 1 p.m. on Sunday.*

★★ ELIZABETH WHITE'S RESTAURANT

983 First Avenue (at 54th Street) PL *9-7850*

This is a restaurant with a neighborhood feeling and with one of the best American-style menus in the city. The service staff is small, but the food is generally excellent. At peak dining hours there is a wait for tables. Luncheons and dinners are both prix fixe and à la carte. Complete luncheons from $1.45; à la carte main courses from 95 cents. Complete dinners from about $2.45; à la carte entrees from about $1.85. *Cocktails, wines. On Saturday the restaurant opens at 5 p.m. Closed Sunday and most major holidays. Reservations accepted.*

★★ EL MATADOR

242 East 58th Street PL *3-1110*

This is a new Spanish-Mexican restaurant with somber lighting, red banquettes, a lot of air conditioning and occasional guitar music. The food may not be distinguished for its authentic nature, but it is palatable nonetheless. The menu embraces such dishes as seviche, or marinated red snapper in lime juice, enchiladas, tacos, tostadas, picadillo and paella. Main dishes cost from about $3.50 to $7. *Cocktails, wines. Open for dinner only. Closed Saturday and Sunday during the summer.*

AE CB DC

★★★ EL PARADOR CAFÉ

561 Second Avenue (near 31st Street) MU *4-8819*

This restaurant, with comfortable decor and first-class service, offers the best Mexican cuisine in town. Dinners are à la carte, and the cost of main courses is about $3 to $5. Fried chicken El Parador ($5), which requires 30

minutes to prepare, is especially recommended. So are the combination plates. *Excellent cocktails, domestic and Mexican beers and Spanish wines. Dinners only. Closed Sunday, New Year's Day, Labor Day, Thanksgiving and Christmas. Reservations are not accepted, and there is frequently a long wait for tables.*
AE

★ EL QUIJOTE

226 West 23rd Street WA *9-1855*

There is a certain tawdry appeal about this well-known Spanish restaurant in the Chelsea Hotel. A large mural depicts the adventures of Don Quixote, and the other walls are hung with a grab bag of paintings in garish colors. The atmosphere is casual in both the dining room and the kitchen. But many dishes are well prepared, including the paellas: the valenciana with chicken, seafood and sausages, and the mariscada with only seafood. The luncheons in particular at El Quijote are a bargain with à la carte main dishes priced from about $1.25 for the ground meat specialty called picadillo à la creole to $1.75 for a generous portion of paella valenciana. A la carte dishes on the dinner menu cost from $2.50 to $4. *Cocktails, wines. Luncheon is not served Saturday and Sunday.*
AE DC

★ EL RADIANTE (offbeat)

640 Prospect Avenue MO *9-8055 and* MO *9-8163*
(near Kelly Street), the Bronx

In spite of the numerous Puerto Ricans in New York, there are relatively few Puerto Rican restaurants of stature; this is probably the best. The food is hearty, and some of the dishes include combinations of rice, pigeon peas, pork and chicken. There are robust meat and vegetable soups, some flavored with coriander. All dishes are à la carte and range from $1.50 for rice and pigeon peas to $3 for paella valenciana. *Cocktails, wines. Open around the clock except for cleaning periods from about 5 a.m. to 6 a.m.*

★★ EMIL'S

23 Park Row WO *2-5866*

This is an expansive, festive, friendly restaurant and one of the best in New York's financial district. Curried dishes—lobster, chicken, shrimp and scallops—are specialties of the house and they are excellent. Otherwise the restaurant bills itself as a seafood house, and the food is generally good. The service is informal but markedly efficient. The menu is à la carte with luncheon main courses from about $2.45 to $4.75, dinner entrees from about $3 to $5.35. *Cocktails, wines. Closed Saturday, Sunday and major holidays.*

AE CB DC

★★ EMPIRE, THE

191 Madison Avenue 683-3465
(between 34th and 35th Streets)

This is a relatively new Chinese restaurant with screens and scrolls and mirrored columns. The Empire is directly across the street from B. Altman & Co. The boast of the place is that it can, unlike most of its competitors, produce Peking duck on one hour's notice. And the duck is good if unauthentic. In lieu of the traditional water–flour–sesame-seed doilies, The Empire serves slices of yeast rolls with the crisp duck skin. The kitchen may tamper with tradition, but the food is generally very good. Luncheons cost from about $1.35 for chow mein to $3.45 for butterfly shrimp. The à la carte menu has main courses from about $2.95 for moo goo gai pan to $12 for the duck, which serves two. *Cocktails, wines. Only à la carte items are available on Sunday, from 1:30 p.m. Closed Thanksgiving.*

★ **EMPRESS, THE**

710 Third Avenue (between 44th and 45th Streets) YU *6-5995*

This is a small, pleasant and somewhat gaudy Chinese restaurant with Chinese-red walls and pink tablecloths. The menu shows imagination and the food can be excellent. As in most Chinese restaurants, it is best to order from the à la carte menu. There are complete luncheons, however, from about $1.75 to $2.70. On the principal menu, available throughout the day, main dishes cost from about $1.90 to $13 (Peking duck). *Cocktails, wines. Only à la carte items are available on Sunday, from 1 p.m.*

AE CB DC

★ **ENGLISH GRILL**

Lower Plaza, Rockefeller Plaza CI *6-5800*

Few restaurants in Manhattan offer a more agreeable view to dine by than the English Grill at Rockefeller Plaza. In the winter there is a wide-angle view of the skating rink, and in summer there is dining out of doors. Many of the main dishes, such as seafood Newburg and pork goulash, are very good, but some of the items, particularly the overcooked, waterlogged vegetables, are lamentable. The wines in carafe are also poor and, considering the quality, costly. The luncheon menu is à la carte with main courses from about $2.75 to $5.95. There are complete dinners from about $4.50 to $6; à la carte dishes in the evening from about $3.25 to $6.50. *Cocktails, wines.*

AE CB DC

ENGLISH PUB, THE

313 Avenue of the Americas (at West 3rd Street) OR *5-3949*

There is considerable charm in the physical setting of The English Pub. There are pewter sconces, carriage lamps and walls of rough white plaster and stained wood, and a guest could only hope that the kitchen and service would be of equal distinction. Unfortunately they are not.

The quality of the lamb chops is good, but they may be served lukewarm; the string beans are waterlogged, as in many another restaurant in New York, and the cheese assortment is, or was on one visit, lamentable. There is a pleasant bar, however, with refreshments on draught, and an outdoor garden for dining. The menu is à la carte with entrees from about $1.75 to $4.75. *Cocktails, wines. Monday through Friday the restaurant opens at 4 p.m. and on Saturday and Sunday at 1 p.m.*

AE CB DC

ERSHOWSKY DELI

39 West 46th Street *247-5630 and 247-5631*

This is one of the town's oldest delicatessens, formerly on the Lower East Side. The slogan is "My Pa Served Your Ma," and the sandwiches are ample and very good. The restaurant's ventilation leaves something to be desired. The cost of the sandwiches is from about 65 cents for chopped liver to $2 for an oversize triple-decker. *Soft drinks and beer. Closed Sunday, New Year's Day, Labor Day, Christmas and all Jewish holidays.*

★ ESPLANADE, THE

969 Lexington Avenue (near 70th Street) UN *1-2015*

A small neighborhood restaurant sandwiched between a grocery store and a bookshop. The management is Swiss, the menu French and Italian. The cuisine is moderately expensive but very good. Many of the dishes, such as the bay scallops sautéed and kidneys Esplanade, are prepared to order. Luncheons are à la carte with main courses from about $1.90 to $3.50. There are complete dinners from about $3.75 to $6 and à la carte entrees in the evening from about $2.40 to $5.50. There is a 25-cent cover charge on a meal when no alcoholic beverage is bought to accompany it. *Cocktails, wines. On Saturday the restaurant opens at 5:30 p.m. Closed Sunday.*

AE DC

★ ESTHER ENG

18 Pell Street 732-0175

Legend has it that Esther Eng and her associates, most of whom were of the Chinese theater, were stranded in New York and opened one of the best of the town's Chinese restaurants, Bo Bo, at 20½ Pell Street. Miss Eng many months ago opened her own establishment at 18 Pell Street, and the food is good, although not up to the nearby Bo Bo's. The decor of Esther Eng is conventional, the reception is warm and the service, on one occasion at least, excellent. There is a complete luncheon from about $1.25 to $1.90. A la carte entrees, available at all times, cost from about $2.50 to $4.50. *Cocktails, wines. Dinner is served Sunday from 11:30 a.m.*

AE CB DC

★ FAGIANO RESTAURANT

1294 Third Avenue (at 74th Street) 535-3416

Another of those restaurants in which some of the parts seem unreasonably better than the whole. Several of the dishes sampled were quite respectable, including the chicken bolognese with prosciutto and mozzarella and the veal francese, which is a quick sauté with lemon. There is piped-in music that seems, if possible, louder than one is normally attuned to, and a pink decor. The tortellini (small meat-filled pastas) seemed overcooked, and the potato croquettes were rather heavy. There are complete luncheons at Fagiano that cost from about $1.75 to $2.75. Complete dinners cost from about $4.75 to $6.75; à la carte dishes from $2 to $5.75. *Cocktails, wines. Closed Monday.*

AE DC

FAMOUS KITCHEN

318 West 45th Street CI 5-9544

A fairly pleasant restaurant in the theater district. The menu is more or less humdrum New York Italian, and

so is the kitchen. Complete luncheons from $2.35 to $4; complete dinners from $4.35 to $6.50. *Cocktails, wines. Closed Sunday and Christmas.*
AE DC

FERDI'S

765 United Nations Plaza MU *6-9436*

This is a convenient spot to dine when visiting the United Nations. In good weather there is a sidewalk café. Both the menu and the cooking are conventional and will seem familiar to those who frequent the city's Italian restaurants. There are special luncheons priced at $2.25. On the à la carte menu main luncheon courses are from about $1.50 to $3.95; main dinner dishes from about $1.75 to $8. *Cocktails, wines. Closed Sunday, most major holidays and, during the summer months, Saturday also.*
AE CB DC

FINALE, THE

48 Barrow Street CH *3-7538*

Largely American and Italian cuisine. The menu is à la carte with main dishes from about $1.95 to $3.95. For an additional 85 cents a choice of appetizer or soup, dessert and coffee are included. *Cocktails, wines. Open for dinner only.*

FIN 'N CLAW

1394 Third Avenue RE *4-4641 and* RE *4-9107*
(between 79th and 80th Streets)

This fish restaurant in upper Manhattan enjoys a neighborhood popularity. The food is conventionally good, but the restaurant's ventilation is less than adequate. The menu is familiar. There are luncheons, not including dessert, from about $1.75 to $2.75. The à la carte menu, available throughout the day, is priced from about $1.95 for broiled porgy to $6.95 for broiled extra-large lobster. *Cocktails, wines. Only à la carte items are available on Sunday. Closed Thanksgiving and Christmas.*

★ FISHERMAN'S NET

493 Third Avenue (near 33rd Street) MU *4-8911*

There is one thing about the vast majority of New York restaurants—their menus are nothing if not predictable. Most of the Italian restaurants are alike, and so are the small French bistros. The menu at the Fisherman's Net resembles a dozen or so others, but the fish is fresh and the service amiable. There are complete luncheons ranging in price from about $1.50 for broiled porgy to $2.25 for striped bass. The à la carte menu available at all meals has entrees from about $2.10 for broiled porgy to $7.35 for a large broiled lobster. *Cocktails, wines. Open seven days a week. Luncheon is not served on Sunday.*

AE DC

★ 500 ON 8TH RESTAURANT, THE

500 Eighth Avenue (at 35th Street) *736-6171*

This is a large restaurant with gauche-modern decor in the garment district. It has one of those thoroughly familiar menus with the usual listings of broiled sole, deep-fried sea scallops, old-fashioned beef stew and on and on, but the restaurant also has an excellent chicken soup with matzoh balls and very good sandwiches. The luncheon menu is à la carte with main courses from about $1.95 to $5.75. A la carte entrees in the evening cost from $2.25 to $6.25. *Cocktails, wines. Closed Saturday and Sunday.*

AE CB DC

★★ FLEUR DE LIS

141 West 69th Street *874-9060*

An uncluttered, provincial-style French restaurant with an extensive menu. The food is hearty in concept and appointment; service is friendly and willing. The pâté is robust and garlicky; the coq au vin and tripe à la mode de

Caen are good, and the restaurant's version of cassoulet delighted one palate. Wines are reasonably priced. The menu is à la carte with luncheon entrees from $1.60 and dinner entrees from about $2.25 to $6.50. *Cocktails, wines. Dinner is served from noon on Sunday.*
AE CB DC

★ **FLOWER DRUM RESTAURANT**

856 Second Avenue (near 45th Street) OX 7-4280

This is a rather spacious and colorful Chinese restaurant whose menu boasts four schools of Chinese cooking. The luncheon menu is prix fixe and somewhat routine with entrees, such as chow mein and shrimp in lobster sauce, from $1.45 to $2.15. The dinner menu, also available at midday, is à la carte and more inspired. The cost of main courses is from about $2.75 to $4.50. *Cocktails, wines. Only à la carte items are available Saturday and Sunday.*
AE DC

★ **FONDA LA PALOMA**

156 West 49th Street 421-5495

With a little imagination this could develop into one of the pleasantest Mexican restaurants in town, and a good one would be welcome in midtown. (The altogether excellent El Parador is downtown.) The food at Fonda La Paloma is very good, whether it is enchilada, taco or stuffed chilies, and a better guacamole would be hard to find. The fault lies in the tables, a bit rickety and too close together, and the service, friendly but painfully slow. One menu at the restaurant serves throughout the day. The menu is à la carte with entrees from about $2.50 for chicken tacos to $6 for steak. *Cocktails, wines. On Saturday the restaurant opens at 5 p.m. Closed Sunday, New Year's Day, Washington's Birthday, July 4, Thanksgiving and Christmas.*
AE CB DC

FONTANA DI TREVI

151 West 57th Street CI *7-5683*

It might be charitable not to go into too much detail about the decor and food at the Fontana di Trevi, Suffice it to say that the decor is on the dark side and dusty, and there are plastic vegetables at eye level along the edge of the banquettes. The stuffed clams are humdrum, most of the antipasto was taken from a tin and the fettucini can be watery. The espresso at Fontana di Trevi is not too bad. The menus are à la carte with main courses at midday from about $2.35 to $5.50; in the evening from about $3.60 to $6.50. *Cocktails, wines. Closed Sunday during July and August.*

AE DC

FOO CHOW RESTAURANT

1020 Lexington Avenue UN *1-4350*
(between 72nd and 73rd Streets)

This restaurant is small and unpretentious and the service is slow, but the menu has imagination and the kitchen seems more than competent. There are complete luncheons from about 99 cents to $1.75. The cost of entrees on the à la carte menu ranges from about $2.10 (Chinese chicken salad) to $12.75 (Peking duck for two or more). *Wines, beer.*

★ FORLINI'S RESTAURANT

93 Baxter Street WO *2-9316*

An earthy, sometimes boisterous, place with a juke-box and a kitchen that is generally commendable. Some of the dishes, such as the noodles with pesto—a garlic, basil and butter sauce—are excellent if a touch robust. The menu is admirably inexpensive. There are à la carte main courses from about $1.15 to $4.50; complete dinners from about $3.25 to $6.25. *Cocktails, wines.*

★ FORNOS

236 West 52nd Street CI 7-9420

There are Latin-Americans and others in town who think of this as one of the best Spanish restaurants in the city. The menus are à la carte with main courses from about $2.50 to $6. To be sure of good food it is best to order several hours or a day in advance. *Cocktails, wines. Closed Sunday and the last two weeks in August.*

FORUM OF THE TWELVE CAESARS, THE

57 West 48th Street PL 7-3450

In New York it is possible to be almost constantly appalled at restaurants with a superficial grandeur and elevated prices that dare in sum to be brazenly pedestrian. The Forum of the Twelve Caesars fits the pattern. There is gloriously starched napery, handsome silver, service plates in bas-relief and in the midst of it all, too often to be called chance, food that is mediocre beyond redemption. The menu is as broad as the gestures of the waiters and, like the waiters, it is mostly show without substance. There are some good dishes all right, including the gazpacho in summer, the leek and sausage pie and the live trout, although that, too, is sometimes overcooked. But the mixed grill! Such a difficult dish to spoil, with the least care. You ask for a lamb chop rare, and it is duly recorded by the waiter. The chop and other meats arrive overcooked and drenched in a heavy sauce, strongly spiced. All dishes are à la carte with luncheon entrees from about $3.25; those at dinner are from about $4.25. There is an excellent and, for this genre of restaurant, reasonably priced wine list. *Cocktails, wines. Luncheon is not served on Saturday. Closed Sunday during the summer.*

AE CB DC

★★★ FOUNTAIN CAFÉ

Bethesda Fountain, Central Park near East 72nd Street

This outdoor café is one of the most delightful of New York's summer attractions and the only outdoor dining spot in the city that really makes sense on all counts. There is no visible automobile traffic with the attendant fumes to be inhaled. There are views of clouds and birds and falling water and even at times a balloon or two floating on strings in the hands of children. There are awnings and kiosks, and the vistas are kindred in spirit to those of the Bois de Boulogne. There is a fascinating menu and the food is by and large first-rate. The menu has listed at times such dishes as a mousse of chicken livers, prosciutto with melon and stuffed artichoke with shrimp rémoulade. Main dishes include terrines of veal and duckling, salmon steak with sour cream and red caviar. The omelets, one of the most popular dishes at the café, have been at times a disappointment—not that they were inexpertly made, but they seemed to have been made too far in advance because of kitchen facilities. The cost of sandwich platters at the café is from about $1.50 to $1.95; main dishes from about $1.65 to $4.95. *Cocktails, wines. The restaurant is open in warm weather only from 11 a.m. until 11 p.m.*

★★ FOUR SEAS

142 Maiden Lane WH *3-6234*

This Chinese restaurant in the financial section of the city is among the most recent to open in New York, and in decor it is perhaps the smartest. The upstairs dining room is simply designed but has walls of carmine and peacock blue. The chef is reputedly of the Szechuan school in China, which is noted for the spiced nature of its dishes. Those at the Four Seas may be a touch too bland for some palates, but the food is generally excellent and prepared with care. There is a single menu for luncheon and dinner, and it is à la carte. The cost of main courses is from

about $2.75 to $7. *Cocktails, wines. Closed Sunday and national holidays.*
AE CB DC

★★★ FOUR SEASONS, THE

99 East 52nd Street PL *1-4300*

The Four Seasons, like cheese and wine, improves with age. It has always been one of the most inventive restaurants in the city, and it is essentially how a New York restaurant should look. It has an opulence that is rare to behold and boasts works of art by Picasso and Miro and a stunning floating sculpture by Richard Lippold. The presentation of the foods, whether a ring of littleneck clams on ice or an exceptionally good seviche in a silver shell, is admirable. One recalls among others a notable dish of poached chicken with thin noodles and a rich broth and a well-made omelet with morels, or woodland mushrooms. All dishes are à la carte with main luncheon courses from about $3.25 to about $8; main dinner entrees from about $4.75 to $9. There is a $1 cover charge at all times. *Cocktails, wines. Luncheon is not served on Saturday during the summer. Closed Sunday.*
AE CB DC

★★ FRANKIE AND JOHNNIE

269 West 45th Street CI *5-9717*

There is a dearth of good eating establishments in the Broadway area, and Frankie and Johnnie, which bills itself as "Simpson's in the Strand," is one of the best. It is an excellent steak house and therefore immensely popular. It is small, crowded at the dinner hour and a trifle noisy. The steaks are first-rate and the service enthusiastic. In addition to grilled dishes, the menu lists such items as chicken in the pot with matzoh balls, shrimp creole and creamed chicken au gratin. The menu is à la carte with main courses from about $4.25 for chicken à la king to $6.75 for filet mignon. The restaurant, which serves din-

ner only, opens at 4:30 p.m. *Cocktails, wines. Closed Sunday, Thanksgiving and Christmas.*
AE DC

★ FRANK LEONE'S

53 East 54th Street PL *9-5941*

Frank Leone is the son of the woman who founded Mama Leone's restaurant many years ago. Although the food at Frank Leone's is quite good and abundant, the impression of one guest is that it could very well be better than it is. The homemade tagliatelle prepared at tableside, for example, tasted on one occasion as if the pasta had been cooked in unsalted water, and it was served lukewarm. Blue-green walls, antique clocks and oil paintings give the restaurant a pleasant atmosphere. There are complete luncheons priced from about $3.25 for linguine with fresh clams to $4 for lobster au gratin. Complete four-course dinners from about $5.50 to $8. *Cocktails, wines. Closed Sunday, New Year's Day and Christmas.*
AE CB DC

★ FRANK'S RESTAURANT

315 West 125th Street *749-7070*

This is a large and pleasant restaurant in Harlem with an American-style menu. It lists such dishes as baked short ribs of beef, lamb stew and shrimp New Orleans style. Some of the fish dishes, such as the broiled striped bass, are excellent. At lunch and dinner all the dishes are à la carte with main courses from about $2.15 (fried smelts) to $5.50 (filet mignon). On Sundays and holidays the menu ranges from $2.50 to $5.75. *Cocktails, wines.*
AE CB DC

FRANK'S SPA

273 Fifth Avenue (near 29th Street) MU *4-2610*

Sandwiches are the hands-down favorite of most New Yorkers at midday, and this is one of the most popular of the town's sandwich emporiums. The fillings are generous and the cost is from about 65 cents to $1.20. There are also hot dishes and salads from about $1.20 to $1.60. *No alcoholic beverages. Closed Saturday and Sunday.*

FRAUNCES TAVERN

54 Pearl Street (at Broad Street) BO *9-0144*

The history is here no doubt. This is, as the literature says, "one of America's oldest buildings." It was built in 1719 and was acquired in 1762 "by Samuel Fraunces as the Queen's Head Tavern, scene of Washington's farewell to his officers on December 4, 1783." There are also musty decor and elderly waiters, but the "olde worlde" ambiance is considerably done in by the loud piped-in music. The menu is limited, good at times but dull. The seafood is fair to middling. The roast beef was of obviously good quality but served cold. The vegetables, including the once-frozen peas and carrots, arrived at the table cold, and the salad was of a tearoom variety. And on and on. There is one menu for lunch and dinner. Main courses cost from about $2.75 to $6. *Cocktails, wines. Luncheon is not served on Saturday. Closed Sunday and, during July and August, Saturday also.*

AE CB DC

★★★ FRENCH SHACK, THE

65 West 55th Street CI *6-5126*

The French Shack ranks with the best medium-priced French restaurants in New York. The kitchen is far more than merely competent. Some of the specialties of the house, which do not, incidentally, invariably appear on the menu, are well above average and include cassoulet and veal with fines herbes. There are two faults to be found with the restaurant: it is generally crowded, and a few of the tables are too close for comfort. The service staff is few in number and, although the service is industrious, it sometimes seems annoyingly slow. The cost

of a complete luncheon is from about $3.50 to $5. Dinner is à la carte with main courses from about $3.75 to $6.50. *Cocktails, wines. On Sunday the restaurant opens at 5 p.m.*
AE DC

★ FRIAR TUCK

914 Third Avenue (near 55th Street) *688-4725*

The Friar Tuck, another in a long list of would-be English pubs in Manhattan, opened recently and almost overnight has become one of the busiest restaurants in the city. The piped-in music can scarcely be heard above the din of voices. There are cobblestone walls, beams, red tablecloths and candlelight, and the restaurant is on two levels. The lower one resembles a dungeon. Two dishes were eaten with pleasure at the Friar Tuck. A mutton chop with kidney came off exceptionally well and so did the roast prime ribs of beef. Some of the dishes, such as the shepherd's pie, seem ordinary, and the sauces for other meat dishes have a pasty look. A word should be said for the miniskirted waitresses. All of them seem models of enthusiasm and efficiency. Complete luncheons are priced from $2.25 to $2.60. A la carte dishes from $1 for a hamburger to $7.25 for sirloin steak. *Cocktails, wines.*
AE CB DC

FUJI RESTAURANT

238 West 56th Street CI *5-8594*

Small but stylish, the Fuji is a pleasant Japanese restaurant. The food is good, but oddly enough, that most popular of Japanese dishes, sukiyaki, is made here with an excess of celery; it is, therefore, a disappointment and tastes like chop suey. The seating is Western style. Dinners and luncheons are both prix fixe and à la carte. Complete luncheons from $2.50; complete dinners from $3.75. A la carte entrees from about $1.25 to $4.25. *Cocktails, wines. Luncheon is not served Saturday and Sunday. Closed Tuesday, Thanksgiving and Christmas. Reservations accepted.*

FUNDADOR

117 West 47th Street JU *6-9363*

An unabashedly garish restaurant, unabashedly loud when the jukebox plays. The menu combines Mexican, Spanish and Latin American cooking with mucho garlic. It is best not to go when pressed for time; the service is leisurely Spanish. There are luncheon specials that cost about $1.75. The à la carte menu has main dishes from about $1.75 for omelets to $3.95 for paella with lobster. *Cocktails, wines. Open seven days.*

AE CB DC

FUSCO'S

18 Beaver Street WH *4-4580*

This restaurant is rather plush and offers French-Italian cuisine. There is an à la carte menu with main courses from about $2.75 to $5.50. Complete dinners cost from about $3.75 to $7.50. *Cocktails, wines. Closed Saturday and Sunday.*

AE CB DC

★★ GAETANO'S RISTORANTE

1190 Lexington Avenue (at 81st Street) 249-4278

There are so many commendable things about this colorful, recently opened Italian restaurant that one deplores mentioning the bad. The decor, with its candy-striped draperies and red tablecloths, is bright, a bit garish and altogether pleasant. The first course of vegetables à la grecque, stuffed artichokes and roasted peppers was above average in inspiration. It was followed by linguine, then a well-seasoned veal parmigiana with an excellent tomato sauce plus fresh, not frozen, peas. After this came a first-rate salad, and then dessert. The sad fact was that the linguine was overcooked and served lukewarm, although of a fine flavor; the spumoni at the end of the meal had a stored quality, and the grapes served with nuts looked downright impoverished. Mark it, however, that dining at Gaetano's is more of a pleasure than a disappointment, and it is reasonably priced. There are only a few tables and a reservation is imperative. The cost of a complete dinner is $6. *Cocktails, wines. The restaurant opens at 6 p.m. Closed Sunday, Monday, New Year's Day, Thanksgiving and Christmas.*

★★ GAGE AND TOLLNER

372 Fulton Street, Brooklyn (near Borough Hall) TR *5-5181*

This establishment, founded in 1879, is four years older than the Brooklyn Bridge and just about equally revered. The most notable entrees on an extensive menu are the steaks, fish and seafood. There are about 50 ways of preparing oysters and clams listed on the menu. The turn-of-the-century decor with arched mirrors is admirable. The à la carte menu, available all day, ranges in price from about $2.25 for sausages to $6.50 for a single sirloin steak. Special lunches, served Monday through Friday, cost about $2.50 to $3.75. The restaurant closes at approximately 9 o'clock each evening. *Cocktails, wines. Closed Sunday, New Year's Day, July 4, Labor Day, Thanksgiving and Christmas.*

★ GAIETY EAST

684 Lexington Avenue PL *9-3455*
(between 56th and 57th Streets)

If there is one type of dining establishment that is as much a part of the New York scene as the Brooklyn Bridge, it is the delicatessen. The forte, of course, is sandwiches, both hot and cold, filled with such gustatory delights as pastrami, corned beef and chopped chicken liver. Also available generally are borscht with sour cream, chicken soup with matzoh balls and a good supply of relishes. One of the best and also one of the fanciest delicatessens is the Gaiety East. There are tables and counter service, and the food is on the whole excellent. The cost of sandwiches is from about 70 cents for a cheese sandwich to $2.50 for sturgeon, lettuce, tomato and Bermuda onion. There are also hot dishes, such as stuffed cabbage for $2.35. *Soft drinks and beer. There is an all-night phone service. The restaurant closes only between about 4 a.m. and 6:30 a.m.*

★ GALLAGHER'S

228 West 52nd Street CI *5-5336*

This is a noisy, bustling steak house with some dishes—the barley soup, for instance—of genuine merit. There is no quarreling with the quality of the steaks that are served, although the sirloin at $6.95 may be sliced a trifle thin for gourmands who are steak fanciers. The menu, in addition to steak, includes such entrees as lamb chops, lobster and chicken. The salads, even though they are made with iceberg lettuce, are of good flavor. The potatoes Gallagher—deep-fried wedges with skin on—are so-so. All dishes are à la carte with main courses from about $3.75 to $6.95. *Cocktails, wines. On Saturday and Sunday the restaurant opens at 4 p.m.*

AE CB DC

★★ GATE OF PEIPING, THE

33 Irving Place *982-5678*

One day recently, when a member of the kitchen staff failed to show, there were a few delays at The Gate of Peiping, but it is generally an admirable Chinese restaurant. The food is prepared with concern and imagination from soups to main courses. There are complete luncheons that cost from about $1.25 for a combination plate to $2.90 for lobster Cantonese; complete dinners from about $1.50 for chicken chow mein to $3.25 for the lobster. A la carte dishes cost from about $2 for diced chicken with Peking sauce to $2.90 for shrimp balls. *No alcoholic beverages. Closed Sunday during July and August.*

★★ GATTI'S

246 East 40th Street MU *6-7670*

Casual elegance is the atmosphere engendered by the brick walls lined with wine racks, stately archways, rolling service carts, strolling musicians and waiters in peasant-style striped shirts and cummerbunds at the Trattoria Gatti. A fairly large and popular restaurant on three floors, it is divided into small rooms to give an intimate setting. The extensive à la carte menu offers a wide variety of Italian dishes, generally well prepared, as well as a selection of steaks and chops. The restaurant several years ago opened a supplementary kitchen to prepare the pasta products and ice cream specialties served. Scaloppine alla Gatti and misto di pesce livornese (Italian-style fish stew) are recommended specialties of the house. All dishes are à la carte with main luncheon courses from about $2.50 to $5.95; main dinner courses from about $3.25 to $6.75. *Cocktails, wines. On Saturday the restaurant opens at 5:30 p.m. Closed Sunday.*

AE CB DC

★★★ GAUGUIN ROOM, THE

The Gallery of Modern Art LT *1-2311 and* LT *1-2721*
2 Columbus Circle

Visitors to afternoon or evening performances at Lincoln Center should not overlook The Gauguin Room on the ninth floor of The Gallery of Modern Art. This is one of the pleasantest dining rooms in New York. The Polynesian food, although specialized, is delicious, and it is prepared with admirable care. There is an excellent assortment of appetizers including crab-meat puffs, tempura shrimp and barbecued pork with pineapple. The curries, whether of shrimp, chicken or filet mignon, are well spiced, and the steak teriyaki is first-rate. There is no handsomer cocktail lounge in all the city, and the drinks are served in generous portions. It is true that there is a $1 admission fee to enter the gallery in order to gain access to the restaurant, but the food is worth it. The menus are à la carte with main courses at noon from $2.75 to $4.50, in the evening from $3.25 to $6.50. *Cocktails. Wines are available, but beer is recommended. Closed Monday. Tuesday through Friday the restaurant is open from noon to 8 p.m., and dinners are available from 5 p.m. The last seating is 7 p.m. On Saturday and Sunday the restaurant is open from noon to 6 p.m., and the last seating is 5 p.m.*

★★ GENE'S

73 West 11th Street OR *5-2048*

This is an enormously agreeable Italian restaurant with a kitchen that is superior to most of its kind in the city. And the management seems to be painstaking in caring for customers. There is an interesting appetizer and main course called shrimps Robert, the pasta dishes are good, particularly the fettucine Alfredo with prosciutto, and the breast of capon Gismonda is excellent. The veal at Gene's is only of average quality, but its preparation is admirable. Complete luncheons cost from $2.25 to $3.50; à la carte dishes at midday from $1.25 to $3.25. Complete dinners cost from $3.85 to $6.50; à la carte dishes in the evening from $3.25 to $6. *Cocktails, wines. On Sunday dinner is served from 1 p.m.*

AE DC

★ GIAMBELLI

238 Madison Avenue MU *5-8727*
(between 37th and 38th Streets)

A small, pleasant restaurant with Italian food that is at times excellent. At luncheon in particular Giambelli's is crowded. Complete luncheons from about $3.60 to $6; dinners à la carte with entrees from about $3.60 to $6.90; *Cocktails, wines. On Saturday the restaurant opens at 4 p.m. Closed Sunday, most major holidays, the first two weeks in July and, during July and August, Saturday also.*

AE CB DC

★ **GIAMBELLI 50th**

46 East 50th Street MU *8-2760*

Italian menu and a kitchen that is rarely above par. Complete luncheons from about $4.20 to $6.50. Dinners are à la carte with entrees from about $3.60 to $8. *Cocktails, wines. Closed Sunday, New Year's Day, Thanksgiving and Christmas.*

AE CB DC

GIAN MARINO'S

716 Lexington Avenue PL *3-8480*
(between 57th and 58th Streets)

The best thing to be said of Gian Marino's, perhaps, is that the restaurant is conveniently close to Bloomingdale's and Alexander's. Many of the main courses are heavily laced with oil and some of them, the chicken alla siciliana, for example, are robust with garlic. The pasta dishes can be excellent, however, although the bolognese sauce that accompanies the tagliarini is pedestrian. All dishes are à la carte with main courses at midday from about $2.25 for eggplant parmigiana to $4.75 for minute steak. Entrees in the evening cost from about $2.75 for spaghetti marinara to $6.50 for broiled sirloin steak. *Cocktails, wines. Luncheon is not served Saturday and Sunday. Closed New Year's Day and Christmas. During July and August the restaurant is closed Sunday.*

AE CB DC

GINGER MAN, THE

51 West 64th Street SC *4-7272*

The only thing that seems to have remained constant since the Ginger Man opened in 1964 is the decor. The food is certainly not the same. However, the entrance area was full at 12:45 on a Monday afternoon (filled with guileless tourists, it would appear). A couple were ushered into a back room where there was an unpleasant musty

odor and piped-in music bouncing off a tin roof to such an extent that a captain eventually noticed and turned the volume down. An omelet Grandmère lacked a fresh herb flavor and was devoid of salt and pepper. An order of shashlik was overcooked, dry, tough and gristly. The rice was reheated. A roulade Leontine—a chocolate roll—was still frozen in the middle. A mousse of chocolate was ordinary. All dishes à la carte with main courses at midday from about $2 for a cheese omelet to $4.25 for sirloin; in the evening from about $2.50 to $5.25. *Cocktails, wines. Open seven days a week.*
AE CB DC

★★ GINO'S RESTAURANT

780 Lexington Avenue (near 61st Street) TE *8-9827*

In any list of New York restaurants with Italian cuisine Gino's should be ranked among the best. The food is not altogether subtle, but its character is laudably good South Italian. There is a faithful, knowing clientele and the restaurant is generally crowded. The menu is extensive and both lunch and dinner are à la carte. Main luncheon courses from about $1.95; dinner courses from about $2.35. *Cocktails, wines. Closed Thanksgiving, Christmas and New Year's Day. Reservations not accepted.*

★★★ GIORDANO RESTAURANT

409 West 39th Street WI *7-9811*

This is a raffish, excellent Italian restaurant in an unlikely neighborhood near the entrance to the Lincoln Tunnel. It is the sort of place about which people say, "Don't praise it too highly, you may spoil it." There are brick walls and posters and a relaxed clientele. The veal and fish dishes are recommended in particular. There is no menu, and the cost of main courses at lunch and dinner ranges from about $2.75 to $7.75. There is a garden for outdoor dining during the summer months. *Cocktails,*

wines. On Saturday and Sunday the restaurant opens at 4 p.m. Closed New Year's Day, Thanksgiving and Christmas.
AE DC

★★ GIOVANNI

66 East 55th Street PL *3-1230*

The kitchen at Giovanni's is for the most part excellent, and the restaurant's appetizers are among the most creditable in town. The cold clams aspic, celery root rémoulade, herring, stuffed eggs and head cheese vinaigrette are all of high order. The trouble with the restaurant is the seating. The tables are too close together, and listening to a stranger's conversation is often unavoidable. Both luncheon and dinner are prix fixe; complete meals at midday from $3.50, and in the evening from $7.50. The menu is French and Italian. *Cocktails, wines. Closed Sunday, New Year's Day, Memorial Day, Labor Day, Columbus Day, Thanksgiving, Christmas and the month of July.*

★★ GLOUCESTER HOUSE

37 East 50th Street PL *5-7394*

Manhattan does not boast an altogether great fish and seafood house with extraordinary gustatory creations. However, if there were a sweepstakes for Manhattan's most outstanding one, the Gloucester House might come off best. The decor is plain, polished and atmospheric without seeming coy. The food is plain and good, with most dishes in the broiled and steamed category. Best of all, the fish is fresh. All dishes are à la carte and the same menu serves for both lunch and dinner. The cost of main courses is from about $2 (parsley omelet) to $13.25 ("jumbo" lobster) with potatoes and salad. *Cocktails, wines. On Sunday the restaurant opens at 1 p.m. Closed Thanksgiving and Christmas.*

★★ GOLD COIN

994 Second Avenue (between 52nd and 53rd Streets) PL *8-1251*

This is one of the best of the city's "bourgeois" Chinese dining spots. The food may be somewhat Westernized, but it is first-class nonetheless. Complete luncheons from about $2 to $4; dinners à la carte with main dishes from about $2 to $6.50. *Cocktails, wines. On Saturday and Sunday the restaurant opens at 3 p.m. Closed the first two weeks in August, Thanksgiving and Christmas.*

AE CB DC

★ GOLD COIN

835 Second Avenue (near 45th Street) OX *7-1515*

This is a relatively new Chinese restaurant and the offshoot of the well-thought-of Gold Coin a few blocks north. There are several things to recommend it, but a few dishes in the new establishment have been a disappointment. The food is palatable enough and the ingredients are of good quality, but the dishes do not seem to have the unusual excellence of the original Gold Coin. There are complete luncheons at about $2.50 and à la carte main courses from about $2.50 to $3.95. Dinner is à la carte with main courses from $2 to $6.50. *Cocktails, wines. On Saturday and Sunday the restaurant opens at 3 p.m. Closed Thanksgiving, Christmas and New Year's Eve.*

AE CB DC

★ GOLDEN COACH

578 Second Avenue OR *9-4669 and* OR *9-4670*
(near 32nd Street)

This Chinese restaurant in the Kips Bay Shopping Center has a pleasant atmosphere and the waiters are agreeable. The special luncheon is ordinary and the à la carte dishes, available at all meals, range from so-so spareribs to a most palatable combination of chicken and lobster. Complete luncheons from $1.30 to $2.75; à la

carte dishes from about $1.75 to $6. *Cocktails, wines. On Sunday dinner is served from 2 p.m.*
AE DC

★★ GOLDEN HORN

122 West 49th Street CI *6-2235*

This restaurant serving Armenian food has relatively new surroundings, and the effect is altogether pleasant. The atmosphere is colorful and bold, reminiscent of the Arabian Nights, and the food, as it has been in the past, is generally excellent. The dishes are in the Middle Eastern tradition and include such fare as stuffed vine leaves, salad with feta cheese, lamb and eggplant specialties. There are complete luncheons from $2.35 to $5.25; also à la carte, with main courses from about $1.50 to $3.45. Complete dinners from about $4.25 to $6.75; à la carte main courses from about $3 to $5.50. *Cocktails, wines. On Sunday dinner is served from 3 p.m.*
AE DC

★ GOLDIE'S NEW YORK

244 East 53rd Street PL *9-7245*

This solidly established institution is far better known as a night-spot with eminently listenable piano music. On the other hand, the food is quite palatable at both lunch and dinner. There is a hot and cold buffet at midday with such dishes as breast of chicken Jeannette, cold salmon in aspic and cold roast beef. Recently there was excellent hot corned beef with cabbage. As far as the decor is concerned, the restaurant is on the dark side, and the buffet is poorly displayed in its lack of illumination. Among the hot luncheon dishes from the kitchen the chicken pancake is very good and so is the ragout of beef, although the latter was recently served with cold noodles. The dinner menu lists chicken tarragon, steak, chops and shrimp scampi. All dishes are à la carte. At midday main courses are priced from $2.50 to $3.50. In the evening from $4 to $6.25. *Cocktails, wines. Closed Saturday and Sunday during the summer. Closed Sunday only during the winter.*

★ GONDOLA

729 Third Avenue MU *2-9658*
(between 45th and 46th Streets)

The decor of the Gondola restaurant, with its red-carpeted wall behind the bar and red pinpointed lighting, is real fancy. Some of the dishes, particularly those made with fish and seafood, are excellent, and some, including the meat sauces for spaghetti, are ordinary. On Wednesday there is available a reasonably gratifying osso buco accompanied by a risotto made with genuine Italian rice. The most admirable thing about this restaurant, perhaps, is the service, about as agreeable as you are likely to find in New York. Luncheon is à la carte with main courses from about $2 to $5.75. Dinner is à la carte with entrees from about $2.75 to $6. *Cocktails, wines. Closed Sunday and all holidays.*
AE CB DC

GOOD TABLE, THE

45 Lexington Avenue (at 24th Street) MU *4-9041*

Fondue bourguignonne, the guest-participation dish in which all hands cook bite-size portions of meat in hot oil before dipping in various sauces, is a specialty of the house at The Good Table. There are sputtering pots wall to wall at peak dining periods, and the fare is generally well received. But meat is only of medium quality, and the sauces are ordinary. The restaurant's picadillo, a Latin-American ground meat dish with rice, is very good, however, and the chilled gazpacho is excellent. Other specialties are beef Andalouse style and chicken in mustard. Dishes on the à la carte menu cost from about $2.75 for cannelloni to $3.50 for the fondue. A complete fondue dinner, including wine, is $6.50 and is available every day except Monday. *Wines and beer. The restaurant opens at 5 p.m. Closed New Year's Day, Thanksgiving and Christmas.*

★★ GRANADOS RESTAURANT

125 MacDougal Street OR *3-5576*

This is one of the most notable of New York's Spanish restaurants. The cooking is not grand luxe, but is more on the order of what may be found in a well-run casa de huespedes, or boarding house, in Spain. There is an excellent dish made with shrimp lightly seasoned with garlic, scallions and tomatoes and a sauce listed as salsa de la casa. In midsummer there is an interesting gazpacho containing sour cream and seedless grapes. Some of the dishes, such as pork with pine nuts, have a commendable flavor, but the meat is of medium quality. The restaurant's flan, at times, is overcooked. The restaurant, located in Greenwich Village, has tables close together, and at peak dining hours they are generally filled. The menu is à la carte with main courses from about $3 for eggs à la malagueña to $6.50 for a steak specialty. *Cocktails, wines. The restaurant opens at 5 p.m. There is a sidewalk café for outdoor dining May through September. Closed Thanksgiving.*
AE CB DC

GRAND CENTRAL TERMINAL

★Oyster Bar and Restaurant *(*MU *9-0776).* The chefs here have the blithe and wonderful notion that calories were never invented. The fame of this institution is worldwide and is based primarily on rich and buttery seafood stews and pan roasts. Unfortunately the deep-fried dishes do not come off as well. Seafood stews start at $2.25. *Cocktails, wine and beer.*
AE CB DC

★ GRAND TICINO

228 Thompson Street GR *3-8876*

There are numerous Italian restaurants in Greenwich Village, and this one has as much character as any. The waiters shuffle along, the walls are a drab green and the food is on the robust side. The ventilation could be better, but customers who dote on the place are legion. The same menu serves throughout the day and the cost of entrees is from about $1.20 to $3.90. *Cocktails, wines. Closed Sunday, Thanksgiving and Christmas.*

★★ GREAT SHANGHAI, THE

2689 Broadway (near 102nd Street) UN *4-5906*

Almost anyone with a penchant for reasonably priced, well-prepared Chinese food should find much to reward him on the menu of The Great Shanghai. The restaurant, near Columbia University, is spacious, and, despite the mass production, the kitchen is competent. There are Chinese egg rolls and won ton soup on the menu, but, happily, more adventurous dishes are listed as well. There are complete luncheons from about $1.25; complete dinners from about $1.60. The à la carte menu lists main courses from about $1.50 to $5. *Cocktails, wines. Dinner is served Sunday and holidays from noon.*

DC

GREAT WALL

146 West 45th Street JU *6-3107*

A goodly number of toilers in the Times Square area patronize and admire the Great Wall, perhaps because, as in many other Chinese restaurants, there are complete luncheons that start at 99 cents. The Great Wall's kitchen is routine and the decor is nondescript, but the food is palatable. The cost of luncheons ranges from 99 cents to $3.60 for broiled choice sirloin steak, of all things. The à la carte menu has main courses from about $1.25 to $4. *Cocktails, wines.*

GREEN TREE, THE

1034 Amsterdam Avenue (at 111th Street) UN *4-9106*

This is a family-style restaurant with Hungarian cuisine. The specialties of the house are such dishes as stuffed cabbage, goulash and chicken paprikash. Both the food and the prices are down to earth, and the portions are copious if not downright overwhelming. A la carte luncheon dishes from 85 cents to 99 cents; complete dinners from about $2 to $3. The restaurant is popular with Columbia University students. *No alcoholic beverages. Closed Sunday, July 4 and Labor Day.*

** GROTTA AZZURRA

387 Broome Street CA *6-9283*

Longtime patrons of the Grotta Azzurra are some of the most avid restaurant-goers in town. The food is always of first quality and generally prepared with admirable care. The trouble is that the management and the waiters seem generally preoccupied with old customers and consequently the casual visitor may get off-the-cuff treatment. But those who wait their turn should find much to their liking, whether it is fish, fowl or pasta. The menu is à la carte with entrees priced from about $2.25. *Wines, beers. Closed Monday.*

* GROUND FLOOR, THE

CBS Building, 51 West 52nd Street *751-5152*

As this book was being compiled, there was a change of management at The Ground Floor. The new director, Charles Chevillot, is the son of the owners of the Hotel de la Poste in Beaune, France. With luck and good guidance, this could become one of the most estimable restaurants of New York. Severely modern and stark in design, it is a welcome departure from the onrush of imitative new restaurants of the past decade. Made of glass and globes, wood and stone, The Ground Floor has the mood and feel of Manhattan. Under the previous di-

rection there were numerous flaws in both kitchen and service. It can only be surmised—or hoped—that some dishes from the original menu of The Ground Floor will be retained. Among the appetizers the grilled langoustines—small, lobster-like crustaceans—were especially good. A blanquette of veal prepared by the chef, current when this volume was compiled in late autumn, was commendable. All the foods served at The Ground Floor are or were à la carte. At midday the cost of appetizers ranges or ranged from about $1.50 for herring to $4.10 for a dozen Chincoteague oysters; main courses from about $3.95 for broiled sea bass to $7.75 for partridge. In the evening the appetizers are the same price as at noon; main courses from about $4.25 for the sea bass to $7.75 for the partridge. There is an extensive list of overpriced wines. *Cocktails, wines. Luncheon is not served on Saturday. Closed Sunday.*
AE CB DC

GUIDO

166 West 48th Street JU *6-9350*

Italian cuisine. The menu is prix fixe with complete luncheons from $1.75 to $2.25; complete dinners from $3.50 to $5. *Cocktails, wines. Closed Monday, Christmas and, during July and August, Sunday also.*

HACIENDA LA PALOMA

29 West 56th Street *582-4620*

This is a relatively new Mexican restaurant with a fairly pleasant decor that embraces brick and tiles and colored glass. Several of the dishes at their best are worthwhile, but they would not include the bland and dull guacamole that began one meal or the overcooked flan (caramel custard) that ended it. In between there was a very good breast of chicken with green mole sauce and an acceptable platter of various dishes including enchiladas, tacos, tostadas, tamales and beans. Not distinguished but palatable. At the same time the kitchen would not serve

the nachos, an appetizer made with tortillas and cheese, as a first course. And natilla, a rummed Spanish cream, was not available for dessert. At lunch and dinner all dishes are à la carte. Main courses cost from about $2.75 to $6. *Cocktails, wines. Closed Sunday.*
AE CB DC

HAMBURG HEAVEN

There are two Hamburg Heavens in the city and they sell plain hamburgers and variations of them as well as other sandwiches, soups, salads and desserts. The restaurants are at 18 East 56th Street (EL 5-5355) and 9 East 53rd Street (752-3040). *No alcoholic beverages.*

★ HANOVER SQUARE RESTAURANT

1 Hanover Square WH *4-9251*

This is a colorful restaurant with a turn-of-the-century atmosphere and an interesting menu that lists such German dishes as schnitzel à la Holstein and hasenpfeffer. The dish called chicken in the pot is served with some of the best marrow dumplings in all the city. Many of the restaurant's customers toil on Wall Street. A la carte luncheon dishes from about $2; complete dinners from about $2.70. Dinners are served only until 8 p.m. *Cocktails, wines. Closed Saturday, Sunday and holidays.*
AE CB DC

★ HARBIN INN

2637 Broadway (at 100th Street) MO *6-3450*

Under the proper circumstances the food at the Harbin Inn is excellent. The proper circumstances involve a meal for four or more guests, preferably ordered in advance. It is best, of course, to have someone who speaks Chinese in the party. The lone diner may take his chances with mediocrity unless he knows the menu. There are complete luncheons from about 80 cents to $3.25; complete dinners from about $1.20 to $3.50. The à la carte menu lists main courses from about $1.75 to $8.50. *Cocktails, wines. Closed Chinese New Year's Day.*

HAROUT'S

14 Waverly Place AL *4-4190*

This is a neat and spacious room with Middle Eastern cuisine in Greenwich Village. There are brick walls, tin chandeliers and, at times, a musician who plays the oud. There are interesting appetizers, such as stuffed vine leaves, and several main courses mostly made of lamb. Luncheon, largely sandwiches, is à la carte from about 55 cents to 85 cents. Main courses at dinner cost from $2.60 to $2.95. *No alcoholic beverages, but customers may bring their own wines. On Friday and Saturday supper is served from 10:30 p.m. to 3 a.m. Closed Sunday.*

HARVEY'S SEA FOOD HOUSE

509 Third Avenue (at 34th Street) MU *3-7587*

A more or less characteristic New York seafood establishment with a routine kitchen. Complete luncheons from about $1.65 to $2.75. A la carte dishes from about $2.45 to $6.45. *Cocktails, wines. Only à la carte items are available Saturday and Sunday.*

AE CB DC

★ HEADQUARTERS RESTAURANT

108 West 49th Street CI *5-4790*

A vast and notably popular restaurant with a menu that is principally American and as solidly down to earth as ham and eggs. The food is generally creditable, the sandwiches excellent and the service about as impersonal as it can get without being mechanical. At midday there are complete luncheons from about $2.40 to $3.50; à la carte main dishes from about $1.95 to $5.50. In the evening there are complete dinners from about $3.60 to $6.50; à la carte entrees from about $2.50 to

$6.50. There are special children's dinners priced from $2.50 to $3.50. *Cocktails, wines.*
AE CB DC

★ HELLENIC PALLAS

141 West 47th Street JU *6-9430*

Next to Chinese restaurants those with a Greek kitchen are among the best bargains in New York. The food at the Hellenic Pallas is very good and reasonably priced, with main courses on the à la carte menu from about $1.50 for broiled porgy with lemon sauce to $2.75 for a combination roast lamb platter. At midday there are complete luncheons from about $1.40 to $1.75. *Wines and beer. The restaurant is closed Sunday during the summer months.*
AE CB DC

★ HENRY STAMPLER'S FILET MIGNON

Central Park West at 61st Street PL *7-3165*

This is a conventional steak house with grilled meats, salads and casseroles. Luncheons are both prix fixe ($2 to $3.75) and à la carte ($3.50 to $6.75). Dinners are à la carte with main courses from about $3.50 to $6.75. *Cocktails, wines.*
AE CB DC

HERB EVANS RESTAURANT

1920 Broadway (at 64th Street) *799-5800*

Someone has likened eating at Herb Evans Restaurant with dining on the subway. The noise level is unbelievable, a category into which might also be lumped the service and the food. And for this you need a reservation. A rushed waiter instructed his customers to "Mix your own drinks." A clam bisque lacked the least trace of fresh clam flavor. It was summer, and half a cantaloupe, carefully chosen from among the appetizers, was so underripe the spoon refused to make a dent. The specialty of the day, softshell crabs, were overcooked, and although a steak

came off with slightly more distinction, it was not browned on the outside. Cocktail glasses and swizzle sticks remained on the table throughout a meal, and a cup of espresso, although listed on the menu, was unavailable. All dishes are à la carte with main courses from about $2.50 to $6.50. *Cocktails, wines. Closed Sunday during the summer.*
AE DC

★ HIDE SUKIYAKI

304 West 56th Street JU *2-0030*

A small, upstairs restaurant with a friendly atmosphere and a very good Japanese kitchen. The menu is unpretentious and so is the food, which runs along the lines of sukiyaki, teriyaki and grilled dishes. The Hide, open evenings only, is convenient to the upper-Broadway theaters. There are à la carte dishes from about $1.25 to $3.50; complete dinners from about $2.95 to $3.95. *Sake and beers. The restaurant opens Sunday at 4 p.m., weekdays at 5 p.m. Closed Saturday.*

HOB NOB RESTAURANT

108 East 41st Street MU *5-0246 and* MU *5-0247*

The Hob Nob is a popular and cozy businessman's rendezvous. The menu is not inspired, but the food nonetheless can be quite palatable. Specialties include such dishes as beef Stroganoff, veal scaloppine and, at noon, the inevitable London broil. All dishes are à la carte with main courses at midday from about $2.50 to $6.25; in the evening from about $4.50 to $7. *Cocktails, wines. On Saturday the restaurant opens at 4 p.m. Closed Sunday and all legal holidays.*
AE CB DC

★ HO HO RESTAURANT

131 West 50th Street CI *6-3256 and 246-3278*

The name of the restaurant is Ho Ho, but the menu is generally ho hum. The restaurant recently opened

next door to La Fonda del Sol in comparably opulent but gaudy surroundings. The food is competently prepared, but it is not distinguished in its seasoning. There are the usual offerings of chow mein, pepper steak and moo goo gai pan. One of the most interesting dishes on the menu is the bok opp shoong made with minced squab, water chestnuts, bamboo shoots and ham. There are complete luncheons that cost from $1.25 to $2.50; complete dinners from $2.90 to $4.90. A la carte dishes cost from about $3 to $5.75. *Cocktails, wines. Open until 4 a.m.*
AE DC

★ HONG FAT RESTAURANT

63 Mott Street WO *2-9588*

This is a very small and decidedly offbeat restaurant in Chinatown. Soft-noodle dishes are the specialty of the house, but almost all the foods are interesting and excellent, whether fried squab or Chinese-style crab. The service is imperiously indifferent, and for an ultimate meal it is best to speak Chinese or be accompanied by someone who does. Portions are copious and all dishes are à la carte from about $1 to $4. *No alcoholic beverages. Open 24 hours a day.*

★ HORN & HARDART AUTOMATS

This is the wonderful world of the nickel-in-the-slot. The restaurants—there are about 50 around Manhattan and Brooklyn—have long been a favorite of children and many of their elders. The offering of foods is extensive, and baked beans is the best-known dish. The vegetables are generally excellent. *The restaurants are open at varying hours and some are closed on Sunday.*

★★ HOUSE OF CHAN

Seventh Avenue at 52nd Street PL *7-4470*

This is a large, efficient and popular Chinese restaurant near Times Square. The ingredients in the kitchen

are of undisputed quality, but where seasonings are concerned the chef is far from adventurous. Most dishes seem toned down for the tourist trade. One of the nice things about the House of Chan is that it is open for supper until 1:30 a.m. There are complete luncheons that cost from about $1.75 for egg foo young to $2.95 for lobster with vegetables. The à la carte menu is priced from about $1.85 to $5.25. *Cocktails, wines. Only à la carte items are available on Sunday, from 2 p.m.*
AE DC

HOUSE OF LOUIE

143 West 47th Street *586-9893*

Suffice it to say that the House of Louie has one of the most conventional menus and kitchens of all the city's Chinese restaurants. In addition to the usual listings of chow mein, there is an American luncheon that offers chicken salad and roast turkey with cranberry sauce. Louie's premises are respectably clean, and the service is routine. There are complete luncheons from $1.40 to $2.85. A la carte dishes are priced from $1.85 to $4. *Cocktails, wines. Luncheon is not served Sunday.*

HOUSE OF MENG

1278 Third Avenue (at 73rd Street) RE *7-5110*

This is a small, noisy but tastefully put together Chinese restaurant that is a great favorite with residents of the neighborhood. Although the food is respectable, it is bland and unsophisticated. The menu will seem thoroughly familiar to anyone conversant with most of the town's Chinese dining rooms. There are complete luncheons from about $1.55 for chicken chow mein to $3.75 for lobster Cantonese; à la carte dishes from about $3.55 for braised sea bass to $6.15 for sizzling steak. *Cocktails, wines. Luncheon is not served Sunday.*
AE DC

★★ HOUSE OF MILANO

311 Second Avenue (at 18th Street) 475-9266

This is a rather garish-looking Italian restaurant with a chef capable of turning out numerous dishes that are well above average. Remembered with particular pleasure is the delicately seasoned chicken San Remo, sautéed and crowned with Italian ham and melting cheese, and with it an unusually well cooked pasta with a light tomato sauce. Most of the pasta dishes, in fact, seem to be prepared with care, including the manicotti. A dish of saltimbocca (veal and ham) was good but bland. The House of Milano has a jukebox that is frequently active, and one wall with red carpeting is typical of the decor. The restaurant is open for dinner only and the menu is à la carte, with main courses from about $2.75 to $6.50. *Cocktails, wines. Closed Monday.*

★ HOY YUEN

117 West 48th Street CI 5-5959

Customers may not be dazzled by the kitchen's expertise at the Hoy Yuen, but it is certainly an acceptable Chinese restaurant in the Times Square area. The quality of the food's preparation can range from an excellent hung shue gai, made with fried boneless chicken, to an ordinary platter of pork with overcooked cellophane noodles. The Hoy Yuen is particularly crowded at midday, one reason being perhaps that complete luncheons may be had from $1 to $2.20. The à la carte menu lists main dishes from about $1.60 for chicken chow mein to $5.25 for Chinese steak. *Cocktails, wines. On Sunday the restaurant opens at 2 p.m.*
AE CB DC

★ HYDE PARK RESTAURANT

998 Madison Avenue (at 77th Street) RE 4-0196

The Hyde Park offers an extensive potpourri of international dishes, but the menu is primarily Jewish and

American. The food is well prepared and there are daily specialties, such as sauerbraten, boiled beef in sauerkraut soup and stuffed cabbage. There are complete luncheons from about $2.10 to $2.95 and à la carte dishes from about $1.40 to $6.95. In the evening there are special dinners from about $4.85 to $6.95 and à la carte items from about $2.95 to $6.95. Sunday brunch, served from noon to 3 p.m., costs from $2.75 to $3.75. For children under 12, brunch is $1 less. *Cocktails, wines. Supper is served from 10 p.m. to 1 a.m.*

AE CB DC

HYE ORIENTAL FOOD SHOP

539 Second Avenue (at 30th Street) MU *3-2555*

The principal point of interest about this small and largely undistinguished food shop is the oriental pizzas. The actual name of Hye's special dish, which is Lebanese in origin, is lahmajin, made with a thin pastry crust spread with ground lamb, beef, tomatoes, parsley and other seasonings. It may be eaten on the premises or purchased frozen and baked at home. The cost of each pizza is 25 cents. *No alcoholic beverages. Lahmajin is available daily from 11 a.m. to 7 p.m., Sunday from noon to 2 p.m.*

★ IDA DE FRANCE

1540 Second Avenue (at 80th Street) TR *9-9870*

There are mixed feelings about this exceedingly popular French restaurant on the upper East Side. The mock-elegant surroundings include a blue carpet with floral pattern, salmon-colored walls and artificial hanging ferns. The food ranges from hors d'oeuvres that are ordinary to very good broiled dishes and veal scallops parmesan. The restaurant seems reasonably priced. The luncheon menu is à la carte with main courses from about $1.95 for omelets to $3 for filet mignon. There are complete dinners from about $5.25 to $7.75 and à la carte

dishes from about $4.25 to $7. *Cocktails, wines. Closed Monday and Christmas.*
AE CB DC

★★ IL BAMBINO

94 University Place (at 12th Street) OR *5-9844*

This restaurant is inexpensive and has a satisfactory Italian menu. When weather is favorable there is outdoor dining. The kitchen's scaloppine is commendable. Luncheon and dinner are both table d'hôte and à la carte. Complete luncheons from about $1.75 to $3; à la carte dishes from about $1.40 to $2.50. Complete dinners from $3 to $4.25; à la carte main dishes from about $1.50 to $4. *Cocktails, wines. Luncheon is not served on Saturday. Closed Sunday, Christmas and New Year's Day. Reservations accepted.*

★ ÎLE DE FRANCE

20 West 72nd Street *799-2254*

Dining well in the vicinity of Lincoln Center at reasonable (or any) cost poses something of a problem. One of the few good restaurants in the area is the Ile de France in the Franconia Hotel. The decor is nondescript, the menu will look all too familiar to those who know the town's restaurants French-bistro style, but the kitchen has merit and the food is reasonably priced. And unlike restaurants at closer proximity to Lincoln Center, it is almost always possible to get a table here. Complete dinners from about $3.25 to $5.15; à la carte entrees from about $2.75 for coq au vin to $4.25 for Dover sole. *Cocktails, wines. Open for dinner only. Closed Monday.*

★★ INDIA HOUSE RESTAURANT

201 East 34th Street MU *4-9367*

A true curry bears only a vague resemblance to most of the homemade dishes in this country made with curry powder. All the dishes at the India House have their own spices and flavors, and they are very good. Several foods, the shrimp for example, may seem overcooked to some local palates, but they are long-cooked in the traditional manner. The restaurant has, by the way, an excellent pungently condimented soup called mulligatawny. In addition to curries, the India House has skewered dishes: keema, which is a spiced chopped-meat dish, and chicken breast stuffed with cheese, which sounds un-Indian. The India House is brightly garish and the service is friendly. Special three-course luncheons cost from $1.25 to $1.75. Complete dinners from about $3.40; à la carte entrees from about $1.95 to $3.95. *On Saturday and Sunday the restaurant opens at 5 p.m.*

AE CB DC

INN OF THE CLOCK

United Nations Plaza Building *752-0424*
866 United Nations Plaza (at 48th Street)

If you lived in the new and impressive United Nations Plaza Building and if it were raining and taxis were hard to come by, it might offer a good excuse to have lunch or dinner at the Inn of the Clock on the first floor. The decor is pleasant and resembles a stage set of an inn with clocks, oak and antiquelike lighting fixtures. The food is adequate but nothing to revel in; the service polite but imprecise. Among pleasant dishes remembered was a first course of crab with avocado, and the chicken in a dish called chicken in pot. An order of rare roast beef was of good quality but served lukewarm. One also recalls an overly aged Liederkranz and an overly cornstarched rhubarb pie in an overly air-conditioned room. If you drop in on a rainy night, order the single lamb chop with water cress and baked potato. The menus are à la carte. At noon the cost of main courses is from about $2.75 to $5.50; in the evening from about $3.50 to $6.50. *Cocktails, wines. Open seven days a week.*

AE DC

★ **INTERNATIONAL CHEESE CLUB RESTAURANT**

153 Chambers Street *964-0024*
(between Hudson and Greenwich Streets)

This restaurant may be worth a visit simply because it is one of a kind in the city. It is on the second floor of a well-known cheese store, Cheese of All Nations, and the fare includes samplings of various cheeses plus dishes made with cheese, such as soupe à l'oignon, hot grilled cheese, hot scraped cheese, quiches and Welsh rarebit. The food is so-so. The menus are à la carte with main dishes at midday priced at $2; those in the evening $2.50. The restaurant closes at 9 each evening. *Various wines; no cocktails. Closed Sunday.*

AE DC

★★★ **ISLE OF CAPRI**

1028 Third Avenue TE *8-9858*
(between 60th and 61st Streets)

There is more of a basic Italian feeling about the Isle of Capri than in dozens of its counterparts. It is an unpretentious restaurant with bare marble tables, and the dishes, one supposes, could be referred to as "home style." The menu shows commendable imagination, and the food, although bourgeois, is almost without exception excellent. All dishes are à la carte with main dishes from about $2 to $3 at midday; $2.25 to $3.95 in the evening. *Cocktails, wines. Closed Sunday.*

AE DC

★ **ITALIANISSIMO**

422 Third Avenue MU *5-4940*
(between 29th and 30th Streets)

This pleasant little Italian restaurant has a garden in summer and a cozy atmosphere in winter. The food is good but not inspired, and the service is friendly. The menu lists a wealth of pasta, seafood and meat dishes and a variety of appetizers, including antipasto Italianissimo

($2.50), an assortment of hot stuffed vegetables. The veal scaloppine with peppers and mushrooms ($3.50) sampled on one occasion had good flavor, but the veal was not very tender. Portions are enormous. Luncheons, without appetizer, from about $1.90; dinner entrees from about $1.95 to $7.50. *Cocktails, wines. Closed Sunday, Labor Day, Christmas and New Year's Eve.*
AE DC

★★ ITALIAN PAVILION

24 West 55th Street JU *6-5950*

An agreeable decor, courteous service and reasonably imaginative à la carte menus, at luncheon and dinner, mark the Italian Pavilion. Specialties, many of which show care in preparation, include crêpes Pavilion, osso buco milanese and vitello tonnato as well as gnocchi and fettucine. Luncheon main courses from about $2.50 to $5.75; dinner entrees from about $2.75 to $6. The restaurant's garden (heated in winter) is open the year around. *Cocktails, wines. Closed Sunday, New Year's Day, Memorial Day, July 4, Labor Day, Thanksgiving and Christmas. Reservations accepted.*
AE CB DC

JACK DELANEY'S STEAK HOUSE

72 Grove Street (at Sheridan Square) AL *5-7905*

This is a Greenwich Village establishment with a neat atmosphere and a piano. The steaks and chops can be good, but they can also be ordinary. All dishes are à la carte with main luncheon dishes from about $1.75 to $2.95; main dinner courses from about $2.35 to $4.95. *Cocktails, wines.*
AE CB DC

JADE COCKATOO

1 University Place GR *7-3532*

If the Jade Cockatoo were in a city with less outstanding competitors among Chinese restaurants, it would doubtlessly rate higher marks. As it stands, however, it is a respectable neighborhood restaurant with food that is appetizing but not notably exciting. Some of the sauces seem a bit too thickened with cornstarch. There are complete luncheons from about $1.35 to $3.35; complete dinners from about $2.35 to $4.10. A la carte dishes from about $1.65 for egg foo young to $5 for steak kew. *Cocktails, wines. Dinner is served Sunday from 1 p.m.*

AE DC

★ JADE PALACE

210 East 53rd Street EL *5-5096*

This is a spacious Chinese restaurant in midtown Manhattan. In keeping with the name, the Jade Palace is carpeted and upholstered in green, wall to wall. The food is generally good and the portions are copious. There are complete luncheons from about $1.40 to $3.10. The à la carte menu, available for luncheon and dinner, lists main entrees from about $2.95 to $5. *Cocktails, wines. The restaurant opens at 5 p.m. on Saturday and at 4 p.m. on Sunday.*

AE CB DC

JAGER HOUSE

1253 Lexington Avenue (at 85th Street) RH *4-3820*

This restaurant has a heavy, old-fashioned atmosphere and a menu that is for the most part German. The draught beer is good. Complete luncheons from about $2.50; à la carte entrees from $1.35 to $2.75. Complete dinners from about $3.25 to $6.50; à la carte main courses from about $2.25 to $5.50. *Cocktails, wines.*

AE CB DC

★★ JAI-ALAI

82 Bank Street *989-5826*
(near Eighth Avenue between 11th and 12th Streets)

There are numerous restaurants in Manhattan with Spanish kitchens, and at their best the food is very good. One of them is the Jai-Alai, and the dishes, whether a casserole of seafood, paella, or pork with almond sauce, are palatable. There is one reservation about dishes sampled at the Jai-Alai—those containing clams are slightly sandy. Otherwise the preparations are cordially recommended, and the food is reasonably priced. At midday a main course plus appetizer or soup costs from $1.55 to $1.75. The à la carte menu is priced from about $1.80 for a mushroom omelet to $4.50 for sirloin steak. *Cocktails, wines.*

AE CB DC

J. & T. CHILI HOUSE

244 West 48th Street LT *1-4622*

This is a rough-and-ready chili house in the theater district. The restaurant has a host of admirers, and for those who dote on earthy, spicy chili similar to that found in many roadside establishments in the Southwest, it isn't bad. There are various chili combinations including chili with meat, with rice, with spaghetti and with elbow macaroni. The cost is from about 90 cents to $1. There are also steaks and chops, and the cost is from about $1.25 to $3.50. The restaurant's boast is "The only chili house open until sunrise." *Cocktails, wines.*

JANE DAVIES

145 West 55th Street CI *7-0176*

The food at this 38-year-old restaurant may not be distinguished, but it is honest, and there is virtue in that. It is cooked along the lines of tearoom fare and the portions are generous. The menu lists such dishes as broiled fish, calves' liver, meat loaf and various salads. The decor is basic. The cost of luncheon with main course and dessert ranges from about $1.35 to $3.95. The cost of a complete dinner with appetizer is about $2.95 to $4.95. *Cocktails, wines. Dinner is served Sunday and holidays from noon. Closed Christmas.*

JANSSEN'S

430 Lexington Avenue (at 44th Street) LE *2-5661*

This is a restaurant with a Continental kitchen and such German specialties as garnished sauerkraut, wiener schnitzel and German pancakes. There is game in season. Complete luncheons from about $3.50 to $3.85; complete dinners from about $4.95 to $6.95. A la carte main dishes range in cost from about $2.75 to $6.75. *Cocktails, wines. On Saturday the restaurant opens at 4 p.m. Closed Sunday.*

AE CB DC

★★ JAPANESE STEAK HOUSE

225 West Broadway *226-5915*

One of the pleasantest innovations on the Manhattan dining scene in recent years is the Japanese restaurant. In a genre by themselves are the Japanese steak houses, in which guests are seated around large rectangular tables with solid metal slabs on which the food is cooked and served. The food at the Japanese Steak House is generally excellent, although the vegetables tend to taste a trifle overcooked. Complete luncheons from $2.75 to $3.50; complete dinners from $6.50 to $7.50. *Cocktails, wines. Luncheon is not served Saturday. Closed Sunday.*

AE DC

★ JENEDI'S

13 East 47th Street *688-0778*

The surroundings in Jenedi's are a little haphazard —with wavy plastic banquettes, motley groupings of bright floral art on the walls and tables too close for comfort—but the food is a cut above that of the average

Italian restaurant in the city. There are several excellent dishes on the menu including very good fettucine, excellent osso buco (but recently accompanied by a watery rice), sautéed chicken breast with prosciutto and melted cheese. All dishes are à la carte. Main courses at midday from about $2 to $5.25; in the evening from about $3.50 to $6. *Cocktails, wines. Closed Saturday and Sunday.*
AE CB DC

JIM DOWNEY'S

705 Eighth Avenue (at 44th Street) PL *7-0186*

This restaurant has been called the struggling actor's Sardi's. It is primarily a steak house and the menu is Irish-American. On Thursday the specialty of the house is corned beef and cabbage. The kitchen is for the most part run of the mill. All dishes are à la carte with main luncheon courses from about $1.85 to $6.50 and main dinner courses from about $2.85 to $6.50. *Cocktails, wines, Irish coffee. Supper is served from 11 p.m. to 2 a.m. Closed Christmas.*
AE CB DC

JIMMIE WALKER'S

866 Third Avenue (at 52nd Street) LE *3-7440*

The exterior of this new restaurant on Third Avenue is a bit imposing. Inside, the atmosphere is like a tearoom or coffeehouse, but with a bar. The menu is predictable, with its shrimp platter and pastrami and corned beef and cabbage. The best thing at Jimmie Walker's may be the peanuts, which are there in plentiful supply and available to all comers. But even the hot horseradish could not disguise the insipid, dry, thin slices of corned beef with unbuttered cabbage and unbuttered potatoes. The menu is à la carte at midday with main courses from $1.45 to $3.50; in the evening from $1.75 to $3.95. *Cocktails, beers and ale. Closed Sunday.*
AE DC

★★ JIMMY'S GREEK-AMERICAN RESTAURANT

6 Water Street 269-9458

Jimmy's is one of the oldest-established and most-talked-about of Manhattan's numerous Greek restaurants. The dishes are long-cooked and well seasoned and bear a welcome resemblance to the foods of small rustic Greek restaurants. Jimmy's moved two blocks from its original address in 1966 and lost part of its charm in transit. The food is the same, but the earthy, Plaka-district atmosphere has been exchanged for a rather sterile, American-cafeteria decor. On the other hand, the restaurant can now accommodate more customers than before, but reservations are still in order. Dishes include such fare as roast lamb, Greek macaroni with meat, lamb fricassee, stuffed vine leaves, meat balls and the usual assortment of Greek pastries. Guests are served in the kitchen by the chef. The cost of main courses is about $3, with an additional charge for side dishes. *There is no bar, but guests may bring their own spirits, beer or wine. The restaurant is open Monday through Friday for luncheon from noon to 2 p.m. It is open two nights a week, Tuesday and Thursday, by reservation only, from 6 p.m. to 8:30 p.m. Closed Saturday and Sunday.*

★★ JIMMY'S LA GRANGE

151 East 49th Street PL *3-3899*

This small, interesting restaurant boasts only one menu, and that is in the owner's head. On a first visit, chicken Kiev (chicken breast stuffed with butter and herbs) is almost mandatory, and it is very good. Other specialties include saltimbocca, which, as served at the restaurant, has a layer of spinach between the ham and the veal. Complete luncheons from about $4.25. Dinner is à la carte with entrees from about $4.75. *Cocktails, wines. On Saturday the restaurant opens at 6 p.m. Closed Sunday.*

★ JOE ALLEN

326 West 46th Street *581-6464*

There are numerous visitors to New York, frequently from abroad, who ask to be taken to a typical American restaurant, and this is in that category. The restaurant serves chili, shrimp creole, omelet and chicken pot pie, and the food is very good. The kitchen offers an excellent black bean soup, and, when available and at its best, the chicken pot pie is cordially recommended. Faults to be found on visits to the restaurant include lukewarm dishes and service that is far too casual. The decor, with its exposed brick walls and photographs, is pleasant enough. All dishes are à la carte with main courses from about $2.10 to $5.50. *Cocktails, wines. Open for dinner only, from 4 p.m. Closed Christmas.*

★ JOE AND ROSE

745 Third Avenue (at 46th Street) EL *5-8874*

A popular midtown restaurant with Italian food. There is no menu at luncheon, but the cost of the meal is from about $3.50 to $4.25. Dinners are à la carte with entrees from about $3. *Cocktails, wines. Closed Sunday and the first two weeks in August.*

AE DC

JOE'S

44 Court Street, Brooklyn TR *5-6000*

Joe's is a Brooklyn landmark of many years' standing. It is a vast establishment with an anachronistic combination of antique paintings, plastic flowers and walls that are gaudy modern (pronounced "modrun"). The cuisine, if that's the right word, goes from knockwurst to roast fresh tom turkey with Joe's stuffing, but it seems primarily Italian. The luncheon menu is à la carte with main courses from about $1.75 to $3.25. In the evening there is a complete dinner that costs $5.25; à la carte dishes from about

$2 for spaghetti to $6 for filet mignon. *Cocktails, wines. Closed Saturday and Sunday.*
AE CB DC

★★ JOE'S RESTAURANT

79 Macdougal Street GR *5-9119*

This is an Italian restaurant in Greenwich Village that is notably unpretentious and has food that is simply prepared and gratifying. It is also reasonably priced. At lunch and dinner the menu is à la carte with main courses from about $1.50 to $5.50. *Cocktails, wines. Closed Tuesday.*

JOHN BARLEYCORN PUB

209 East 45th Street YU *6-1088*

This is another in the lengthy list of recently opened restaurants with a "dear old Erin" atmosphere, and it is physically one of the handsomest. It has stained glass and pewter serving plates and pretty waitresses with engaging brogues. The food is quite ordinary, but the public seems to love it and at noon a table for two is hard to come by. The menu at midday lists such specialties as Madras curry of lamb (the Madras Chamber of Commerce should take action), Dublin broil with a somewhat floury mushroom sauce, shepherd's pie, grilled dishes and Irish stew. The dinner menu is more or less the same. There are luncheon entrees from about $1.95 to $5.75; dinner entrees from about $2.25 to $5.75. *Cocktails, wines. On Saturday the restaurant opens at 6 p.m. Closed Sunday.*
AE DC

★ JOHNNY JOHNSTON'S CHARCOAL ROOM

846 Second Avenue (at 45th Street) MU *4-7250*

Steaks charcoal-broiled in full view. The cost of complete luncheons is from about $2.25 to $3.25; à la carte entrees from about $3.75 to $6.50. Dinners are à la carte with main courses from about $2.95 to $6.75. *Cock-*

tails, wines. On Saturday and Sunday the restaurant opens at 2 p.m. Closed New Year's Day and Christmas.
AE CB DC

★ JOHN'S RESTAURANT

302 East 12th Street GR *5-9531*

The management's attitude may border on the lofty, but if one likes well-cooked Neapolitan cuisine, this small restaurant may be worth a visit. The tomato sauces and rum cake are excellent. Dinners are à la carte with main courses from about $3.50 to $5. *Cocktails, wines. Open for dinner only. Closed Monday, New Year's Day, Easter, Thanksgiving and Christmas and from July 1 through Labor Day.*

★★ JOY GARDEN

48 Mott Street WO *2-9787*

This small upstairs restaurant has one of the most interesting menus in Chinatown. Chop suey and chow mein are available, but more imaginative dishes, such as fried squabs and steamed whole sea bass, happily dominate the à la carte bill of fare. Complete luncheons cost from 85 cents to $3.25. The same à la carte menu serves for luncheon and dinner, with main dishes priced from about $1.70 to $4.95. *No alcoholic beverages. Only à la carte items are available on Sunday.*

JULIUS LOMBARDI

181 West 10th Street (corner Seventh Avenue) WA *9-9485*

An Italian restaurant whose choicest dishes are grilled foods such as steaks and chops. At the midday meal there is frequently standing room only. The restaurant staff is small, and even at uncrowded hours the service can be painfully slow. The same menu serves for both luncheon and dinner, and all dishes are à la carte. Pasta dishes from about $2.75; grilled dishes from about $4 to $7.50. *Cocktails, wines. Closed Saturday, Sunday and all legal holidays.*
AE DC

★ JUMBLE SHOP STEAK HOUSE

176 Macdougal Street (at West 8th Street) SP *7-2540*

This establishment is a short walk from many of the nightclubs and off-Broadway theaters in Greenwich Village. The menu offers Italian and charcoal-broiled dishes, and the results range from commonplace to good. Complete dinners from $3.75 to $5.50; à la carte entrees from $2.95 to $5.50. *Cocktails, wines. Open for dinner only, Monday through Saturday from 4 p.m. and Sunday from 3 p.m. Closed Christmas.*

AE CB DC

KABUKI

115 Broadway *962-4677*

This restaurant was scheduled to open in its new location at a date too late for review in this guide. In its old address at 64 Wall Street it was considered one of the best Japanese restaurants in the city.

★ KAMEHACHI

41 West 46th Street *765-4737*

New Yorkers have taken to Japanese food with awesome enthusiasm. Restaurants that serve sushi, sashimi and the like are increasing and flourishing. One of the recent entries, and a very good one where food is concerned, is the Kamehachi. There is a bar for sushi (raw fish with vinegar rice), and specialties include broiled eel and tempura. The prices are modest, in the vicinity of $1 to $2. There is one annoyance, and that is the limited staff. At times there are lengthy waits between courses. *American and Japanese beer. Closed Sunday, New Year's Day, Labor Day and Thanksgiving.*

★ KARACHI

144 West 46th Street CI *5-9643*

This second-floor restaurant is easy to bypass, but curry lovers manage to seek it out. Prices, although

inevitably not as low as they used to be, are modest. Curries are on the mild side and hot sauce is available. The usual assortment of meat, fish, poultry and vegetable curries is served; also a variety of "bengal" breads, relishes and chutneys. There is a small assortment of desserts, including a delicious rosewater-flavored custard. There is a special $1.30 luncheon and complete dinners from $2.65. *No alcoholic beverages. Dinner is served from noon on Saturday and from 12:30 p.m. on Sunday.*
AE DC

★★ KASHMIR RESTAURANT

108 West 45th Street CI *7-8785*

The atmosphere is plain and the service enthusiastic though slow at the Kashmir, but the food is gratifying. It should be noted that most of the dishes, whether beef kurma or tandoori chicken, are well spiced and some of the condiments powerfully hot. The menu lists both à la carte dishes, from about $2 for chicken curry to $2.75 for chicken biriani, and complete meals from about $2.65 to $5.25. There is a special luncheon at $1.25 served Monday through Friday. *Beer and wine.*
AE DC

★ KATZ'S DELICATESSEN

205 East Houston AL *4-2246 and* AL *4-2247*
(at Ludlow Street)

One of the best known of New York's delicatessens. The à la carte menu, which is available all the time, lists sandwiches from 60 cents (salami) to $1 (combination with turkey). Frankfurters, with mustard and sauerkraut, cost 25 cents. Combination platters start at 95 cents. *Beer and soft drinks. Closed on Jewish holidays.*

★★ KEEN'S ENGLISH CHOP HOUSE

72 West 36th Street WI 7-3636

One of the oldest restaurants in the city, Keen's has an appropriate tavern decor dominated by thousands of "churchwarden" clay pipes that hang from the ceiling. The menu relies heavily on steaks, roasts and chops, generally well prepared, with such typical English dishes as mutton chops, beefsteak and kidney pudding (Monday only) and, on occasion, imported Dover sole. Prix fixe luncheons from about $2.20, with à la carte main courses from about $3.25 to $6.25. Complete dinners from about $4.75 to $7.50; à la carte main dishes from about $3.75 to $7.75. *Cocktails, wines. On Sunday the restaurant opens at 4 p.m. Closed Sunday during the summer months.*

AE DC

★★ KENERET

296 Bleecker Street OR 5-9587

This is a Syrian restaurant in Greenwich Village, and the food is quite special. It may not appeal to the most fastidious palates, but for those who enjoy fairly robust salads, eggplant dishes and the North African specialty called couscous, it is excellent. Keneret is, in fact, one of the few restaurants in New York that offers couscous—a buttery, tender cereal served with a hot or mild sauce containing meat and vegetables. The restaurant is a large, faintly illuminated place with a brick wall and fish-net decor, and the service is pleasant, if slow. All the dishes at Keneret are seasoned with creditable imagination, but the music is a bore. A blaring jukebox in the corner is activated at intervals. The cost of main dishes at Keneret is from about $2.75 to $3.75. *Cocktails, wines. Open for dinner only.*

★★ KENNY'S STEAK PUB

Lexington Avenue at 50th Street EL *5-0666*

Kenny's Steak Pub is a large, dimly lighted and expensive steak house in midtown Manhattan. The restaurant is neat and the reception is warm, but the portions, whether of salad or a main course, may seem overly copious. The service is swift and efficient, perhaps a touch too much so. For those who dote on first-quality steaks, however, the restaurant should have great appeal. All dishes at Kenny's are à la carte with main luncheon entrees from about $1.95 to $4.25 and main dinner courses from about $3.25 for a salad platter to $7.75 for boneless sirloin steak. *Cocktails, wines. On Saturday and Sunday the restaurant opens at 5 p.m.*

AE CB DC

KING DRAGON

1273 Third Avenue (at 73rd Street) YU *8-3433*

Chinese cooking. The complete luncheon ranges in cost from about $1.65 to $2.85. A la carte main courses cost from about $2.25 to $6.10. *Cocktails, wines. Only à la carte items are available Sunday, from 1:30 p.m. Closed Thanksgiving.*

AE CB

KING HENRY IV

142 East 53rd Street PL *2-5566*

French menu and a somewhat conventional cuisine. For laughs, perhaps, the luncheon menu lists meat balls bordelaise and meat balls du chef. Complete luncheons from $1.75 to $3.75; complete dinners from $3.75 to $8. *Cocktails, wines. On Sunday the restaurant opens at 5 p.m.*

AE CB DC

★ KING OF THE SEA

879 Third Avenue (between 53rd and 54th Streets) EL *5-9309*

This is one of New York's largest and oldest sea-food houses, and one always feels that it should be better than it is. The menu is elaborate, but the food, although appetizing enough, is generally not distinguished. There are a few unusual entrees, such as crab fingers with mustard dressing and, when available, Florida stone crabs. There is a single à la carte menu for lunch and dinner with main courses from about $1.95 for broiled kippers to $5.85 for the largest Maine lobsters. *Cocktails, wines.*

AE DC

★★ KING WU

18 Doyers Street WO *2-8480*

There are many restaurants in Chinatown, but few achieve the goodness and admirable authenticity of King Wu. The decor of the establishment is not elegant, just basic. A la carte dishes at both lunch and dinner from about $1.75 for shredded pork to $12 for Peking duck, which must be ordered in advance. Complete lunches from 95 cents to $2.75. Full-course dinners for two at midday from $4.60; in the evening from $4.90. *No alcoholic beverages, but excellent tea. Reservations for six or more will be accepted.*

KIPPY'S

240 West 52nd Street *581-4772*

This is a steak and lobster restaurant in the Broadway area that was reputedly designed at a cost of nearly a million dollars. The results are physically fairly felicitous. The restaurant has wall-to-wall carpeting, soft lighting, nice napery and a good-looking square balcony around the main dining room. The reception is cordial and the cocktails are giant size. A few nice things may be said for the food. The steaks are excellent, the américaine sauce for a lobster was recently well seasoned, and there is a good relish tray with olives and pickles. The service at Kippy's is too chaotic to be called indifferent. When one couple recently ordered broiled chicken, one of the orders arrived pink and undercooked. Hailing a waiter required considerable patience, and when this was pointed out to a captain, he added with resignation and wondrous candor, "Our waiters are truly extra-great collectors of checks." The lobster that bathed in that américaine sauce was, incidentally, chewy, and the restaurant's oxtail soup (the menu notes it is made with "a recipe from early 1800's") tasted strikingly like alphabet soup. All the dishes at Kippy's are à la carte. Main dishes at midday cost from about $2 to $7.25; in the evening from about $4.25 to $7.95. *Cocktails, wines. Luncheon is not served Saturday and Sunday.*

AE DC

★ KIRBY ALLEN RESTAURANT, THE

797 Madison Avenue RH *4-9835*
(between 67th and 68th Streets)

If anyone wishes to show a foreigner a restaurant that serves typical New York food he should go no farther than The Kirby Allen. It has certain tearoom aspects, but the dishes are all there from the molded salmon aspic salad and roast loin of pork with applesauce to pineapple upside-down cake and chocolate pie with whipped cream. The food is prepared with reasonable care but no special inspiration. The service, on the other hand, is by waitresses, and it is about as pleasant as you will find in the city. The cost of luncheons with copious portions is from about $1.50 to $2.75; complete dinners from about $2.85 to $4.75. *Closed Saturday, Sunday, legal holidays and the last three weeks of August.*

★★ KITCHO RESTAURANT

103 West 44th Street *581-6670*

There are numerous enthusiasts for Japanese food who say this is the best of the city's many Japanese restaurants. The dining room is physically no thing of beauty, but the kitchen is rewarding whether it offers such basics as sukiyaki and tempura or a notable pork and mushroom dish on skewers, kushikatsu. A la carte dishes at midday cost from about $1 to $2.50; special luncheons from about $2.25 to $3.50. Complete dinners are about $4 to $5.50. *Cocktails, wine, Japanese beer and sake. The restaurant opens at 5 p.m. on Sunday. Closed Saturday and major holidays.*

★ KLEINE KONDITOREI

234 East 86th Street RE *7-7130*

This is one of the smallest, neatest and perhaps the best of the so-called German restaurants in the section of New York known as Yorkville. The menu, the same for lunch and dinner, lists such dishes as goulash, liver dumplings and sauerkraut. The cost of each day's specialties is about $2. Dinners are à la carte with main dishes from about $1.75 to $3.35. *Cocktails, wines.*

★★ KOBE STEAK HOUSE

145 West 49th Street *765-3146*

Anyone who has never dined in one of the several Japanese steak houses in Manhattan is missing an exceptional opportunity to sample excellent international cookery. The dining rooms are equipped with large rectangular tables with heavy metal slabs in the center where the food is cooked. Guests, generally six, sit around the tables. The Kobe is typical, with a menu that offers a choice of steak, shrimp, pork or chicken. The foods are quickly cooked, cut into bite-size pieces and served with sauces containing soy and sesame seeds. Accompaniments include bean sprouts, green pepper, onion and mushrooms, also quickly cooked on the metal slab. A complete

steak house luncheon is priced from about $2.50 to $2.95 with à la carte dishes from about $3.50 to $5. Complete dinners cost from $4.95 to $7.95 with à la carte dishes from $3.95 to $6. *Cocktails, wines. Open seven days a week.*
AE CB DC

★ KOON SHING TEA HOUSE

202 Canal Street *964-2410*

One of the joys of the Chinese kitchen can be the assortment of appetizers with various fillings such as chopped chicken, shrimp, pork or beef, most of them steamed. The brightly lit Koon Shing is a new teahouse that boasts on its menu more than 50 varieties of hors d'oeuvres and pastries, and some of them are a delight. The cost is from about 15 cents to 50 cents, and there is a special tea lunch with seven appetizers, enough for a complete meal, that costs $1. The lunch is served Monday through Friday from noon to 3 p.m. The restaurant also has noodle dishes, soup dishes and the like that cost from about 95 cents to $2.75. The restaurant is, come to think of it, one of the biggest bargains in Chinatown. *There is no bar.*

★ LA BOURGOGNE

123 West 44th Street JU *2-4230*

One of the nicest things about La Bourgogne is its proximity to the Broadway theaters. The food is French, of course, and the specialty of the house is the cheese soufflé. The luncheon menu is table d'hôte and ranges in cost from $2.50 to $3.95. Dinners are both prix fixe and à la carte with complete meals from $3.75 to $6.95. *Cocktails, wines. Closed Sunday.*
AE DC

★★ LA CABANA

146 East 57th Street *758-3242*

This is a relatively new Argentine restaurant with a brief, interesting menu and food that is fascinating. It has the taste of authenticity. There is, for example, excellent broiled chicken delicately flavored with cumin and garlic; grilled skirt steak of considerable merit; and, among the appetizers, empanadas or Argentine turnovers and rolled beef stuffed with hard-cooked eggs. The decor of La Cabana is also beguiling. There are potted palms, ceiling fans with globe lamps, a polished marble fireplace and an expansive entrance. Some people may be put off by the service, which is casual in a Latin way, but the foods are grilled to order and that in itself is something to praise. The cost of a complete luncheon is $4.95; of a complete dinner, $7.95. *Cocktails, wines. Closed Sunday during the summer.*

AE DC

★★★★ LA CARAVELLE

33 West 55th Street JU *6-4252*

This is the finest restaurant in New York on almost every count. The direction under Fred Decre and Robert Meyzen is enormously professional. The waiters have as much style and experience as you are apt to find in Manhattan; but most important, perhaps, the chef, Roger Fessaguet, is a fiercely dedicated young man, and the food from his kitchen, whether it be sauces or dessert, is almost consistently outstanding. The cold dishes such as salads, poached fish and foods in aspic are especially noteworthy. There is a comfortable decor, and the clientele represents, for the most part, the beau monde of New York and world society. The cost of a complete luncheon is $7; of a complete dinner $10.25. *Cocktails, wines. Closed Sunday and for several weeks during summer.*

LA CAVE HENRI IV

201 East 52nd Street PL *5-6566*

French cuisine of varying merit in a fairly elaborate Manhattan cellar. Complete luncheons from about $1.75 to $3.50; complete dinners from about $3.50 to $7.50. *Cocktails, wines. On Sunday the restaurant opens at 5 p.m.*

★★ LA COMÉDIE

2005 Broadway (at 68th Street) 799-6768

This may well rank as the best of the restaurants in the vicinity of Lincoln Center, and it is one of the largest luxury restaurants in the world. It was designed by Jean and Pierre Pagès, and they have achieved compartmentation in the 400-seat dining room by table and banquette arrangements and by visual effects in the choice of colors, fabrics, murals and wall hangings. Considering the size, the vast majority of the dishes come off admirably. As to the seating and service, that is something else again. In the Lincoln Center area there is no steady and predictable flow of customers such as there might be in an established restaurant in the East Sixties. When the Center's houses play to capacity, restaurants enjoy a crush equal to Grand Central at rush hour. The guests arrive simultaneously. They nervously regard their watches, order cocktails and ask to be dispatched in time for an 8:30 curtain. At other times, when things are dull, waiters stand around, arms linked, legs crossed, leaning idly against the dining room scenery. Thus there are occasional delays in being seated at La Comédie, and the service will never be fast enough for some anxious ticket holders. Remembered with pleasure are the assorted appetizers, the oxtail ragout, a blanquette of veal and crab florentine. Recalled with less favor, overcooked kidneys, the assorted cheeses and an order of beignets soufflés, or fritters, that tasted of overly used fat. Both the luncheon and dinner menus are table d'hôte. The cost of a complete meal at midday is from about $3 to $6; in the evening from about $6 to $9. The

supper menu, served from 10:30 p.m. until midnight, is à la carte with main courses from about $2 for an omelet to $6.50 for filet mignon. *Cocktails, wines. Open seven days a week. Luncheon is not served on Sunday.*
AE

LA CONCHA

206 West 79th Street TR *4-8205*

Cuban champions of this restaurant insist that it serves the best Spanish and Cuban food in town. There are shredded beef, rice with chick-peas and, of course, paella valenciana, the famed seafood-and-rice casserole. Much of the food may be rewarding, but the paella has been on occasion woefully disappointing. The menu is à la carte with main courses from about $1.60 for an onion omelet to $3.50 for the paella. Combination Mexican platters cost from about $3 to $3.25. *Cocktails, wines. Open for dinner only.*
CB DC

★★★★ LA CÔTE BASQUE

5 East 55th Street *688-6525*

For one man's taste, this is the most beautiful restaurant in America. The murals, painted on canvas by Bernard Lamotte, are captivating. Particularly enchanting is a view of the harbor at Saint Jean de Luz. The tiny fishing vessels, the cafés along the quay and the tiled roofs of the town are executed with such perspective and such vivid colors that the scene is a tour de force. The cuisine at La Côte Basque is classic and at its best superb. The kitchen is at times wayward, a remark that can be applied to almost any in Manhattan. The table service is professional. The cost of a complete luncheon is $7; of a complete dinner $9.75. There is no à la carte menu. *Cocktails, wines. Closed Sunday and, during the summer, Saturday also.*

★★ LA CRÊPE RESTAURANTS

48 West 55th Street 247-1136
15 Greenwich Avenue CH 3-2555
1974 Broadway (at 68th Street near Lincoln Center) TR 4-6900
59 Nassau Street (corner Maiden Lane) 732-8680

The first of these generally admirable establishments opened in 1965 and its success was instantaneous. The principal dishes are large, thin, Brittany-style crêpes, and there are 55 fillings, including snail butter, eggs, sausage, caviar and cheese. They range in cost from about 40 cents for a plain crêpe to $2.75 for one with lobster Thermidor. If there are faults to be listed, it is that the service is at times slow, the crêpes are occasionally served lukewarm and, on one occasion at least, bits of tomato skin were evident in a crêpe provençale. The restaurants are open until 1 a.m. with the exception of the Nassau Street branch, which closes at 9 p.m. *The restaurants on Nassau Street and on Broadway serve cocktails, beer and wines; the other two serve only beer and wines. The Broadway restaurant is open seven days a week; the Nassau Street restaurant is closed on Saturday and Sunday. The Greenwich Avenue restaurant is closed on Monday.*

★★ LA CROISETTE

1063 First Avenue (at 58th Street) PL 9-2630

La Croisette is in the genre of several recently opened restaurants, with murals in bright colors evocative of various regions of France. The name comes from the boulevard that borders on the bay at Cannes, one of the most famous promenades in the world. The restaurant has a kitchen of general excellence that offers at times such dishes as duck with apples and chicken with woodland mushrooms. Both the luncheon and dinner menus at the restaurant are prix fixe. The cost of a complete meal at noon is from about $3.50 to $4 and in the evening from about $5.50 to $8. *Cocktails, wines. On Sunday the restaurant opens at 5 p.m.*

AE DC

★★★★ LAFAYETTE

202 East 50th Street   *421-4640*

A recent addition to a growing list of small, dignified and relatively elegant restaurants in Manhattan. The name of the restaurant is celebrated with a flourish. There are tricolors vertically imprinted on the cloth wall-coverings, and above a functional fireplace framed with French tiles there is the Lafayette heraldic emblem. The menu is interesting and the kitchen is generally excellent. Both the luncheon and the dinner menus at the Lafayette are table d'hôte. The cost of complete luncheons ranges from about $4.50 for an omelet to $7 for an entrecôte. Complete dinners range from about $6.75 for veal kidneys in cocotte to $9 for tournedos. *Cocktails, wines. Closed Sunday.*

★ LA FONDA DEL SOL

123 West 50th Street   PL *7-8800*

There is an exceptional charm about the surroundings of the Fonda del Sol. It is a brilliantly conceived place with an amusing menu but a kitchen that seems to have lost a good deal of inspiration since its inception a few years ago. To give credit where it is due, the "parade of typical Latin American appetizers" is interesting and the desserts, including the mocha parfait and pomegranate ice, are generally outstanding. But on two visits two main courses, the once-distinguished barbecued ribs of beef and the stuffed beef "Argentine way," tasted and looked as though they had been prepared the day before. And both were served lukewarm. The luncheon menu is à la carte with main courses from about $2.75 to $5.50. There are complete dinners that cost from $6.75 to $8.75. *Cocktails, wines. Open seven days. Luncheon is not served on Sunday during July and August.*

AE CB DC

★★ LA FORTUNA

16 East 41st Street MU *5-4890*

This Italian restaurant, opened several years ago, has gained a deserved popularity. It is a fairly handsome, comfortably appointed place with limited seating capacity. It may be a trifle expensive for some pocketbooks, but the food is prepared with care and the sauces are good. All dishes are à la carte. The cost of main courses at midday is from about $2.75 to $5.50; in the evening from about $3 to $6.50. *Cocktails, wines. Luncheon is not served on Saturday. Closed Sunday, most major holidays and, during the summer months, Saturday also.*

AE CB DC

★ LA GALETTE

341 East 43rd Street *689-5444*

Someone seems to be trying very hard to produce good food at this relatively new restaurant, and the effort is frequently worthwhile. There is, for example, an excellent hot stuffed cabbage, which may be ordered as an appetizer or main course, and an interesting mixed grill called fatanyeros, a Transylvanian specialty with pork chops, wiener schnitzel, steaks and sausages. The food is generally Hungarian. Some of the dishes seem a trifle ordinary, including the goulash and the vegetables. The menus are à la carte and at midday the cost is from about $2.25 for the stuffed cabbage to $3.50 for minute steak. In the evening entrees are about $2.85 to $6.50. *Cocktails, wine. Closed Saturday for luncheon and Monday for dinner. There is a garden for outdoor dining during the summer.*

AE CB DC

★★★★ LA GRENOUILLE

3 East 52d Street PL *2-1495*

In some respects this is a strikingly beautiful restaurant, particularly as to the multicolored roses or other bouquets found there in abundance. La Grenouille also

boasts a distinguished kitchen, and some of the specialties include littleneck clams Corsini and striped bass with beurre blanc (white butter sauce). The sauces are generally as good as you are apt to find in the city. A regrettable aspect, however, is that the tables are so close together, and it lessens the grandeur that the restaurant should have. The cost of a complete luncheon is $7.25; of a complete dinner $10.25. *Cocktails, wines. Closed Sunday and most major holidays.*
AE

★★ LA GRILLADE

845 Eighth Avenue (at 51st Street) *265-1610*

The owners of La Grillade were formerly with the well-favored Le Caneton on the Upper East Side, and apparently the same high standards apply here. This is a fairly small, pleasant restaurant with jigsaw murals on the walls and friendly service by French waitresses. The menu is not startlingly original, but the food is generally good, whether it is the house pâté or roast lamb with flageolets. A walk from the restaurant to Lincoln Center is not unthinkable. Complete luncheons cost $2.75; complete dinners from about $3.95 to $5.15. A la carte items at midday from about $1.90 to $5; in the evening from about $2.75 to $5.25. *Cocktails, wines. On Saturday and Sunday the restaurant opens at 5 p.m. Closed July 4 and Labor Day.*
AE DC

★★ LA GROCERIA

333 Avenue of the Americas (at West 4th Street) CH *2-3200*

This is conceivably the most colorful restaurant in Greenwich Village, and the atmosphere is in conservative good style. The restaurant is triangular, and the walls are lined with boxes and tins of pasta, olive oil, tuna and olives, all of which are for sale—thus the name La Groceria. The menu is stereotyped, and the food is not altogether different from that found in a score or more

small Italian restaurants in Manhattan. The food is good nonetheless, and the veal Francese is recommended in particular. There is one menu and it is à la carte. The cost of main dishes is from about $1.25 for spaghetti with tomato sauce to $3.95 for minute steak. *Cocktails, wines. The restaurant's sidewalk café is open April through November. The restaurant opens at 4 p.m. Monday through Friday, at noon Saturday and at 1 p.m. Sunday. Closed Christmas.*
AE CB DC

★★ L'AIGLON

13 East 55th Street PL *3-7295 and* PL *3-7296*

This is a neat, air-conditioned and comfortable restaurant that has the virtue of being open all summer. The menu is both French and Italian, and at its best the food is very good, although some of the portions may seem a touch too ample for discriminating appetites. Both the luncheon and dinner menus are prix fixe and à la carte. At midday the cost of a complete meal is from about $4.50 to $4.75; à la carte entrees from about $2.75 to $7. Complete dinners cost from about $7.25 to $8.75; à la carte dishes from about $3.75 to $7.50. The service corps at L'Aiglon is large, but it is at times inattentive. *Cocktails, wines. On Sunday the restaurant opens at 5 p.m. Closed New Year's Day, July 4, Labor Day, Thanksgiving and Christmas.*
AE DC

★ LA LOCANDA

228 East 45th Street *682-9307*

An Italian restaurant that seems to have a potential not fully realized. There is no doubt in one mind that the chef has an unusual skill; the menu is well varied and the food is cooked to order. If you ask for spaghetti al dente, you get spaghetti al dente. The food is South Italian, and there is an apparent odor of garlic in the dining room, but, worse, there is a very loud and distracting television over the bar. There are excellent seafood

dishes at La Locanda, and the combination dish of veal and chicken is recommended. There is a single à la carte menu for lunch and dinner with main courses from $1.90 to $5. *Cocktails, wines. Closed Sunday.*
AE DC

LA MAGANETTE

892 Third Avenue (at 54th Street) *753-4565 and 753-4566*

This is a relatively new restaurant whose name is a dialect word for macchinetta, or espresso machine. The restaurant is a place of brick and stone, marble and plastic banquettes, and the preparation of the food varies from a lamentably uninspired antipasto della casa to an interesting scaloppine la Maganette with prosciutto, eggplant and mozzarella. Even the latter tastes a bit too strongly of wine. There are complete luncheons from $2.50 to $2.95. Dinner is à la carte with main courses from about $2 for spaghetti with tomato sauce to $6.25 for steak. *Cocktails, wines. On Saturday and Sunday luncheon is à la carte. Closed Christmas.*
AE CB DC

LANZA RESTAURANT

168 First Avenue (between 10th and 11th Streets) OR *4-7014*

The atmosphere at the Lanza is informal and the food on occasion lacks subtlety, but those who relish a robust cuisine may find Lanza's of interest. There is a single à la carte menu for lunch and dinner. The menu is lengthy and the food is reasonably priced. Entrees cost from $1.50 to $2.75. *Cocktails, wines. Closed Monday, New Year's Day, Easter and Christmas.*

LA PETITE MAISON

108 East 60th Street PL *5-5667*

A small and pleasant enough restaurant with competent French and Italian cuisine. Luncheons are table d'hôte and cost from about $3 to $4.25. Complete dinners

from about $4.85 to $8; à la carte dishes from about $3 to $6.50. *Cocktails, wines. On Sunday the restaurant opens at 5 p.m. Closed New Year's Day and Christmas.*
AE CB DC

★ LA PETITE MARMITE

53 West 56th Street JU *6-9823*

This establishment has champions who consider it one of the best small French restaurants in town. The food is generally prepared with care. Complete luncheons from $2.50 to $4; complete dinners from $4.25 to $6.25. *Cocktails, wines. Closed Sunday and most major holidays.*
AE CB DC

★★ LA PIAZZETTA

144 East 52nd Street PL *3-3131*

At first glance the menu of La Piazzetta does not look substantially different from those at scores of other Italian restaurants in the city. The menu lists the expected linguine with clam sauce, scampi marinara and spaghetti dishes, but there seems to be someone in the kitchen who cares. The pasta dishes taste freshly made, and the fettucine Alfredo, although not prepared at tableside, is worthwhile. The tables are small and close together, but the reception is warm and friendly. All dishes are à la carte. Main courses at midday are from $1.50 to $5.25; in the evening from $2.25 to $5.85. *Cocktails, wines. On Saturday the restaurant opens at 5 p.m. Closed Sunday and all major holidays.*
AE CB DC

★ LA PLACE

42 East 53rd Street PL *3-8415*

This is a small, relatively new restaurant with tables too close together for comfort. The menu is generally French, with the usual dishes along the lines of coq au vin, frogs' legs provençale and sole amandine. At mid-

day the restaurant is crowded. Both luncheon and dinner menus are à la carte. Main courses at lunch cost from about $2.95 to $5.25 and at dinner from about $5.25 to $7.50. The restaurant's garden (heated in winter) is open the year round. *Cocktails, wines. On Saturday the restaurant opens at 5 p.m. Closed Sunday, July 4 and Christmas.*
AE CB DC

★★ LA POPOTTE

232 East 58th Street PL *2-9292 and* EL *5-8965*

If the sum of this restaurant were on a par with some of its parts, it would count among the most agreeable in town. The decor is pleasant. The deep-fried mushrooms served with tartar sauce are exceptional, the assorted hors d'oeuvres are excellent and so are the cream soups. The entrees are good, but they do not invariably sustain the luster of what has gone before. The chicken with sauce smitane, for example, may be a trifle overcooked; the frogs' legs provençale are served with a glaze sauce that is a trifle heavy. Compared with some of its counterparts, La Popotte's menu seems fairly priced. The cost of a four-course meal ranges from about $5.15 to $9.25. *Cocktails, wines. Open for dinner only, until 11:30 p.m. Closed Christmas.*
AE CB DC

★★ LA POTINIÈRE

60 West 55th Street CI *5-6764*

La Potinière has a highly satisfactory French kitchen. This is a large restaurant and the service is competent. The decor, on the other hand—particularly the murals—is too busy and frivolous for considerations of elegance and style. Both luncheon and dinner are prix fixe with complete meals at midday from $2.90 to $6.25 and in the evening from $4.90 to $8.50. *Cocktails, wines. On Sundays and holidays the restaurant opens at 5 p.m.*
AE

★★ LA POTINIÈRE DU SOIR

47 West 55th Street CI *5-4266*

From some points of view this is one of the pleasantest French restaurants in Manhattan. At its best the cuisine is first-rate; it is also reasonably priced. One disquieting note, however, is the piped-in music, which is occasionally loud and distracting. Complete luncheons from $3.25 to $6.50; complete dinners from $5.10 to $9. *Cocktails, wines. The restaurant is open until midnight Monday through Friday and until 1 a.m. Saturday. Luncheon is not served Saturday. Closed Sunday and for three weeks beginning and including the last week of July. Reservations accepted.*

AE

LA REINE

139 East 52nd Street PL *3-3394*

La Reine is a small restaurant with a dozen tables, discreet lighting and a cordial reception. The kitchen, on the other hand, seems ordinary. On one visit an appetizer of mussels ravigote was a bit sandy, the assorted hors d'oeuvres, routine. The main dishes consist of palatable but undistinguished fare such as supreme of capon Gismonde, veal scaloppine and shrimp with wild rice. The cost of complete luncheons is from about $2.95 to $5.50. Dinner is à la carte with entrees from about $3.95 to $7.50. *Cocktails, wines. Luncheon is not served Saturday. Closed Sunday and, during the summer months, Saturday also. Closed New Year's Day, Washington's Birthday, July 4, Labor Day and Christmas.*

AE DC

★★ L'ARMORIQUE

246 East 54th Street PL *3-3787 and* EL *5-9086*

Guests at L'Armorique are greeted by the chef and host in his toque blanche. Specialties of the house seem generally to be more the chef's creations than works of classic cuisine, but the results can be excellent. The restaurant's recommendations usually include snails ($1.90),

though the coquille Nantaise ($2) is delicious. The lobster flambé à L'Armoricaine is another specialty—lobster pieces in the shell in a sauce lightly flavored with anise ($6.90). The entree prices start at $4.75. *Cocktails, wines. Open for dinner only. Closed Monday, New Year's Day, Christmas and from June 15 to September 15.*
AE CB DC

★ LARRÉ'S FRENCH RESTAURANT

50 West 56th Street CI *7-8980*

The impressive things about Larré's are the prices and a few dishes that are a trifle out of the ordinary for Manhattan. There is a club luncheon (entree, dessert and coffee) for $1.85 and a complete dinner for $3.50. One of the unusual dishes is raie, or skate, served with black butter and capers, a specialty of the house. Like most of the dishes at Larré's, it is very good but not overly distinguished. The à la carte menu offers entrees from $3 for an omelet to $5.50 for broiled steak. *Cocktails, wines. Closed Sunday.*

★ LA SCALA

142 West 54th Street CI *5-1575*

A fairly pleasant Italian restaurant with a conventional menu. At lunch and dinner all food is à la carte with main dishes from about $2 to $6. *Cocktails, wines. Open until 12:30 a.m. Closed Thanksgiving and Christmas.*
DC

★★ LA STELLA

102-11 Queens Boulevard, Forest Hills IL *9-9511*

Of course you may not know who is dining next to you at La Stella, and the police have been known to interrupt a meal midway, but the kitchen of this small establishment in Forest Hills has much to recommend it. All food is cooked to order, whether it is linguine with clam sauce, the hot antipasto or the main courses. The hot

antipasto with its shrimp marinara, stuffed clams and stuffed mushrooms is as good as one is apt to find in all New York. The walls of La Stella are salmon pink, and there are vases on the walls with artificial flowers, but the linen is immaculate and the service recently was hard to fault. There is a lot of noise and music from a radio, and it is difficult to hear your table companion, much less the conversation at neighboring tables. One menu serves throughout the day, and all dishes are à la carte with main courses from about $1.40 for spaghetti with marinara sauce to $5.75 for steak pizzaiola. *Cocktails, wines. Closed Monday.*
AE DC

LA STRADA

134 West 46th Street CI 5-9472

Italian cuisine. The menu is à la carte at luncheon and dinner. Luncheon entrees start at about $2.75; dinner entrees begin at about $3.50. *Cocktails, wines. Closed Sunday.*
AE DC

★ LA STRADA EAST

274 Third Avenue (between 21st and 22nd Streets) GR 3-3760

A neighborhood restaurant with an interesting Italian menu. The food at times is excellent. All foods are à la carte with main luncheon courses from $2.25 to $3.25; dinner entrees from $3.25 to $5.95. *Cocktails, wines. Closed Saturday and Sunday during the summer.*
AE CB DC

★★★ LA TOQUE BLANCHE

359 East 50th Street PL 5-3552

This is a generally excellent and popular French restaurant with a menu that shows more imagination than most. On occasion such specialties as quiche Lorraine, tripe à la mode de Caen and cassoulet Toulousain are available. The restaurant is larger than many in its class and the service is attentive. Complete luncheons from $3.50 to $4.90; complete dinners from $6.25 to $8.25. *Cocktails, wines. On Sunday the restaurant opens at 6 p.m. During the summer months luncheon is not served Saturday. Closed New Year's Day, July 4, Labor Day and Christmas. Reservations suggested.*

★★ LA VENERE WEST

117 West 58th Street *765-1427*

This is a relatively new Italian restaurant, and for the most essential element, the food, it is cordially recommended. The pasta dishes, particularly the fettucine, are prepared with considerable care, and so are the veal dishes. Recommended in particular is the veal alla chef with an excellent brown sauce. Among the appetizers there is an interesting cold eggplant dish with olives and pine nuts, and the salads are commendable. The walls of La Venere West are painted green, and there is aqua-colored Venetian glass on all the tables. Opera music is piped in, and the table service is not markedly efficient. The kitchen deserves patronage, but one wonders what would happen on a crowded night with only two waiters. Complete luncheons cost $2.90; complete dinners are $5. There is also an à la carte menu with entrees from $3 to $6. *Cocktails, wines. On Saturday the restaurant opens at 5 p.m. Closed Sunday, New Year's Day and Christmas.*

AE CB DC

★ LE ALPI

234 West 48th Street JU *2-7792*

An Italian restaurant with, happily, more things plus than minus. The fettucine is excellent, the veal is of good quality and, although the staff seems small, the service in general is enthusiastic. On the negative side, soups have in the past lacked substance and the American-style coffee is dreary. There is a four-course luncheon that costs from about $2.75 to $5. There are two complete

dinners at $5.95 each plus an à la carte menu that lists main courses from about $3 to $5.50. *Cocktails, wines. Luncheon Saturday is à la carte. Closed Sunday and Christmas.*
AE CB DC

LE BERRY

321 West 51st Street 247-9540

There are dozens of small French bistros in the Broadway area and one of them is Le Berry. It is an atmospheric place, but the food at best is routine. Complete dinners cost from about $3.50 to $5. *Cocktails, wines. Luncheon is not served.*

★★ LE BIARRITZ

325 West 57th Street 245-9467

Several restaurants with chefs as proprietors have opened in New York, among them Le Biarritz. A. Vaillant was formerly chef of the Potinière du Soir, and his new establishment is neat and comfortable. Specialties of the house include an excellent crêpe Biarritz, and other dishes remembered with pleasure are veal Marengo, chicken à l'estragon and a crisp duckling Montmorency. At first glance the restaurant's menu looks conventional with its sole meunière, trout amandine and so forth, but there is much to recommend the kitchen. Luncheon is à la carte with main dishes from $1.75 to $3.50. Complete dinners cost from $4 to $6.50. *Cocktails, wines. On Saturday and Sunday the restaurant opens at 5 p.m.*
AE DC

★★ LE BISTRO

827 Third Avenue (between 50th and 51st Streets) EL *5-8766*

One of the neatest of New York's small French restaurants, Le Bistro also boasts of loyal French clientele. Both the hors d'oeuvres and main courses are of a high order, and the service is attentive. The tables are a fraction too close together and the restaurant is frequently

crowded. Complete luncheons from $3.75 to $5.50; complete dinners from $4.95 to $7.50. *Cocktails, wines. Closed Sunday, New Year's Day, Washington's Birthday, Memorial Day, July 4, Christmas and from the middle of August through Labor Day.*
AE DC

LE BOEUF À LA MODE

539 East 81st Street RH *4-9232*

A restaurant on the upper East Side of Manhattan with a most ordinary French kitchen. Complete dinners from $5 to $5.75; à la carte entrees from about $4 to $6.25. *Cocktails, wines. Luncheon is not served. Closed Monday.*
AE CB DC

LE CAFÉ ARNOLD

240 Central Park South CI *6-7050*

Although the Arnold bills itself as a restaurant français, the menu is French, Italian and American. The food is more often than not routine. Luncheon is à la carte with main dishes from about $2 to $5. Complete dinners from about $5 to $7.50. *Cocktails, wines. Closed Sunday.*
AE CB DC

★★ LE CHAMBERTIN

348 West 46th Street PL *7-2154*

This is one of the pleasantest restaurants in the theater district from the standpoints of the quality of the food and relative lack of hurly-burly. The menu at lunch seems commonplace, but at dinner it does have such less-than-inevitable dishes as poached turbot, short ribs and duck with cherries. The sweetbreads maison are delicious, and the beef is rare and tender. Complete luncheons from $2.25 to $3.50; complete dinners from $4.25 to $6.25. *Cocktails, wines. Closed Sunday and the first two weeks of July.*
AE DC

★★ LE CHANTECLAIR

18 East 49th Street PL *5-7731*

Where price is concerned, Le Chanteclair is outside the grand-luxe category of Manhattan restaurants, and in its league it has a very good kitchen. There is a neat decor focused on a mural of the Place de la Concorde, and the service is above average. The problem is that the tables are too close for comfort, and because of the restaurant's success, which is considerable, there may be a long wait for a table, particularly at midday. The assortment of cheeses at Le Chanteclair is, as it is in most New York restaurants, lamentable. Both luncheon and dinner are prix fixe, with complete luncheons from about $3.95 to $6.75; complete dinners from about $5.50 to $7.95. *Cocktails, wines. Closed Sunday, the first three weeks in July, New Year's Day, Thanksgiving and Christmas.*

AE CB DC

★ LE CHÂTEAU RICHELIEU

48 East 52nd Street PL *1-6565*

At its best the food at Le Château Richelieu is inspired, but it is quite capable of being routine. The same may be said of the restaurant's wines. All dishes are à la carte with main luncheon dishes from $3.50 for mushroom omelet to $8 for sirloin steak. Main dinner dishes from about $4.50 to $8. *Cocktails, wines. Closed Sunday.*

AE CB DC

★★ LE CHEVAL BLANC

145 East 45th Street MU *2-9695*

This is one of the most active French bistros in the city, and although the menu is not burdened with inspiration, the food is of general excellence. One problem, however, is due to the popularity of Le Cheval Blanc. At peak dining periods both of the restaurant's dining rooms are filled. It is best to go early or late for lunch. Complete luncheons from about $3.15 to $4.75; complete dinners

from about $4.25 to $6.25. *Cocktails, wines. On Saturday the restaurant opens at 5 p.m. Closed Sunday, New Year's Day, Washington's Birthday, Memorial Day, July 4, Labor Day, Thanksgiving and Christmas.*
AE CB DC

★★ LEE'S RESTAURANT

36 Pell Street WO *2-8191*

This is said to be the oldest restaurant in Chinatown. Although the management has changed, the food is very good; the tea lunch, which consists of several small Chinese specialties served at midday, is excellent. There is a complete luncheon from about 95 cents to $2.50; a complete dinner from about $1.75 to $3.25. The à la carte menu lists main courses from about $1.75 to $4.75. *No alcoholic beverages.*

★ LE GOURMET

49 West 55th Street CI *7-4423*

French cuisine. The menu at midday is prix fixe with complete luncheons from about $2.75 to $3.95; complete dinners from about $4.50 to $7. *Cocktails, wines. On Sunday the restaurant opens at 5 p.m. Closed Saturday during the summer months.*
AE CB DC

★★★ LE MANOIR

120 East 56th Street PL *3-1447*

This is a handsome restaurant with cheerful, comfortable surroundings and a menu of unpretentious dishes that are generally first-rate. Some of the fish dishes are outstanding, particularly the poached bass with whipped butter sauce. The meat entrees, such as sweetbreads in champagne and chicken with mushrooms and artichokes, are generally good. The menu is table d'hôte and à la carte with complete luncheons at $4.50 and dinners from

$7.50. *Cocktails, wines. Closed Sunday, New Year's Day and Christmas.*
AE DC

★ LE MARMITON

216 East 49th Street MU *8-1232*

Le Marmiton is very well known in New York and recently opened at a new address. The decor is neat and standard French provincial, and the menu shows no more imagination than is found in a score of other restaurants around the city. On one occasion chicken en casserole was served with overcooked wild rice, and the veal kidneys were in a bordelaise sauce that tasted too strongly of burnt onion. The most interesting item sampled was the coquille of seafood with scallops and white wine as a first course. It was well glazed and well flavored. There are complete luncheons from about $3.75 to $6; complete dinners from about $5.50 to $8.25. *Cocktails, wines. On Saturday the restaurant opens at 5 p.m. Closed Sunday and, during June, July and August, Saturday also. Closed all major holidays.*
AE CB DC

★★★ LE MISTRAL

14 East 52nd Street *421-7588 and 421-7589*

New York has within recent years become host to several restaurants with stylish interiors, but it is a compliment allowable to few to say that the food is on a par with the decor. Such praise may be accorded Le Mistral, however. This addition to the town's roster of luxury restaurants is a place of estimable charm with a kitchen of considerable merit. The cost of dining there is $5.95 for the complete luncheon and $8.75 for the complete dinner. *Cocktails, wines. During the summer months, luncheon is not served Saturday. Closed Sunday, New Year's Day, Washington's Birthday, Thanksgiving and Christmas.*
AE DC

★★ LE MOAL

942 Third Avenue (between 56th and 57th Streets) MU *8-8860*

This is a well-established, frequently crowded French bistro with a bill of fare that is well rounded, if standard, for the city. There is the usual duck bigarade and grilled chicken, and the food is generally good, though at times overcooked. The luncheons are notable in that they are relatively inexpensive. The midday menu is prix fixe with complete meals from about $2.75 to $4.60. The evening menu is à la carte with main courses from about $3.20 to $4.75. *Cocktails, wines. Dinner is served from 1 p.m. on Sunday. Closed New Year's Day, Thanksgiving and Christmas.*
AE CB DC

★ LEONE'S

239 West 48th Street JU *6-5151*

Leone's offers quantities of food in a colorful setting, and the sheer abundance is most impressive on an initial visit. Thereafter it may begin to pall. A fine place, nonetheless, for visitors to the city. The cost of an extensive dinner is $5.50. *Cocktails, wines. The restaurant is open for dinner only: weekdays 4:30 p.m. to 1 a.m.; Saturday 4 p.m. to 1 a.m.; Sunday 2 to 10 p.m.*
AE CB DC

★★★ LEOPARD, THE

253 East 50th Street PL *9-3735*

This restaurant, in a building that was formerly a private residence, seemed a trifle naïve and pretentious when it opened about three and one-half years ago. It has, however, matured into something both responsible and honestly worthwhile, with food that is prepared with exceptional skill and care. There is no printed menu; for each meal, a limited but well chosen selection of entrees is outlined by a captain or maître d'hotel. Recently this included a choice of grilled filet mignon with Choron sauce (béarnaise flavored lightly with tomato); chicken

with tarragon; sirloin au poivre; and stuffed fillet of striped bass. These were preceded by a gossamer pie that the captain promised as a quiche but was in truth an onion tart and smoked salmon. There was also a choice among first courses of prosciutto with melon or eggplant caviar. Next a choice of soups, a consommé with claret or a purée of sweet peas, both of which were excellent. There was salad and dessert. In a critical sense, a dish of braised leeks came off poorly. The flatware on the table was slightly tarnished and the wines—which are included in the price of the meal, incidentally—were nothing remarkable. The Leopard's muscadet, a wine of the Loire Valley, was thoroughly drinkable but a bit on the harsh side; the Château Lamartine, 1962, good without any particular distinction. The overall atmosphere is that of a plush bistro that could, like the flatware, do with a bit of polish. The cost of a complete luncheon at The Leopard is $6.50; a complete dinner from $12.50 to $15.00. *Cocktails, wines. Closed Sunday.*
AE

★★ LE PAVILLON

111 East 57th Street PL *3-8388*

In the days of its glory Le Pavillon was the ultimate French restaurant on this continent. It was, in fact, the model and principal training ground for hundreds of chefs, waiters and the like, and the man responsible was the legendary Henri Soulé, who opened the restaurant in 1939. When he died in 1966 the spirit of the place went with him. The next year Le Pavillon was taken over by another management under the direction of Claude C. Philippe, and it remains a place of certain elegance and luxury. But however much one might devoutly wish it, Le Pavillon does not exist in all its former grandeur. In its finest moments the kitchen perpetuates to a great extent the cuisine for which the restaurant was celebrated. But even that is not without fault, and the service today falls short of its former mark. The waiters at Le Pavillon now seem to collide with less grace than they did in former days. All the dishes at Le Pavillon are à la carte. Main courses for luncheon cost from $3 to $7.75; dinner $5 to $9.75. There is an irritating charge for bread and butter, at lunch $1 and in the evening $1.50. It is an index of some sort to say that the cost of one of the most reasonably priced wines is $18. *Closed Sunday.*

AE CB DC

★★ LE PÉRIGORD

405 East 52nd Street PL *5-6244*

This is far and away the best French restaurant in the Beekman–Sutton Place area. Several of the dishes are distinguished, including the duck pâté, the langoustines au gratin and the various preparations of striped bass. The turbot sampled on one occasion was dry. The decor of Le Périgord is nondescript, with bright, almost fluorescent murals, grillwork, potted plants and low ceiling. The cost of a complete luncheon is $4.25; of a complete dinner $8.50. *Cocktails, wines. On Saturday and Sunday the restaurant opens at 6 p.m. Closed New Year's Day and Christmas.*

AE DC

★★ LE PONT NEUF

212 East 53rd Street *751-0373*

This is a relatively new French restaurant, and the food is both reasonably good and reasonably priced. The decor consists of murals that will give many diners the feeling of déjà vu, but the surroundings are pleasant enough. Luncheon is prix fixe at $3.75; dinners are à la carte with main courses from $3.50 to $6.50. *Cocktails, wines. Luncheon is not served Saturday and Sunday. Closed Sunday during June, July, August and September. Closed Thanksgiving and Christmas.*

AE DC

★★ LE POULAILLER

43 West 65th Street 799-7600

This is the long-awaited and newest enterprise of the owners and chef of New York's esteemed La Caravelle restaurant. Le Poulailler means the poultry coop, and it is a handsome, spacious place with an airy, delicate decor by Jean Pages. It is next door, more or less, to Lincoln Center, and that is a point in its favor. As to the atmosphere, on the walls there are linear drawings of the Paris opera, views of Paris bridges and sketches of game birds in cages. The menus for lunch, dinner and supper are wholly adequate, although not as dazzling, perhaps, as dedicated patrons of La Caravelle might have hoped. Much of the food is of an à la minute sort, with such dishes as omelets, poached eggs, chicken in cream sauce and sauerkraut in champagne. The food is generally well prepared, and remembered with special favor on one occasion were the bay scallops in a light wine sauce with mushrooms and a ragout of beef. The cost of a complete luncheon is $4.25; of a complete dinner $8. *Cocktails, wines. Closed Sunday.*

DC

★★ LE PROVENÇAL

21 East 62nd Street TE *8-4248*

A small but rewarding French restaurant with the same familiar menu (coq au vin, boeuf bourguignon and so on) but a thoroughly competent kitchen. The service is just a cut above par, but the chef seems to care. The restaurant is popular and therefore crowded. Both luncheon and dinner are table d'hôte with midday meals from about $3.25 to $5.50; dinners from about $4.95 to $6.95. *Cocktails, wines. Closed Sunday, most major holidays and from August 1 through Labor Day.*

AE DC

★★ L'ESCARGOT

987 Third Avenue (near 59th Street) PL *5-0968*

Pleasant is the word for this L-shaped, pint-size French restaurant. It applies equally to the decor, the service and the food. The snails for which the restaurant is named are subtly seasoned and are served as an appetizer or as a main course. The menu is somewhat predictable, but it is extended daily by two plats du jour. Such dishes as calf's brains are rewarding; the pâté is robust and good. Complete luncheons (entree, dessert and coffee) from about $2.35 to $4.50; dinners (appetizer added) from about $4.35 to $7.50. *Cocktails, wines. Closed Sunday.*
AE

★ LES CHAMPS

25 East 40th Street LE *2-6566*

This is a large, modern and popular restaurant. Although the name is French, the menu offers a mélange of dishes, such as curried chicken, goulash and broiled fish. The food is reasonably well prepared. Luncheons are à la carte with main courses from about $2.50 to $5.95. Dinners are à la carte with entrees from about $4.25 to $6.95. *Cocktails, wines. On Saturday the restaurant opens at 5 p.m. Closed Sunday, New Year's Day and Christmas.*
AE CB DC

★★ LES PYRÉNÉES

251 West 51st Street CI *6-0044*

Les Pyrénées, with its neat and pleasant ambiance, has long been established as one of the better middle-class French restaurants in New York. The composition of the menu offers few surprises, but the food, such as roast lamb and poulet chasseur, is generally well prepared. Complete luncheons from $2.75 to $3.50; complete dinners from $4.75 to $6.50. *Cocktails, wines. On Sunday the restaurant opens at 4 p.m.*
AE DC

★★ LE STEAK

1089 Second Avenue (near 57th Street) *421-9072*

This is a steak house, purportedly French, that enjoys an enviable fault, an excess of success. At the peak of the dinner hour there are masses of people at the bar waiting for tables. It is crowded, with a noise level at times like that of Bedlam, but the food is good. There are only twenty tables in this neat, L-shaped restaurant, and a single menu serves from day to day. The meal consists of a very good, crisp salad as a first course, grilled steak with a maître d'hôtel sauce faintly flavored with tarragon and a choice of dessert or frommages (sic). The steak is of prime quality and the desserts are excellent. The cost of dinner is $5.95. The wines are reasonably priced; a choice Moulin à Vent, 1962, costs $5.50. *Cocktails, wines. Open for dinner only. Closed Sunday.*

★ L'ÉTOILE

Sherry Netherland Hotel PL *1-7025*
Fifth Avenue and 59th Street

This is a fairly new, elegant-looking brasserie whose decor offers a welcome change from the stale and all-too-frequent murals of provincial scenes with which the walls of most French restaurants hereabout have been garnished in recent years. To call it a brasserie is to say that the food is of a casual sort as opposed to haute cuisine. Unfortunately both food and service here leave much to be desired. Within memory, for example, a guest ordered jambon persillé, or ham in parsley aspic with a vinaigrette sauce. The dish arrived without sauce. The sauce was requested and the waiter brought oil and vinegar. The guest insisted on vinaigrette sauce and with some reluctance it was produced. "Why," the guest asked, "didn't you serve it in the first place?" "Most people don't like it," the waiter said. That's candor, but the sauce was excellent—more distinguished than other more complicated dishes, including a cheese soufflé and a stuffed striped

bass. A paillard of veal, a thin, flattened steak of excellent quality, quickly grilled over charcoal, is well remembered. The best dishes to be had, in fact, seem to be those that are the least complicated to prepare. Luncheons are à la carte; à la carte dishes cost from about $2.25 to $5.75. Complete dinners cost from $6.25 to $8.75. Supper dishes from $1.25 to $4.75. *Cocktails, wines. Luncheon is not served on Saturday and Sunday during July.*
AE CB DC

★ LE VALOIS

45 East 58th Street MU *8-7630*

The menu at Le Valois is lengthy, and the cuisine ranges from excellent (roast chicken with tarragon) to ordinary (London broil with mushroom sauce). All dishes are à la carte with main luncheon entrees from $3 to $5.50; main dinner dishes from about $4 to $7. *Cocktails, wines. Closed Sunday and, during July and August, Saturday also.*
AE DC

★★★★ LE VEAU D'OR

129 East 60th Street TE *8-8133*

In its finest moments this is the ultimate restaurant with bourgeois cooking in Manhattan. The chef, Lucien Guillemaud, is a master of his art, whether it is in turning out a lobster américaine, tripe à la mode de Caen or a simple dish of boiled beef. The trouble with Le Veau d'Or is its enormously warranted success. There is frequently a long wait for a table, even though the tables for some tastes are already too close together. The atmosphere is wholeheartedly French, and one of the proprietors, Georges Baratin, is one of the kindest and most knowledgeable of restaurateurs. During the summer, when there are vacation periods for the staff and owners, Le Veau d'Or does not function as smoothly as it should. Complete luncheons cost from about $3.10 to $3.95; complete dinners from about $4.95 to $7.10. *Cocktails, wines. Luncheon is not served on Saturday; closed Sunday.*

★ LIBORIO

150 West 47th Street JU *2-6188*

A popular and interesting restaurant with Latin-American food including such novel dishes as stuffed pot roast and stewed goat meat. Complete dinners are $4.50 to $6; à la carte entrees from $3.25 to $5.75. Luncheon is not served. There is entertainment in the evening. *Cocktails, wines. Closed Monday.*

AE CB DC

★ LICHEE TREE, THE

65 East 8th Street GR *5-0555 and* GR *5-0959*

This is an expensive Chinese restaurant in the heart of Greenwich Village. The decor is Chinese modern and the menu is well varied. The cuisine is, on occasion, very well prepared; the service is so-so. Luncheons and dinners are both prix fixe and à la carte. Complete luncheons from about $1.75 to $2.75; complete dinners from about $3.25 to $6.50. A la carte dishes from about $2.50 to $7.50. *Cocktails, wines. Dinner is served Sunday from 1 p.m. Reservations accepted.*

AE CB DC

★ LINDY'S

1655 Broadway (at 51st Street) CO *5-0288*

The food at Lindy's, one of the city's oldest restaurant landmarks, can be excellent, particularly such dishes as salmon, sturgeon, chopped liver and blintzes. It is a convenient place to go for an after-theater snack. The tables are close together, however, and the service at times is too abrupt for total comfort. At luncheon there is a prix fixe menu with complete luncheons from about $1.85 to $3.25 and an à la carte menu with entrees from about $1.55 to $4.95. Complete dinners from about $4.25 to

$6.95; à la carte dinner entrees from about $1.95 to $5.95. *Cocktails, wines.*

★ LIN HEONG

69 Bayard Street WO *2-8195*

This is a small but burly and popular restaurant in Chinatown. Customers frequently share tables with other customers, and the food is generally excellent. The fish and seafood dishes, such as the poached sea bass with fermented black beans, are particularly recommended. All dishes are à la carte with main courses from about 96 cents for soft-noodle dishes to $2.50 for lobster preparations. *Open seven days a week, 24 hours a day. No alcoholic beverages.*

★ LITTLE KITCHEN, THE

242 East 10th Street *477-4460*

Part of the wonder and pleasure of dining in New York is the extraordinary variety of its restaurants. The Little Kitchen is a place that has been recently much publicized for "soul food," or food that is characteristically Southern. This embraces such dishes as fried chicken, barbecued spareribs, chitterlings, candied yams and various greens such as mustard and collard. The Little Kitchen is presided over by a woman known as Princess Pamela, and her tiny kitchen produces an interesting table with the tasty and well-seasoned spiritual fare listed above plus baking-powder biscuits. The Little Kitchen, it must be added, is small, and warm when crowded. There are only eighteen tables. The cost of a copious meal is from about $1.35 to $1.75. *No alcoholic beverages. Open for dinner only.*

LOBSTER, THE

145 West 45th Street JU *2-0400*

This is a well-known, conventional but moderately priced fish and seafood house in the Times Square area

that, if autographed photographs can be used as an index, gets its share of celebrities. There are two dining rooms, one as uninteresting as an airplane hangar, the other with stark walls and modern art. The menu lists tried and true broiled fish and lobster dishes. At midday the à la carte menu has entrees from about $1.95 to $4; complete luncheons from about $2.95 to $5. Complete dinners cost from about $3.95 for broiled mackerel to $7.95 for the shore dinner including broiled baby lobster. *Cocktails, wines. On Sunday the restaurant opens at 3 p.m.*
AE DC

★★ LONGCHAMPS

There are nine Longchamps restaurants in convenient locations about Manhattan and, all things considered, the food is very good. The menus are extensive and the dishes are American and Continental, with such entrees as corned beef, London broil and beef goulash. The menus are à la carte, and the cost of main dishes is from about $2.25 for an omelet to $6.85 for sirloin steak. One of the pleasantest of the nine restaurants is that in the Manhattan House, Third Avenue at 65th Street. Other locations are 253 Broadway, at City Hall; Fifth Avenue at 12th Street; Fifth Avenue at 34th Street (*see* Mark Twain Riverboat); Broadway at 41st Street; Lexington Avenue at 42nd Street; Madison Avenue at 49th Street; Madison Avenue at 59th Street; and Madison Avenue at 79th Street. *Cocktails, wines. The restaurants are open seven days a week except for the one at Broadway and 41st, which is closed Sunday, and the one near City Hall, which is closed Saturday and Sunday. The latter are the only two also closed for holidays.*
AE CB DC

★★ LONG RIVER

10 West 45th Street 867-6496

This is a relatively new and relatively handsome Chinese restaurant conveniently close to Broadway

theaters. There are beaded room dividers, framed embroidery and Chinese art, and the service is pleasant. The menu is not startlingly different from what one is accustomed to in a dozen other Chinese restaurants in Manhattan, but the food is competently prepared. The portions are vast, and the combination platters, piled to overflowing with chow mein, chop suey and the like, look almost unappetizing. The platters, served with tea and dessert, are priced from about $1.75. At lunch and dinner à la carte dishes cost from about $1.45 for egg foo young to $5.50 for steak. *Cocktails, wines.*
AE DC

★ LORD & TAYLOR'S SOUP BAR

Fifth Avenue at 38th Street (10th floor) WI *7-3300*

Men and women shoppers alike crowd the two dozen chairs here for one of the most limited menus in town. But shoppers who enjoy the man-size bowl of excellent Scotch broth rarely hunger for more. In hot weather the broth gives way to chilled vichyssoise. Dessert the year round is deep-dish apple pie. With milk or coffee, the total tab comes to $1.10. *Open daily from 11 a.m. to 3:30 p.m., Saturday to 4 p.m. Closed Sunday.*

LORELEI

233 East 86th Street SA *2-9926*

German-American. An à la carte menu lists entrees from about $2.50 to $6.50. Complete dinners may be ordered for about 75 cents more. *Cocktails, wines. Open for dinner only. Closed Monday.*

LOTUS, THE

228 East 86th Street LE *5-0099*

Chinese cuisine. At both luncheon and dinner special prix fixe meals begin at about $2. The à la carte menu lists entrees from about $2. *Cocktails, wines.*
AE DC

★★ LOTUS EATERS

880 Third Avenue (near 54th Street) *688-1410*

This is a relatively new, reasonably handsome and corking good Chinese restaurant in midtown Manhattan. It is best to order from the à la carte menu rather than rely on the spareribs–fried rice–chow mein format of the luncheon menu. Such a menu is available, however, and it is inexpensive, with complete meals from about $1.45 for roast pork–fried rice to $3.10 for lobster Cantonese. The à la carte items cost from about $2.75 for fried shrimp balls to $4.50 for hot spiced lobster out of the shell or five-flavored fried squab (both of which are excellent, by the way). There is one minor distracting note and that is the ventilation in the dining room. It is not perfect. *Cocktails, wines.*

AE CB DC

★★ LOTUS EATERS FIFTH

182 Fifth Avenue (between 22nd and 23rd Streets) *929-4800*

Anyone who is fascinated by Chinese cooking that is far from run of the mill should find much to admire in this comparatively new Chinese restaurant. There are numerous insidiously good dishes, such as a delectable pork ball and spinach soup, hot and sour soup, chicken with special sauce (a thin soy sauce with scallions and ginger), ginger-flavored shrimp and spiced shredded chicken. The chef makes much use of oil and spices, and, for those who ask, the dishes will be made quite hot, Szechuan style. Lotus Eaters Fifth is a big restaurant, largely undecorated and with piped-in music. The service is friendly but with no particular style. There are complete luncheons that cost from about $1 to $3; à la carte main dishes are priced from about $1.40 to $3.60. *Cocktails, wines.*

AE CB DC

★ LOUISE

225 East 58th Street EL *5-8133*

A great favorite with many New Yorkers. The Italian menu is familiar, but the kitchen is generally competent. The cost of dinner is from about $6.25 to $8. *Cocktails, wines. Open for dinner only. Closed Sunday, Thanksgiving, Christmas and the first two weeks in July.*

★★ LOUISE JR.

317 East 53rd Street EL *5-9172*

The food is generally good at this restaurant with the odd name, and the portions are copious. There is also plenty of noise, particularly near the kitchen. The antipasto in itself is sufficient for a meal, and the table d'hôte menu adds soup, a main course, dessert and fresh fruit. The menu is à la carte and table d'hôte with complete luncheons from about $4 and complete dinners from about $6.50. *Cocktails, wines. On Sunday the restaurant opens at 4:30 p.m. Closed Monday.*
AE CB DC

LOUIS SHERRY AT PHILHARMONIC HALL

64th Street and Broadway PL *3-0200*

The captain of Louis Sherry at Philharmonic Hall knew a thing or two when he extended the dessert order and announced: "Now you come to the best part of the meal." Everything about this restaurant, where one is stared at by passers-by, is geared to "getting you to the theater on time." The impression gained is: "It is best not to ask questions or be tardy in your choice." There are prix fixe and à la carte menus. An individual quiche at one dinner was reasonably good, but a consommé in the course of the same meal didn't deserve the title "double," and it wasn't hot. A breast of chicken was cooked too far in advance. It was stringy and sauceless, and the tarragon mentioned on the menu was absent. A piccata of veal was dry, lukewarm and flat. But, as the captain said, the des-

serts aren't bad. An individual pecan pie came off reasonably well and so did an apple strudel. The restaurant is open for dinner and supper. There is a complete dinner that costs $7.50 and à la carte main courses cost from $4.75 to $6.25. A la carte main courses at supper cost $2.75 to $3.85. There are sandwiches from $1.45 to $2.25. *Cocktails, wines. Open seven days a week.*
AE DC

LOUIS SHERRY'S PLAZA CAFÉ AT PHILHARMONIC HALL

64th Street and Broadway PL *3-0200*

A pleasant place for outside dining when weather permits. The menu remains the same all day from lunch through supper. There are modest food offerings, and beverages include soft drinks and cocktails. The menu includes crêpes with minced chicken and mushrooms, avocado with crab meat, sandwiches and so forth, plus desserts. The cost of dishes is from about $1.35 to $2.85. *Cocktails, wines. Open seven days a week.*
AE DC

★★★ LÜCHOW'S

110 East 14th Street GR *7-4860*

Lüchow's is a landmark of more than 80 years, and, as such, it has a special eminence. It smells profoundly at times of red cabbage and sauerkraut, and it is one of the noisiest restaurants in the city. It is also one of the most colorful. At times there are German bands playing oom-pah-pah, and children love it. There are festivals galore, numbering among them the bock beer festival, the venison festival and the goose festival. The food at its best is excellent. One of the major faults is that the portions are enormous and sometimes arrive at the table lukewarm. Lüchow's is schmaltzy enough to border on the sophisticated, and the beer is cold. There are few places in town where one can dine as well on a limited budget.

Complete luncheons from $1.75 to $2.95; complete dinners from $3.75 to $4.75. There is also an à la carte menu. *Cocktails, wines. Closed Monday.*
AE CB DC

★ LUM'S GARDEN

111 West 49th Street CI *7-8757*

Those who prize Chinese food will find several things to admire at Lum's Garden, provided they make their selection from the à la carte menu. Recommended in particular is the yook soong, which is made with bits of meat and egg and topped with crisp but tender rice noodles. There are complete luncheons from about 95 cents to $2.95 and à la carte dishes from about $1.50 to $5. *Cocktails, wines. Dinner is served from 12:30 p.m. on Sunday.*

★ LUNA'S RESTAURANT

112 Mulberry Street CA *6-8657*

This is a long-established, garish, overly bright Italian restaurant in Little Italy. It has a tile floor, gaudy art and no cloakroom. The tomato sauces are, nonetheless, robust, cooked with whole cloves of garlic and, in their genre, excellent. The portions are enormous, whether veal with peppers or spaghetti marinara. The fritto misto, or mixed seafood fry, is very good and very fresh. All dishes are à la carte. The cost of main courses is from about $1.15 for a simple spaghetti dish to about $4.50 for steak. The lobster fra diavolo sampled on one occasion cost $8.50. It wasn't worth it. *Wines. Open noon to 5 a.m.*

★★★ LUTÈCE

249 East 50th Street PL *2-2225*

There is an indisputable charm about this small restaurant which, in some ways, seems the most Parisian of New York's restaurants. The kitchen has improved since it opened some years ago, and some of the specialties show great taste and imagination. Count among them a pâté of fresh fish in crust, a combination of fish in a mosaic pattern. There is a cunning small bar here, in the summer a pleasant outdoor garden, and when the restaurant is crowded, over-all it seems more festive than jammed. One could wish that the owner, Monsieur Surmain, would dress in a more reserved and elegant style to better match his surroundings. There is a complete luncheon at $6.50. The dinner menu is à la carte with main courses from about $6.75 to $8.50. *Cocktails, wines. Luncheon is not served on Saturday. Closed Sunday during the winter, Saturday and Sunday during the summer.*

★★ MME. ROMAINE DE LYON

32 East 61st Street *758-2422*

This revered and worthwhile New York institution, which specializes in omelets, has recently moved to new premises and it is all to the good. Mme. Romaine's omelets bear such names as Rond Point, Bordelaise, Talleyrand and Mozart. And her menu with several hundred omelets, ranging from plain ($2.25) to one called Périgord ($8) with foie gras, truffles, Madeira and Pernod, is just as impressive as ever. Physically, Mme. Romaine's omelets may not be invariably things of beauty, but they are excellent to the taste. The only off-note in the small, two-room restaurant is the ventilation. At times the odor of cooking is evident. The menu, which offers salads, brioches and croissants, is à la carte. *There is no bar, but wines and apéritifs are served. Open 11:30 a.m. to 3 p.m. Monday through Saturday; 6 to 10 p.m. Tuesday through Friday. Closed Sunday and most major holidays.*

★ MAMA LAURA RESTAURANT

230 East 58th Street MU *8-6888*

There are numerous faithful customers who consider this one of the best Italian restaurants in Manhattan. Many of the dishes, such as the boneless chicken Dorato, are very good, but the over-all quality of the kitchen is

uneven. Luncheons are à la carte with entrees from $2.25 to $4.50. A la carte main courses in the evening from $3.25 to $8. *Cocktails, wines. On Saturday and Sunday the restaurant open at 5 p.m. Closed Thanksgiving and Christmas.*
AE CB DC

★ MAÑANA

1136 First Avenue (at 62nd Street) *838-9847*

This is a busy, ambitious little Mexican restaurant with food that its customers fairly rave about. It is good, more El Paso than Mexico, and its seasonings are not for shy palates. Much of it is mucho caliente. There are eight combination plates embracing such dishes as tacos, enchiladas, tamales, tostadas and chilis rellenos. The interior with its exposed bricks and overhead pipes is pleasantly shabby, the service friendly. The disturbing thing about Mañana is the ventilation, which is poor and particularly noticeable at the point of arrival. There is one menu. A la carte dishes are priced from 90 cents to $1.75. Combination platters cost from $2.10 to $2.65. A pitcher of sangria —the iced Mexican wine drink—costs $2.95. The restaurant, incidentally, also caters at-home parties. *It is open from noon to 6 a.m. Cocktails, beers. Open seven days a week.*

★★ MANDARIN HOUSE, THE

133 West 13th Street WA *9-0551*

This is an excellent Chinese restaurant and one of the best in the city outside Chinatown. It will rarely disappoint. There are complete luncheons from about $1.40 to $2.10; complete dinners from about $2.85 to $4.10. A la carte main dishes from about $2.25 to $12 (Peking duck). *Cocktails, wines. Dinner is served Sunday from noon.*
AE CB DC

★★★ MANDARIN HOUSE EAST

1085 Second Avenue (at 57th Street) PL *5-9631*

There are some residents of the fashionable East Side who declare that they have gourmandized on every entree of the Mandarin House East, and for a very good reason. The food is prepared with particular excellence; to name a few of the delicacies, there are the sliced chicken in fish-flavored sauce, the river shrimp in hot spiced sauce, a delectable North China egg dish made with shredded pork and wrapped in thin pancakes and the various chicken dishes with nuts. The decor of the Mandarin House East is a curious combination of Indian and Chinese. There are complete luncheons that cost $1.95. The à la carte menu lists main courses from about $2.25 to $3.95. *Cocktails, wines. Luncheon is not served Saturday and Sunday.*

AE CB DC

MANERO'S STEAK HOUSE

126 West 13th Street CH *2-4767 and* CH *2-4793*

Where atmosphere is concerned, this is a large and pleasant steak house in Greenwich Village. The food is something of a mixed bag, however, and on occasion even the steaks leave something to be desired. Children are welcome, and there is a special dinner priced at $1.95 for children under 10. There are complete luncheons from $1.95 to $3.25; à la carte entrees from $2.75 to $4.90. Complete dinners from $3.50 to $8; à la carte items from about $1.75 to $4.95. *Cocktails, wines. On Saturday and Sunday the restaurant opens at 3 p.m. Closed Christmas.*

AE CB DC

★★ MANGANARO'S AND MANGANARO'S HERO-BOY RESTAURANT

488 and 492 Ninth Avenue LO *3-4619*
(between 37th and 38th Streets)

There is considerable distinction in the food served both in Manganaro's vast and fabled grocery store and in the Hero-Boy Restaurant next door. First-rate "heroes" are served in both, but there is, in addition, an excellent assortment of hot Italian dishes served in the rear of Manganaro's. The menu varies each day, but there is spaghetti and other pasta with various sauces, soups and so forth. The sauces in both establishments are made on the premises, and they are interesting and good. The ingredients for the heroes include salami, cheese, prosciutto, peppers, pickled eggplant, tuna, meat balls and eggs scrambled with green peppers. They cost from about 65 cents to $34.50, and that's no joke. They do prepare a special six-foot hero for the latter price and it serves 30 people. *Only beer and soft drinks are available. The restaurant is open until 7 p.m. Closed Sunday.*

★★ MANNY WOLF'S

Third Avenue at 49th Street *355-5030*

At peak dining periods there is usually a wait for tables at this 71-year-old steak house. The food is almost consistently of high quality, whether it is a charcoal-broiled chateaubriant or chicken in pot with matzoh balls. The tables are too close together, and the noise level is notably high. Luncheons are prix fixe and à la carte, with complete luncheons from about $2.50 to $3.75; à la carte from about $2.25 to $6.95. Dinners are à la carte with main courses from $4.25 to $8.25. *Cocktails, wines. Dinner is served from 2 p.m. on Sunday.*
AE CB DC

★★ MARCHI'S

251 East 31st Street OR 9-2494

One of New York's most unusual North Italian restaurants, Marchi's has no printed menu. There is an extensive antipasto, homemade lasagne, a fish course, a roast course (generally chicken and veal), vegetables, salads, cheese, fruits, dessert and coffee. One price: $6.75. *Cocktails; appropriate Italian wines, $4.50 to $4.75 a bottle. Open for dinner only: 6 to 9:30 p.m. weekdays; 5 to 10:30 p.m. Saturday. Closed Sunday. Reservations recommended; frequently they are imperative.*

AE

MARCO POLO

21 East 8th Street *677-3355 and 677-3356*

The Marco Polo is a relatively new, immaculate, polished Chinese restaurant in one of the most civilized precincts of Greenwich Village. It is not a bad place to dine if you are in the neighborhood, because the food is generally palatable. On the other hand, the kitchen would not win a prize for adventurous seasoning; a guest was told on one occasion that chicken in cellophane would require 40 minutes, and some of the dishes seem too much thickened with cornstarch. A complete luncheon costs from about $1.50 to $3.75. The à la carte menu has entrees from about $1.95 to $6. There is a special dinner at $5. *Cocktails, wines. Dinner is served from noon on Sunday.*

AE CB DC

MARIA

141 East 52nd Street EL 5-9342

A popular restaurant in midtown Manhattan. The menu is by no means distinguished by its originality, but the food can be palatable. There are complete luncheons priced at $3; complete dinners at $5.50. There is also an à la carte menu with main courses from about $3 to $3.50.

Cocktails, wines. On Saturday the restaurant opens at 5:30 p.m. Closed Sunday.

★★ MARIO

140 West 13th Street CH *3-9310*

One of those very good small Italian restaurants, this one in Greenwich Village. The restaurant is inexpensive and frequently crowded. The tomato sauces are down-to-earth but excellent. Complete luncheons from $2; complete dinners from $4. *Cocktails, wines. Closed Sunday during July and August. Reservations recommended.*
AE CB DC

★ MARIO'S VILLA BORGHESE

65 East 54th Street PL *1-2990*

This is a spacious and pleasant Italian restaurant with a menu that is principally Italian but has a few Yankee entrees. The quality of the food ranges from pedestrian to excellent. Luncheons are prix fixe and cost $4. Dinners are prix fixe and cost from about $6.50 to $8.50. *Cocktails, wines. Closed Sunday and legal holidays.*
AE CB DC

★ MARIO'S VILLA D'ESTE

58 East 56th Street PL *9-4025*

There is an extensive menu here, and the feeling is that if the chef would concentrate on fewer dishes, it would be improved over-all. The food is acceptably good but not distinguished. There is a cold seafood appetizer with a piquant sauce that can be recommended. The scampi, however, on one visit were tough and overcooked, and the veal kidneys had not been cored. The London broil was New York typical. There is excellent rum cake and good coffee. There are complete luncheons that cost $4.25. Complete dinners are priced from about $6.75 to

$9. *Cocktails, wines. Open seven days a week. Luncheon is not served on Sunday.*
AE CB DC

★★ MARK TWAIN RIVERBOAT

Empire State Building (Fifth Avenue at 34th Street) PL *9-2444*

This stationary riverboat, paddlewheel and all, boasts a somewhat flamboyant decor by Oliver Smith, the Broadway set designer. It is, in truth, a Longchamps Restaurant; thus the menu is extensive and the quality of the food is generally high. The luncheon menu is à la carte with main courses from about $1.95 to $6. There are complete dinners from $4.75 to $6.75 and à la carte main dishes from about $2.50 to $6. In the evening, one glass of wine is offered without cost to each guest until 8 p.m. in the lower night club section of the Riverboat, until 10 p.m. in the upper restaurant section. *Cocktails, wines. Dinners are served on Sunday from noon.*
AE CB DC

★★ MARNEL'S RESTAURANT

131 East 47th Street EL *5-8904*

This is a relatively small restaurant with two unpretentious but comfortable dining rooms separated by a kitchen. The service is friendly, if a little breathless at peak periods, when the restaurant is crowded. The menu is largely French, with some Italian dishes, and the food is almost consistently good. Recommended in particular are the coquille of seafood Marnel's and the lobster bisque, a Friday-only specialty. Complete luncheons cost $3.25; complete dinners from about $3.75 to $6. *Cocktails, wines. On Saturday the restaurant opens at 5 p.m. Closed Sunday, New Year's Day, Labor Day, Veteran's Day, Thanksgiving, Christmas and the first two weeks of July.*

★ MARSH'S STEAK PLACE

112 Central Park South CO *5-2470*

This is a popular, colorful steak house that has recently reopened under new management. The most interesting aspect of the restaurant is the serving of spirits. Waitresses in miniskirts bring the bottles and water or soda to the tables and customers serve themselves. This does not apply to mixed drinks such as martinis and Manhattans. Other than that, Marsh's is a friendly place, the steaks are generally excellent, and that's about the sum of all praise. On the reverse side of the coin, such dishes as chopped chicken liver, the salads with various dressings, the shrimp cocktails and so forth are edible but far from distinguished. Three lamb chops, ordered medium rare, were brought to the table grossly overcooked. All dishes are à la carte with main courses at midday from $1.50 to $4.25. In the evening main courses cost from $3.50 for broiled chicken to $6.95 for broiled filet mignon. *Cocktails, wines. Open seven days a week. Luncheon is not served Saturday and Sunday.*

AE CB DC

★★ MARTA RESTAURANT

75 Washington Place GR *3-9077*

There has been a marked change of opinion about this restaurant since it was first visited some years ago. At an earlier date it seemed stereotyped. It still has its faults, but the kitchen seems to offer more of an effort than much of its competition. The hot antipasto, compared with that of many small Italian restaurants in town, is impressive, with excellent broiled shrimp, stuffed mushrooms and mussels Posillipo. The pastas are cooked with care and the marinara sauce is excellent. The veal rolls seem overcooked but tasty. Luncheon dishes are à la carte with main courses from about $1.35 to $4.75. Complete dinners cost from about $4.25 to $6. A la carte dinner entrees

from about $3.50 to $6.50. *Cocktails, wines. Open seven days a week.*
AE CB DC

★★ MARTA'S

249 West 49th Street CO 5-4317

Many of the dishes on Marta's menu will seem familiar to those who know New York's Italian restaurants, but the kitchen here is above average. The restaurant is in the theater district, and, although the staff is limited, the service is pleasant. The veal dishes are good, but the fish dishes and vegetable dishes seem to have special excellence. One menu serves for both luncheon and dinner, and all food is à la carte. Main dishes cost from about $1.50 for spaghetti with butter sauce to $5 for filet mignon fiorentina. *Cocktails, wines. Closed Christmas.*
AE DC

★ MARY ELIZABETH'S

6 East 37th Street MU 3-3018

Mary Elizabeth's is something of a landmark in New York. It has a tearoom atmosphere and is divided into three parts—a main dining room, a men's grill and, downstairs, what is called the Soup Tureen. The food is simply prepared, modestly priced and generally good. Recommended in particular is the Soup Tureen, which specializes in soups and salads. An adequate meal there costs $1.25. It is open Monday through Friday for luncheon only. The dining room and men's grill, open Monday through Saturday at midday and on Thursday only for dinner, offer complete luncheons from about $2.25 to $2.70. A la carte dishes at midday cost from about $1 to $2.10. A complete dinner costs about $2.25 to $3.50 and à la carte dishes in the evening cost from about $1.85 to $2.50. *Cocktails, wines. Closed Sunday and, during the summer months, Saturday also.*
AE CB DC

★ **MARY'S**

42 Bedford Street CH *2-9588*

This is a small, colorful offbeat restaurant with a good deal of appeal where the food is "family-style Italian." There is a dining room with six tables downstairs, a larger room upstairs and a limited service staff. The kitchen is large, with foods such as pasta and fish cooked to order, composed dishes such as lasagna and braciole (stuffed rolled meat) cooked in advance. The restaurant has a fantastically good and hot bean soup. There is no menu, but the waiter recites such dishes as those above plus shrimp marinara and manicotti. All dishes are à la carte. The cost of main courses throughout the day is from $1.70 to $3.50. *Apéritifs, wines; no cocktails. Closed during the summer.*

★ **MAUD CHEZ ELLE**

40 West 53rd Street CI *5-3350*

A rather stylish dining room with a kitchen that has its moments of grandeur, but fleetingly. At times too there is confusion over the wine service. The cost of luncheon is from about $5 to $7; of dinner from about $8 to $12.50. There are also pre-theater dinners from $6.50 to $7.50. *Cocktails, wines. On Sunday the restaurant opens at 5 p.m. During the summer months the restaurant is closed Sunday and for luncheon Saturday. Closed from the middle of August through Labor Day.*

AE CB DC

★ **MAX'S KANSAS CITY**

213 Park Avenue South CA *8-2080*
(between 17th and 18th Streets)

This is one of the most switched-on restaurants in Manhattan. There are waitresses in miniskirts and waiters with beards. Max's is a large, angular, two-level restaurant. At the moment it is wildly popular, and consequently there is at times a wait for tables. The service is a bit

disorganized, but the simply grilled steaks and lobsters are good. The dishes are à la carte with luncheon entrees from about $1.10 for hamburger on a seeded roll to $3.25 for broiled filet mignon; dinner dishes from about $2.50 for broiled swordfish steak to $4.95 for boneless sirloin. *Cocktails, wines. The house wine ($2) served in a pichet, or pitcher, is dreadful. On Saturday and Sunday dinner is served from 1 p.m.*
AE CB DC

MAX'S RESTAURANT

30 West 47th Street JU *6-7340*

This is a small restaurant with Jewish cuisine of Middle European inspiration. The specialties include gefüllte fish, rich broths and cold boiled carp. There is both counter service and table service, and the restaurant is frequently crowded. The cost of main dishes is from about 95 cents to $1.35. The restaurant is open from 7 a.m. to 4:30 p.m. *No alcoholic beverages. Closed Saturday, Sunday and legal holidays.*

MAYAN ROOM, THE

16 West 51st Street LT *1-3580*

If there was ever a restaurant in Manhattan that was long on inspiration and short on execution, it is The Mayan Room. It is a handsome enough room, in tangerine shades, with reproductions of Mayan sculpture. The menu is interesting to read with its tablita mixta, a grouping of broiled meats; chicken adobado, or chicken baked in banana leaves; and pescado, or broiled fish with freshly pickled onion slices. The tamalitas, or cocktail-size tamales, were very good recently, when they were freshly made. On another occasion, in the evening, they were on the dry side. The seasonings for the main dishes are by no means distinguished or interesting, the chicken at times tastes overcooked and recently two orders of fish seemed to have been cooked too far in advance for good taste. The

Mayan Room is crowded at midday. In addition to Mayan dishes the restaurant has what might be called Continental cooking—beef Stroganoff, veal Holstein and the like. All dishes are à la carte, with main courses at midday from $2.45 to $6.25; in the evening from $3.25 to $6.25. *Cocktails, wines. Closed Saturday, Sunday, New Year's Day, Memorial Day, July 4, Labor Day, Thanksgiving and Christmas.*
AE CB DC

★ MAYHEWS

1178 Third Avenue (near 68th Street) LE *5-9222*
785 Madison Avenue (near 66th Street) BU *8-3781*
804 Lexington Avenue (at 62nd Street) TE *8-3580*
774 Broadway (near 9th Street) GR *3-0370*

These are decidedly informal restaurants with quick, casual service. They are worth noting if only for their hamburgers, which are lean and neatly cooked to order. There is a complete dinner menu priced from about $2.15 for an omelet to $5.25 for broiled double lamb chops. The food is generally good, if not remarkably distinguished. The à la carte dishes cost from about 70 cents for hamburgers to $4.25 for the lamb chops. *Cocktails, wines. There is great variance in the hours during which the Mayhews restaurants are open. On weekends and for late evening dining it is best to telephone.*

McBELL'S

359 Avenue of the Americas OR *5-6260*
(between 4th Street and Washington Place)

If there is any difference between Dublin Bay prawns and the run-of-the-gulf shrimp one is accustomed to locally, it is that the former are drier and have less taste. That is the impression gained at McBell's, at any rate. This restaurant boasts an Irish kitchen, and the dining room has a pleasant atmosphere, with stained wood and exposed brick, red tablecloths and double-globe lamps. The corned beef and cabbage is fairly good and the portions are copious, but the steak and kidney pie is not much more distinguished that the so-called prawns. The menu also offers Irish ham, Irish stew and Irish bacon. McBell's would probably be a nice place to celebrate St. Patrick's Day. The menus are à la carte with main courses at midday from about 95 cents for a hamburger platter to $1.95 for the Irish stew; in the evening from about $2.50 for chopped steak to $4.25 for lobster tails. *Cocktails, wines. Closed Christmas and on Good Friday until 5:30 p.m.*

McCARTHY'S FAMOUS STEAK HOUSE

839 Second Avenue (at 45th Street) MU *7-6131*

McCarthy's steak house has been around for a long time and its quality has varied. One of the best things to be said for one meal is that the Caesar salad was tasty and the steaks seemed to be of excellent quality. The decor is reasonably pleasant, with pecky cypress shutters and subdued lighting. A shrimp cocktail was fairly tasteless, and the cheeses poor beyond description. The service is such that when wine was requested, the waiter advised, "In the half bottles I can give you a Médoc, but in the whole bottles I'll have to check." All dishes are à la carte. The luncheon menu has dishes from about $2.50 for an omelet to $3.75 for broiled fish. On the evening menu prices range from about $4.25 for broiled chicken to $6.95 for filet mignon. *Cocktails, wines. On Saturday the restaurant opens at 4 p.m. Closed Sunday, Thanksgiving and Christmas.*
AE DC

★★ McSORLEY'S OLD ALE HOUSE

15 East 7th Street GR *7-9363*

This is one of the most engaging saloons in America. It is a man's world and women aren't allowed. The story goes that a woman named Mother Fresh Roasted, a peanut peddler whose husband had died of a lizard bite during the Spanish-American War, was welcomed in her day for an occasional ale, but that is legend. The bedraggled atmosphere includes portraits of George Washington, a pot-bellied stove, tables with a distressed appearance and the smell of beer and ale. The bill of fare consists of roast beef, fresh ham, Virginia ham, hamburger steak, corned beef hash and chili. The most famous dish, and it is worth the visit, is a platter of ripe Liederkranz cheese, thick slices of sweet Bermuda onion and bread or crackers. The cost of most dishes is from about 50 cents to $1.20. *The bar serves only beers, porter and ale. Open seven days a week.*

★★ MERCURIO

53 West 53rd Street JU *6-4370*

A popular Italian restaurant with an attractively uncluttered decor. Service is generally excellent and the food varies from only fair to extremely good. The wine list includes some of the less well-known Italian imports. The fettucine Alfredo is above average. Main dishes include everything from veal scaloppine to rognocino trifolato (veal kidney with mushroom, truffles and sherry). Table d'hôte luncheons from about $3.50 to $6; à la carte dinner with entrees from about $3 to $9. *Cocktails, wines. Closed Sunday, New Year's Day, Thanksgiving, Christmas and the month of July.*

METROPOLITAN OPERA HOUSE

Lincoln Center

Grand Tier Restaurant (799-3400). Nothing can be all bad in a restaurant that has murals by Marc Chagall, and the Grand Tier Restaurant has two. If you sit at the right table you can see them both; if not, from almost any table you can see one of them reflected in the towering windowpanes out front. On the other hand, the room is crowded and noisy, and customers are rushed through the meal that consists for the most part of mediocre food. Composed dishes, such as breast of capon opera or sweetbreads financière, taste flat when cold or lukewarm, but one recalls a splendid bottle of Chambolle Musigny ($10) that was memorable. Guests are advised that simple dishes, such as chops or roast prime ribs of beef, are the preferable choices from the menu. There are complete dinners at the Grand Tier from about $7.50 to $8.50. There is an à la carte menu with main courses from $5 to $7.50. *Cocktails, wines. Dinner only. Only guests holding tickets to the opera may dine at the Grand Tier on the evening of their performance. Open according to opera schedule. Reservations are essential.*

The Top of the Met (799-3737). The Top of the Met in the Opera House is a place with murals by Dufy, and, like the Chagalls at the Grand Tier Restaurant upstairs, they come off far better than the kitchen. The omelets sampled on one occasion were overcooked and lukewarm, the mixed grill with its two small lamb chops, well seasoned but lukewarm. At midday a few women park their shopping bags and other oddments close to their feet beneath their tables. That must be a commentary on something. There are complete luncheons at the Top of the Met from about $3.50 to $6; complete dinners from $7.50 to $9. *Cocktails, wines. Closed Sunday. Reservations are recommended.*

★ MICHAEL'S PUB

3 East 48th Street PL *8-2272*

This was one of the first pubs in Manhattan. It has a gregarious atmosphere and is crowded and noisy at luncheon. There are some very good dishes available, including the chops, calves' liver and Irish bacon. The pub's trifle is ordinary, but the Stilton is good. Main luncheon dishes from about $2.75 to $6; main dinner entrees from about $3.50 to $6.80. Supper is served from 11 p.m. to 1 a.m. *Cocktails, wines. Closed Saturday and Sunday.*
AE DC

★★ **MIKE MANUCHE**

150 West 52nd Street JU 2-5483

This is a colorful restaurant with a pleasant and masculine atmosphere. At midday, in particular, it is a favorite dining spot of businessmen. The menu is primarily Italian and quite palatable. Both luncheon and dinner are à la carte. Luncheon main dishes from about $2.75 to $6; main dinner courses, served with spaghetti and mixed green salad, from about $4 to $7.50. *Cocktails, wines. Luncheon is not served on Saturday. Closed Sunday.*

AE CB DC

★ **MILLER'S**

233 Broadway CO 7-3156

A large, old, solidly established restaurant on the ground floor of the Woolworth Building. It has an interesting menu with such dishes as lobster meat Vallauris, a sautéed dish awash with butter, numerous fish dishes and such down-to-earth fare as chicken pot pie, corned beef hash and corned beef and cabbage. One of the best-known dishes is listed as côtelette de veau de l'empereur. It is sautéed veal with a light cream sauce, and it is quite tasty. Miller's is crowded with businessmen at midday. All dishes are à la carte with main courses from $1.95 to $6.25. *Cocktails, wines. Closed Saturday and Sunday.*

AE

★ **MINETTA TAVERN**

113 MacDougal Street GR 3-9119

A neat and frequently crowded neighborhood restaurant in Greenwich Village. It has a loyal, genteel clientele, and the quality of the food, which is Italian, ranges from the ordinary to the excellent. The portions for almost all the foods are overly copious and the table service is only average. The restaurant is generally pleasant, nonetheless. At lunch and dinner all dishes are à la

carte from about $1.50 for spaghetti with tomato sauce to $4.75 for steaks. *Cocktails, wines. Closed Monday.*
AE CB DC

★★ MIRKO
408 East 64th Street TE *8-5380*

The menu at Mirko's is basically Russian with its chicken à la Kiev and its shashlik served at times to melodies, plaintive and otherwise, from violin and piano. The food is cooked in a very small kitchen, but it is generally good. The menu, which doesn't seem to vary from month to month, is table d'hôte, with main courses from about $4.75 for filet of sole to $8 for sirloin steak. *Cocktails, wines. Luncheon is not served. Closed Sunday.*

★ MIYAKO
20 West 56th Street CO *5-3177*

This was one of the first of New York's Japanese restaurants. It is a three-story place with a large, crowded dining room and food that is agreeable enough for anyone with only a casual interest in Japanese food. New Yorkers may have become spoiled by a wealth of adventurous Japanese restaurants, and at the Miyako the food seems more Westernized than in some of the more recent ventures. The menu includes the usual tempura, sukiyaki, teriyaki or fish shioyaki, and it is good enough although, by and large, unremarkable. There are complete luncheons from $2.25 to $4; complete dinners from $3.50 to $5. A la carte items cost from $1.50 to $3. *Cocktails, wines. Luncheon is not served on Sunday. Closed Monday and most major holidays.*

★ MOLFETAS CAFETERIA
307 West 47th Street JU *6-9278*

What Molfetas lacks in elegance it more than makes up for with good Greek food. There are roast lamb and braised lamb, stuffed vine leaves and excellent rice, and the cost of any main dish is rarely more than $1. Desserts are along the lines of baklava. The food is hearty, the portions are large and the cafeteria is neat. *Cocktails, Greek wines and beer.*

★ MONA TRATTORIA

567 City Island Avenue, the Bronx 885-1366

There is a certain raffish charm about City Island and its views of boats and boatyards. There is a similar charm about the Mona Trattoria, a small, largely unadorned Italian restaurant near the waterfront. The chief virtue of the restaurant is its pasta dishes, although the turkey breast with prosciutto and white truffles is also rather special. The service staff of the Trattoria is small, and when the restaurant is crowded the service is disorganized. The same menu serves throughout the day. The cost of à la carte dishes is from about $2 for noodles with meat sauce to $4.50 for tournedos Rossini. There is a complete dinner that costs $5.75. *Cocktails, wines. Closed Monday.*

DC

★★★ MON PARIS

111 East 29th Street ~~MU 4-9152~~ 683-4255

There are fewer than 20 tables at the Mon Paris; the service is friendly and with no particular style; but this is one of the finest small French restaurants in New York. The food is prepared with remarkable finesse, and both the food and wines are reasonably priced. Mon Paris is generally crowded at main dining periods. All dishes on the restaurant's menus are à la carte. Main dishes at midday cost from about $2.50 to $3.75 and in the evening from about $3.50 to $6. *Cocktails, wines. On Saturday and Sunday the restaurant opens at 5 p.m. Closed New Year's Day, Washington's Birthday, Easter, Memorial Day, July 4, Labor Day, Thanksgiving and Christmas. Closed Sunday during the summer months. Reservations desirable.*

★ MONT D'OR

244 East 46th Street OX *7-5668*

A plain, pleasant and popular restaurant with a Franco-American kitchen. The menu ranges from spaghetti bolognese to filet mignon with bordelaise sauce. A la carte main luncheon dishes from $2.50 to $3.50; complete luncheons from $2.75 to $3.75. Complete dinners only, from $4 to $6. *Cocktails, wines. On Saturday the restaurant opens at 5 p.m. Closed Sunday.*

AE CB DC

★★ MONTE'S RESTAURANT

97 MacDougal Street OR *4-9456*

Monte's is far from being the most elegant Italian restaurant in New York, but it is one of the neatest bargains in the Italian genre. It is popular with many of the budget-minded and substantial citizens of Greenwich Village, and at times it is difficult to obtain a table. All dishes are à la carte with main courses from about $1.25 for an onion omelet to $4 for a large sirloin steak. *Cocktails, wines. Closed Tuesday.*

★★ MONT ST. MICHEL RESTAURANT

327 West 57th Street LT *1-1032*

This is a pleasant French restaurant with a menu that is tried and true and a kitchen that is competent. The trump and triumph of the Mont St. Michel, however, is available on Thursdays and Fridays and it is couscous, that extraordinary cereal of North African celebrity. There is probably no finer couscous served in America than that at the Mont St. Michel. It is steamed to perfection and served with an assortment of excellent accompaniments including chicken, lamb and cumin-flavored meat balls. There is bouillon too, and a hot sauce served on the side. The cost of the couscous with salad is $3.50. There are complete luncheons that cost from $1.95 to $3.25; complete dinners from $3.50 to $4.75. A la carte

dishes at midday cost from $2.25 to $6 and in the evening from $2.50 to $5.25. *Cocktails, wines.*
AE CB DC

★ MOON PALACE

2879 Broadway (at 112th Street) *666-7517 and 666-7518*

At its best the food at the Moon Palace ranks with the best to be had in any Chinese restaurant in Manhattan. A dish of shredded chicken with abalone and another of pork shreds with soft bean curd were enjoyed recently with uncommon relish, and they will long be remembered. Both the boiled and fried dumplings are first-rate. The problem here, as it is in many Chinese restaurants, is to persuade the management that you have an authentic appetite for food that is leagues removed from chow mein and chop suey. This is a large, unpretentious restaurant, near Columbia University, and it seems vastly popular with the students. The luncheon menu is inexpensive and mundane with complete meals from $1.05 to $2.75. The à la carte menu, available at all hours, lists main courses from about $1 to $4.75. *Cocktails, wines. Dinner is served Sunday from 11:30 a.m. Closed Chinese New Year's Day.*

★ MORGEN'S EAST

34 East 52nd Street HA *1-1331*

★ MORGEN'S RESTAURANT

141 West 38th Street BR *9-7420*

These are neatly run restaurants from dining room to kitchen, and the food is agreeable. The chopped chicken liver, the brisket of beef and the corned beef are excellent. The fresh seafood is good. The luncheon menu is à la carte with main courses from about $2.75 to $5. There is a complete dinner that costs $5 and à la carte items from about $3.50 to $7. *Cocktails, wines. Morgen's East is closed for lunch on Saturday and all day Sunday. The restaurant at West 38th Street is closed Saturday and Sunday.*

★ NAT SIMON'S PENGUIN ROOM

21 West 9th Street GR 7-9450

A candle-lit, subterranean rendezvous that in some respects may seem a trifle gauche. There are blackamoor candelabra and piped-in music and a room that the management calls a "romantic library." The menu encompasses such dishes as half chicken broiled or Southern fried, schnitzel à la Holstein and Yankee pot roast. The specialty of the house, however, is the steaks. They are quite good, if not extraordinary. All dishes are à la carte with main courses from about $3.75 to $6.50. *Cocktails, wines. Luncheon is not served.*

AE DC

NAUTILUS, THE

267 West 23rd Street *675-9840*

A run-of-the-mill fish and seafood restaurant. The fish seems fresh, however, and the service is friendly. All dishes are à la carte with entrees from about $1.10 to $4.95. There is a buffet Sunday afternoon. *Cocktails, wines. On Saturday the restaurant opens at 6 p.m.*

★★ NEAR EAST RESTAURANT

138 Court Street, Brooklyn *624-9257*

This is another of those small, unpretentious and generally excellent Middle Eastern restaurants where one may dine well for one or two dollars. Lamb is the principal meat, and it is cooked at the Near East with numerous vegetables, such as green beans, eggplant and okra. There are also several excellent appetizers—for example, the traditional hummus, a purée of chick-peas, and baba gannough, a purée of eggplant. There is one menu for lunch and dinner, and all dishes are à la carte. Main dishes cost from about 90 cents for stuffed cabbage to $2 for shish kebab. *No alcoholic beverages. Closed Christmas.*

★ NEW MOON INN

2824 Broadway (between 109th and 110th Streets) AC *2-2653*

In its best moments this is an excellent Chinese restaurant, but at times both the service and the food can be indifferent. Complete luncheons from 90 cents to $3.25. Cantonese family dinners range from $4.20 to $4.80 for two to $9.30 to $12.50 for five. *Cocktails, wines.*

★★ NEW SHUN LEE RESTAURANT

2450 Broadway (between 90th and 91st Streets) EN *2-2200*

This is a corking good Chinese restaurant on upper Broadway and a very good place to arrange an extensive banquet. Ignore the luncheon menu, which is both Chinese and American, and order à la carte. A la carte dishes cost from about $1.40 to $3.75 and are generally excellent. *Wines, cocktails. Closed for Chinese New Year.*

★★ NICOLA PAONE

207 East 34th Street *889-3239*

Inasmuch as there are few very good Italian restaurants in New York City, there are several things to admire at Nicola Paone. The menu shows much imagination, although some of the best dishes have curious names like Boom Boom and Nightgown, both rolled-veal dishes, one with mushrooms, the other with eggplant. For New York the service is sufficiently enthusiastic and efficient to marvel at. On the negative side, the restaurant's banquettes are not notably comfortable and the antipasto is dull. Paone's is no recent discovery, and the tables are frequently filled, particularly at midday. All dishes are à la carte with main courses from about $2 to $3.25 at noon; $2.25 to $4.50 in the evening. *Cocktails, wines. On Saturday the restaurant opens at 5 p.m. Closed Sunday.*

AE CB DC

★★ NINGPO RESTAURANT

83 Second Avenue (between 4th and 5th Streets) *473-9761*

The Ningpo, which is in a rather miserable section of Manhattan, deserves far more patronage than it has. The food is obviously prepared by a first-rate Chinese hand, whether it is lobster Cantonese or almond dice-cut chicken. On a recent visit the serving was done by one waitress, and there were few guests. The food is reasonably priced. The cost of main dishes à la carte is from $1.35 to $3.45. There are complete dinners for two that cost $5. *There is no bar. Closed Monday.*

★★ NIPPON

145 East 52nd Street EL *5-9020*

This is one of the finest Japanese restaurants in Manhattan—and they have proliferated within recent years. The restaurant is stylish in concept, and service is by handsome kimono-clad young women. There is a tempura bar, where guests may sit at a counter to dine on a variety of seafoods and vegetables dipped in batter and deep-fried; also a sushi bar, where the traditional service of various kinds of raw fish are served with soy, ginger and wasabi, which is grated horseradish. There are special luncheons at the Nippon that include a clear soup or a bean soup, pickled vegetables, a principal dish, rice and dessert, such as melon. The cost is from about $2 to $3.50. Complete dinners, which are more elaborate, cost from about $5 to $10. There is an à la carte menu with dishes from about $3.50. *Cocktails, wines. On Saturday the restaurant opens at 5:30 p.m. Closed Sunday.*
AE CB DC

★★ NOM WAH TEA PARLOR

13 Doyers Street WO *2-8650 and* WO *2-6047*

Numerous restaurants are a vital part of the color of Chinatown. One of the best for Chinese tea lunches is the Nom Wah Tea Parlor, which serves a large assortment of exotic dumplings and other Oriental appetizers ranging in cost from about 15 cents to 50 cents. A representative luncheon for two is usually about $3. The restaurant is generally crowded shortly after noon, so it is best to get there early, particularly on Saturday and Sunday. *No alcoholic beverages. Open for luncheon only.*

NYBORG AND NELSON COFFEE SHOP

937 Second Avenue *753-1495 and* EL *5-9141*
(between 49th and 50th Streets)

It is regrettable that the food and surroundings in this new upstairs coffee shop are so prosaic, for the idea of the restaurant is admirable. The attempt has been made to re-create sandwiches and other dishes of Swedish inspiration. The food is edible all right, but the real potential is imperfectly realized. The menu consists of open-faced and closed sandwiches, smorgasbord dishes, and Swedish pancakes, which are, by the way, better than most things on the menu. A recent cup of yellow pea soup with white sausages was characteristic: adequate soup that needed an herb of some sort to vary the flavor. The smorgasbord plates offer ordinary meat balls, indifferent sliced ham, eggs with herring, smoked salmon and so on. All dishes are à la carte with sandwiches priced from 80 cents to $1.25. Smorgasbord platters from $1.50 to $1.75. *There is no bar, but an extensive assortment of beers is available. Closed Sunday.*

DC

★ O. HENRY'S STEAK HOUSE

345 Avenue of the Americas (at West 4th Street) CH *2-2000*

Butcher blocks for cocktail tables, gas lamps that formerly illuminated the streets of Baltimore, and sawdust on the floor help make this one of New York's most colorful restaurants. It has a solid mahogany bar, waiters in butcher coats, and stained-glass windows. The draught beer is excellent, but the food is just reasonably good. The

charcoal steaks, for example, have a good flavor, but the texture can be flaccid and chewy. All foods are à la carte with main luncheon dishes from about $1.75 to $5.25. The dinner menu ranges from about $3.25 to $5.50. *Cocktails, wines, beer on draught. There is a sidewalk café for outdoor dining April through November. Closed Christmas.*
AE CB DC

★ OLD DENMARK

135 East 57th Street PL *3-5856*

The Old Denmark is first and foremost a purveyor of Scandinavian delicacies for the retail trade, but it also boasts one table where customers may dine on Danish specialties. There is a seating capacity for eight persons at a time and the table is shared by other customers. The food consists primarily of salads, such as cucumber, mushroom, crab, beet and herring, but there is also liver pâté and smoked salmon. The meal also includes bread, lemon cake and coffee. The cost of the lunch is $2.50. *Open for luncheon only. No alcoholic beverages. Closed Sunday and legal holidays.*

★ OLD FORGE STEAK HOUSE

200 East 17th Street (at Third Avenue) GR *3-1767*

A neat and comfortable steak house with good food and some of the most accommodating waiters in town. Charcoal-broiled dishes are the principal fare. Complete luncheons cost from about $1.85 to $3.50; complete dinners from about $3.95 to $4.95. A la carte dishes throughout the day cost from $3.50 to $5.95. *Cocktails, wines. On Saturday and Sunday the restaurant opens at 3 p.m.*
AE CB DC

OLD GARDEN, THE

15 West 29th Street LE *2-8323*

The several rooms of this landmark are divided by natural brick walls with arches. The food is mostly Yankee style, with such dishes as creamed chicken, breaded veal cutlets, steaks and chops. There is nothing elegant about the menu, but it is well varied; the portions are large and inexpensive. Luncheons are à la carte with main courses from about $1.10 to $1.45; complete dinners from $1.95 to $3.75. *Cocktails, wines. Closed Sunday, the first two weeks in July, most major holidays and, during the summer months, Saturday also.*

OLD HOMESTEAD

56 Ninth Avenue CH *2-9040 and* CH *2-9041*
(between 14th and 15th Streets)

On its poster-size menu this restaurant styles itself "New York's Oldest Steak House"; it was established in 1868. In spite of the opening of an additional dining area, the restaurant is generally crowded with people who have a penchant for wrought-iron decor and step-high steaks. The food preparation is generally commonplace. Entrees include the usual variations on the beef theme plus a large number of "specials," which may be anything from Dover sole to sauerbraten. Luncheons are à la carte with main courses from about $1.60 to $7.25. There are complete dinners from about $4.75 to $8.50; à la carte dishes from about $3.50 to $8.50. *Cocktails, wines. Dinner is served from 1 p.m. on Sunday.*

AE CB DC

OLD HUNGARY RESTAURANT

1327 Second Avenue (near 70th Street) YU *8-2143*

The Old Hungary has a decor as unpretentious as the restaurant's stuffed cabbage, but the food is good and reasonably priced. Complete luncheons, for example, cost $1.75. Complete dinners cost $2.95 to $5.25, and à la carte dishes from $2.60 to $4.35. The roast veal shanks are particularly recommended. *Cocktails, wines. Luncheon is not served on Sunday.*

★ OLD MEXICO RESTAURANT

115 Montague Street, Brooklyn MA *4-9774*

Where the food is concerned, this is an especially good Mexican restaurant in Brooklyn. There are the usual specialties such as tostadas, enchiladas and tamales, but there are the spiced mole dishes as well. There is also an excellent pasta. The restaurant is small. On the negative side, the ventilation is poor and the service is indifferent. For aficionados of Mexican food, however, it can be rewarding. All dishes are à la carte with main courses from about $2.25 for a combination plate to $3.25 for paella with lobster tail. *Wines and beer. Open for dinner only, from 5 p.m. Closed Sunday, New Year's Day, July 4, Labor Day, Thanksgiving and Christmas.*

★ ORIENTAL PEARL

211 Pearl Street WH *3-6490*
(between John Street and Maiden Lane)

When the Chinese food is good at the Oriental Pearl it is capital. The good food includes shrimp with brown sauce and pressed duck with chopped almonds. The menu also boasts such dreary items as chop suey and chow mein. The restaurant is frequently crowded and the tables are close together. Complete luncheons from about $1.35 to $2.95; complete dinners from about $1.45 to $4. A la carte dishes from about $1.45 to $4. *Cocktails, wines. Closed Saturday and Sunday.*

ORIGINAL JOE'S RESTAURANT

217 East 59th Street EL *5-9890*

For many years this restaurant occupied a popular site on Third Avenue. The restaurant reopened a few years ago at the above address with modern decor and an

Italian cuisine that is generally ordinary—but then again, it is modestly priced. A la carte luncheon entrees cost about $1.90 to $3.85. Complete dinners from about $2.90 to $4.75; à la carte main dishes from about $1.60 to $4.45. Filet mignon is $3.95. *Cocktails, wines. On Sunday dinner is served from 11:30 a.m. Closed Thanksgiving and Christmas.*
AE DC

★★ ORSINI'S

41 West 56th Street PL *7-1698*

This restaurant is a joy to behold, the most European-looking of all New York restaurants, and it numbers among its clientele some of the most stylishly dressed men and women you're apt to find in the city. There are fashion designers and models and countless members of the international set. The dining room is on the second floor above a handsome entrance room below. The dining tables are of inlaid tile, presumably Italian, the walls are of exposed brick and rough stucco and there are good-looking fabrics that serve as wall hangings. The service staff is neatly turned out. The menu is long and far more interesting than you will find in most of the city's Italian restaurants. The pasta dishes, particularly those simply made with butter sauces—the noodles Alfredo, for example—are excellent. The veal dishes are good, but a recent order of gamberetti or shrimp alla Nettuno had a tomato sauce that seemed a bit acid and salty; the shrimp were dry and the cooked clams that accompanied them tough. The restaurant's elvetia or rum cake, like that you find almost everywhere in town, smacked of rum flavoring rather than rum, and why that should be is one of the mysteries of the century. All dishes are à la carte with main luncheon dishes from about $2.75 to $5; main dinner courses from about $3.75 to $7.50. *Cocktails, wines. Closed Sunday.*
CB DC

★ **OSCAR'S DELMONICO**

56 Beaver Street BO *9-1180*

New York's old Delmonico Restaurant at the turn of the century was at 494 Pearl Street, and it was one of the world's most celebrated dining rooms. The present Delmonico's is said to have many of the trappings of the original, including the front entrance. The food of the new establishment is Continental, primarily of North Italian inspiration, and, although it may not be in its predecessor's league, it is very good. The menu offers such dishes as breast of chicken Valdostana with cheese and tomatoes, and sliced breast of chicken with noodles in a rich cream sauce. Luncheons are à la carte with main dishes from about $4 to $7.75. Complete dinners cost $9; à la carte entrees from $4.75 to $7.75. *Cocktails, wines. The dining room closes each evening at 10. Dinner is not served on Saturday. Closed Sunday, most major holidays and, during the summer months, Saturday also.* *AE*

★ **OSCAR'S SALT OF THE SEA**

1155 Third Avenue TR *9-1199*
(between 67th and 68th Streets)

This is at the moment New York's reigning fish and seafood emporium, and with very good reason. It is one of the most reasonably priced restaurants in town and the food is honest—no substituting of paprika for improper broiling. Oscar's has recently expanded and has a brand-new front. There is still frequently a wait for tables, at times half an hour or longer, and the people noise is something to contend with. The cost of a two-course meal is from about $2.65 to $6; of a three-course meal from about $2.90 to $6.25. A la carte dishes from about $2.15 to $5.50. *Cocktails, wines. Open seven days a week.*

★ OVIEDO

202 West 14th Street WA *9-9454*

For better or for worse, this is one of the best-known Spanish restaurants in New York, and it has the usual offerings of paella, saffron rice and seafood dishes in green sauce. The kitchen is competent but not distinguished, and, to coin a phrase, it is a colorful restaurant, from the oil-on-velvet paintings recessed in the walls to the jukebox music that blares forth from the bar. The menu is à la carte and main courses are priced from about $1.50 for a Spanish omelet to $3 for the paella with lobster. *Cocktails, wines.*

★ PABLO'S

208 East 58th Street PL *2-3054*

Despite the Spanish name, the menu here is international. The food is prepared with an enthusiasm that is rare in New York, although there may be a trifle too much essence of garlic (or garlic powder) in some of the dishes. The paella and pork satay are particularly recommended. The service is above average, and the decor is neat and sophisticated. Luncheons are à la carte with main courses from about $1.75 to $3.25. Complete dinners from about $5 to $8.25. *Cocktails, wines. Luncheon is not served on Saturday and Sunday. Closed July 4, Labor Day, Thanksgiving and Christmas.*

AE

★ PAGODA RESTAURANT

41 Mott Street WO *2-5650*

This is a spacious second-floor restaurant in the heart of Chinatown. The Pagoda is popular with tourists, and it is an excellent place for dim sum tea luncheons—an assortment of Chinese appetizers—served until 2:30 p.m. each day. There are complete luncheons from about $1.35 to $2.85; complete family dinners cost $2.95 a person. The cost of the tea luncheons varies with the

number of appetizers selected. A la carte dishes from about $1.75. *Cocktails, wines.*
CB DC

★★ PAK-INDIA CURRY HOUSE

111 West 48th Street 586-9614

There is tremendous variety in the numerous curries available at the new Pak-India Curry House. The special luncheon, priced at $1.25 and available on weekdays, represents one of the best bargains in the city. There is a markedly friendly atmosphere about the Pak-India and a pleasant quaintness about the decor, wallpaper murals of Pakistani and Indian scenes, arches and gilded twist columns. The menu lists about thirteen beef curries, three shrimp curries, six chicken curries and so on, and there is a note that any Indian or Pakistani curry not on the menu is available if requested in advance. Complete dinners cost from $2.90 to $5.50. A la carte dishes cost from about $1.90 to $2.75. *Cocktails, wines.*
AE DC

PALACE D'ORIENT

108 Lexington Avenue 684-9393
(between 27th and 28th Streets)

There is one thing about the numerous Middle Eastern restaurants in New York: the food is reasonably priced and palatable. The Palace d'Orient has an Armenian kitchen, and it fits this description. The dishes are based, typically, on lamb with vegetables, and there is the usual assortment of appetizers, including the tarama salad (a citron-flavored fish roe paste that is very good here), stuffed vine leaves and stuffed mussels. The trouble is the chef seems to have an affinity for sweet dishes, and the fillings for the leaves and mussels reflect it. One menu serves throughout the day, and the cost of abundant main courses is from about $1.80 to $3. *Cocktails, wines. Closed Tuesday.*

★ PALLADIUM

20 East 41st Street *684-8352*

The Greek dishes at the Palladium—spinach pie, moussaka and the like—are generally excellent, but unfortunately they are far too few. The rest of the menu is standard American with a smattering of Italian and about as nondescript in its preparation as the restaurant's decor. The menu is à la carte with main dishes from about $2 for an omelet to $4.25 for lamb shish kebab in a combination plate. *Cocktails, wines. Closed Sunday and, during the summer months, Saturday also.*

AE DC

★★★ PALM RESTAURANT

837 Second Avenue (near 45th Street) MU *2-9515*

This is a friendly, rough-and-tumble restaurant with cartoons on the walls and a checkroom attendant who reads the racing forms. It is, nonetheless, one of the finest steak houses in Manhattan. There is no written menu, but it is recited by the waiters and runs along the lines of chicken, chops and roast beef in addition to steaks and lobster. Steaks and lobster cost in the vicinity of $7. The home-fried potatoes at the Palm are extraordinarily good. All dishes are à la carte with luncheon and dinner entrees from about $2.50. *Cocktails, wines. On Saturday the restaurant opens at 5 p.m. Closed Sunday and, during the summer months, Saturday also.*

★★ PANCHO VILLA'S

1501 Second Avenue (corner 78th Street) *734-9144*

This is a welcome addition to Manhattan's roster of Mexican restaurants. The surroundings are neat and interesting, but unfortunately the seating capacity is limited. The chef does a commendable job with such dishes as cheese enchiladas, both dark and green mole sauces, and the usual assortment of tacos, enchiladas and tostadas. Pancho Villa's is open only in the evening, from

5:30 p.m. to 1 a.m. seven days a week, and all dishes are à la carte. The cost of main courses is from about $2.75 to $4.50. The bartender could certainly use a lesson in how to make a margherita. *Cocktails, wines.*

★★ PANTHEON RESTAURANT

689 Eighth Avenue (near 43rd Street) JU *6-9672*

This is one of the oldest of New York's numerous Greek restaurants, and it seems to improve as years go by. It is a friendly place with casual service, and the food is better than you'll find in many small, well-known restaurants in Athens. The menu runs along the traditional lines of well-done lamb dishes with rice or vegetables or both, roast veal and chicken and macaroni dishes. One delight is the avgolemono, or egg and lemon soup made with chicken broth. It is especially good at the Pantheon. The Greek antipasto with its taramasalata, or cold, lemon-flavored red caviar salad, anchovies and feta cheese, is simple and good. All dishes are à la carte with main courses from about $1.25 to $3. *Cocktails, wines. Open seven days.*

★★ PAPPAS

14th Street and Eighth Avenue WA *9-9421*

The atmosphere of this 55-year-old restaurant is bourgeois, but the seafood, particularly the broiled lobster, can be rated with some of the best in the city. The menu also lists casseroles and grilled meat dishes. Luncheons are à la carte with main courses from about $1.50 to $4.50. Complete dinners cost from about $3.40 for veal goulash to $5.75 for broiled whole lobster. *Cocktails, wines. Closed Sunday and most major holidays.*

AE DC

★ PAPRIKA

1529 York Avenue (at 81st Street) RH *4-9227*

This is a small Hungarian restaurant with a few Jewish specialties on the upper East Side. There are only twelve tables, and all the food is cooked in a small kitchen. The food at its best is excellent, and this would include a recent giblet soup, an enormously tasty ragout with sausages and a sampling of freshly made chopped chicken livers. Many of the main courses, including the stuffed cabbage, roast pork and potted steak, are well seasoned, but they also seem overcooked. Among the desserts, the Hungarian pancakes called palacsinta are very good and the rich chocolate cake with three textures is admirable. There are complete meals that cost from about $2.90 to $4.75; à la carte items from about $2.20 to $4. *There is no bar, but wines and beers are available. With the exception of Saturday and Sunday, the Paprika is not open at midday. Closed Monday.*

★★ PARADISE INN

311 West 41st Street LO 3-2581

This Greek restaurant is now comparatively large (there is even a "taverna" upstairs with nightly entertainment), but the food is still generally excellent; prices downstairs are low and service is adequate. There is the expected selection of lamb dishes and, on occasion, moussaka—a delicious eggplant, meat and cheese combination. The same à la carte menu, with main dishes from about $1.20 to $2.75, serves all day. Wine is available by the tall glass (50 cents). *Cocktails, wines.*

★ PARIOLI, ROMANISSIMO

1367 First Avenue (between 73rd and 74th Streets) 734-9951

This is a compact, new Italian restaurant. There are hanging plants, a brick wall with tasseled awning and a maître d'hôtel who seems thoroughly professional. The foods are cooked to order and include such dishes as a meat-filled cannelloni Rossini with cream sauce, rolled breast of chicken Eleanora Duse and veal Quo Vadis with artichokes and peas. The tables are too close for total comfort, a recent bottle of Valpolicella was too tart for pleasure and the restaurant's ventilation leaves something to be desired. All dishes are à la carte with main courses from $1.75 for spaghetti marinara to $5.25 for sliced steak alla Parioli. *There is no bar, but wines and beer are available. Open for dinner only. Closed Monday, Labor Day, Thanksgiving and Christmas.*

DC

PARISIEN

304 West 56th Street JU *6-9321*

The menu at the Parisien is principally French with a smattering of Italian, and it may seem all too familiar to much of the restaurant-going public. The food can be good, however. Luncheons are à la carte with main courses from about $2 to $3.75. There is also a special luncheon at $2.25. Complete dinners from about $4.25 to $7; à la carte entrees from about $2.25 to $7. *Cocktails, wines. On Saturday the restaurant opens at 5 p.m. Closed Sunday and most major holidays.*

AE DC

★ PARKWAY EAST (offbeat)

163 Allen Street GR *5-9815*

A fascinating unroutine restaurant with Jewish cuisine, Rumanian style. There are chopped liver and borscht. There is also a lengthy list of charcoal-broiled meats, chicken in the pot and boiled beef flanken. The food is generally excellent. The menu is à la carte with main courses from about $1.75 to $6.50. *Cocktails, wines. Open for dinner only. Closed for Rosh Hashanah and Yom Kippur. Reservations recommended for Saturday and Sunday.*

★★ PASSY, THE

28 East 63rd Street TE *8-0094*

The Passy has maintained its feeling of elegance relatively well during its many years of location in Manhattan. The service is attentive but leisurely, and the food varies from ordinary to excellent. As in several of the city's restaurants of a certain class, there is an inexplicable and annoying charge on the menu for bread and butter—60 cents at luncheon, 75 cents at dinner. Luncheon entrees cost from about $2.50 to $5.75; dinner entrees from about $3.75 to $6.50. *Cocktails, wines. Dinner is served Sunday, from noon. Closed Saturday, most major holidays and, during the summer months, Sunday also.*

AE CB DC

★★ PATRICIA MURPHY'S CANDLELIGHT RESTAURANT

12 East 49th Street *421-6464*

Patricia Murphy's, which really does have candlelight at both lunch and dinner, may look a trifle prim and proper to some guests, but the quality of the food is excellent and it is cooked with care and some sophistication. There are salads, of course, and sandwiches, but there are also very good dishes on the order of striped bass with a mustard and hollandaise sauce, chicken liver pâté with walnuts, and caviar aspic. There are complete luncheons from about $1.95 to $2.95 and à la carte dishes from about $1.85 to $2.95. Dinners are prix fixe from about $2.95 to $5.95. *Cocktails, wines. Dinner is served from noon on Sunday. Closed Christmas.*

AE CB DC

★★ PAUL AND JIMMY'S PLACE

54 Irving Place OR *4-9463*

Paul and Jimmy's Place is usually crowded because it is one of the best small Italian restaurants in Manhattan. La cucina is Neapolitan. The sauces are good and the striped bass livornaise style is generally excellent. All dishes are à la carte with main luncheon dishes from about $1.75; main dinner courses from about $3. *Cocktails, wines. Reservations frequently essential.*

AE DC

★ PAUL REVERE'S TAVERN AND CHOP HOUSE

Lexington Hotel, Lexington Avenue at 48th Street PL *5-4400*

There is more atmosphere here than you could shake a lantern at, and the dark bar might do well with more illumination. The menu is weighted on the side of seafood, steaks and chops, with odd curry and flamed dishes. The fresh oysters and clams are first-rate, and the steaks and chops are generally good. But there is, to choose at random, an insipid veal and game pie, and a couple of orders of salad, made with that most undistinguished of salad greens, iceberg lettuce, were tossed with a white dressing best not described. The portions, including desserts, are about as large as you'll find in New York, and that is saying something. A brandied apple cobbler was well spiced. The service is confused. The menus are à la carte with main dishes at midday from about $2.45 for swordfish to $5.50 for steaks; in the evening from about $3.95 for chicken to $6.95 for steak and $7.50 for stuffed lobster. *Cocktails, wines. Open seven days.*

AE CB DC

★★★ PEARL'S CHINESE RESTAURANT

149 West 48th Street *586-1060*

Without question this is one of the neatest and best Chinese restaurants in the city. The proprietor is Mrs. Pearl Wong, better known to a devoted following as Miss Pearl. As to the decor, there are freshly painted, brightly lighted orange and salmon walls, and the over-all feeling is one of simple elegance. There is an impressive clientele as well including Richard Rodgers, the composer, Donald Brooks, the fashion designer, Billy Baldwin, the interior designer, and numerous luminaries of Broadway. Miss Pearl offers exceptional variety in her new establishment. She noted recently that the two most popular dishes were the moo shee pork with pancakes and the beef with lotus root, snow peas and tree mushrooms. Among the appetizers, dem sem, or white flour dumplings, and the steamed dumplings made with rice flour are particularly good. The wor wonton, a large bowl of soup with numerous ingredients, is excellent and sufficient for a meal. Complete luncheons are priced from $1.25 to $7.50. Pearl's has one drawback—its size. There are only 20 tables, and at times there is a wait to get one. *Cocktails, wines. Luncheon is not served on Sunday. Closed on Saturday during the summer months.*

★★ PEKING HOUSE

845 Second Avenue (at 45th Street) MU *7-6636*

This is one of the friendliest of the city's Chinese restaurants, and some of the dishes, particularly the quick-sauté dishes and steamed dumplings (listed on the menu as ravioli Chinese style), are excellent. At one meal, however, an order of braised squab tasted as though it had been cooked too far in advance and reheated. The Peking House is fairly small and modern in decor. There are complete luncheons from about $1.40 to $3.75. A la carte dishes on the main menu cost from about $1.95 for chop suey to $6.25 for steak à la Peking. *Cocktails, wines.*

★★ PEN AND PENCIL, THE

205 East 45th Street MU *2-1580*

Bruno's Pen and Pencil is a popular and frequently crowded midtown restaurant that specializes in steaks, chops and roasts, catering to a largely male clientele at luncheon. The à la carte menu is largely the same each day, with some Continental and curry dishes at luncheon, such as Vienna schnitzel Holstein and curry of lamb Singapore. Luncheon main courses are from about $2.95 to $3.95; entrees at dinner are from about $3.95 to $7.85. *Cocktails, wines. On Saturday and Sunday the restaurant opens at 5 p.m. Closed New Year's Day, Thanksgiving and Christmas.* *AE CB DC*

PENTHOUSE CLUB

30 Central Park South PL *9-3561*

The glass-enclosed terrace of this 19th-floor restaurant offers a sweeping and majestic view of Central Park. For the fortunate few who can procure tables overlooking that panorama the restaurant is well worth a visit. The kitchen is, by and large, only so-so. Luncheon is à la carte with entrees from $2.75 to $7.50. Complete dinners cost $7.50. Supper entrees, served from 10 p.m. to 1 a.m., are $3.50 to $7.50. *Cocktails, wines. Dinner is served from 1 p.m. on Sunday.*

AE CB DC

★ PER BACCO

140 East 27th Street LE *2-8699 and* LE *2-8663*

This is a small restaurant with a menu that is more French than Italian and food that is frequently more individual than either. The "Salt n' Bocca" sampled on one occasion was good, and the duck with orange proved quite succulent. The table d'hôte menus include, in addition to the "cheese cigarettes" that are served regularly, hors d'oeuvres and soup. Luncheons are from about $3.25 to $3.75; dinners from about $3.95 to $9. A la carte main dishes at luncheon are from $2.25 to $4.25; at dinner from $2.75 to $7. There is a cover charge of 35 cents at dinner. *Cocktails, wines. On Saturday and Sunday the restaurant opens at 5:30 p.m. Closed Sunday June through September and, during July and August, Saturday also. Closed New Year's Day, Easter, Thanksgiving and Christmas.*

AE CB DC

★ PERGOLA DES ARTISTES

252 West 46th Street *245-9779 and* CI *7-8726*

This is an agreeable small French restaurant in the Broadway area. The reception is cordial, the food is modestly priced and the service is reasonably good although the staff is small. The menu, with duck in orange sauce and fish meunière, is not overly original, but the food is well prepared. Luncheons are à la carte with main courses from about $1.50 to $2.50. Complete dinners from about $3.80 to $6; à la carte entrees from about $2.80 to $5.50. *Cocktails, wines. Closed Sunday, New Year's Day, Thanksgiving and Christmas.*

★★★★ PETER LUGER

178 Broadway, Brooklyn EV *7-7400 and* EV *4-9100*

This is a motley, raffish place with the atmosphere of a respectable neighborhood restaurant. The premises are neat and the bare tables are of polished oak. The important thing, however, is that the steaks at Peter Luger's are exceptional from the standpoint of both quality and grilling. There may be none better in all New York. Luger's is no sudden discovery. It has been around since 1887 and has a faithful clientele. The restaurant is frequently crowded and at times it is necessary to stand in line to wait for a table. There are special luncheons, with such dishes as prime ribs of beef, beef stew and pot roast, that cost from about $1.85 to $2.95. The cost of steaks is from about $6.50, according to weight. Two large grilled lamb chops are $5.25. *Cocktails, wines, beer on draught. On Sunday the restaurant opens at 4 p.m.*

★★ PETER'S BACKYARD

64 West 10th Street GR *3-2400*

This is a busy, noisy, pleasant place and one of the best steak houses in Greenwich Village. The quality of the beef is excellent, and the meat is cooked to a turn over a massive open charcoal pit. The atmosphere is neat and comfortable. The salads, on the other hand, with a sweet tomato dressing, are awful, and although the waiters are friendly enough, their style is largely mechanical. All the dishes are à la carte with main courses from about $3.50 for chopped steak to $7.50 for a T-bone. *Cocktails, wines.*

The restaurant opens at 4 p.m. Monday through Saturday; at 2 p.m. Sunday and holidays. Closed Thanksgiving and Christmas.
AE CB DC

PETE'S TAVERN

129 East 18th Street GR *3-7676*

In its own way Pete's is celebrated for down-to-earth Italian cuisine that is reasonably priced. All the foods are à la carte with main courses at luncheon from about $1 to $1.75 and at dinner from about $1.25 to $5.95. *Cocktails, wines. On Saturday the restaurant opens at 5 p.m. Dinner is served from 2:30 p.m. on Sunday. Closed Christmas.*
AE DC

PHIL GLUCKSTERN'S

209 West 48th Street CI *6-3960*

This restaurant serves kosher food with such Jewish specialties as stuffed miltz, kreplach soup and pickled beef tongue. There are complete dinners from about $3.75 to $6.25; à la carte main dishes from about $2.75 to $4.75. *Cocktails, wines. Luncheon is not served, but the restaurant opens at 1 p.m. on Sunday and holidays.*
AE CB DC

★★ PHILIPPINE GARDEN, THE

455 Second Avenue (near 26th Street) MU *4-9625*

This is a colorful, friendly restaurant that offers, particularly at noon, some of the biggest culinary bargains in town. The cooking is good, if slightly robust at times, and vaguely resembles Chinese cuisine. The menu lists such dishes as fish with vinegar, green peppers and ginger; chicken and pork with cabbage, scallions, bananas, sausages and onions. There are complete luncheons with copious dishes from about $1 to $1.50; complete dinners from about $2.75 to $5. The evening menu is also à la carte with main courses from about $1.50 to $3. *Cocktails, wines. Dinner is served Sunday, from 1 p.m.*

PHIL'S COCKTAIL LOUNGE AND RESTAURANT

187 Third Avenue (at 17th Street) GR *3-9751*

Italian cuisine. A la carte menu available at all times with main dishes from about $2.50. Prix fixe menu available at luncheon only; complete luncheons from $1.85. *Cocktails, wines. On Saturday and Sunday the restaurant opens at 2:30 p.m.*

★ PICCOLO MONDO

1269 First Avenue *249-3141 and 249-3142*
(between 68th and 69th Streets)

This is a relatively new and in some aspects admirable Italian restaurant with gauche modern decor, warm reception and service that is generally commendable. The fettucine Alfredo is excellent, and the soups, which include vichyssoise, minestrone and onion, are worthwhile. The medallions of beef with truffle sauce are very good, the veal Florentine pedestrian. The veal is served on a bed of spinach, and why the chef would serve a dish of spinach as an accompaniment is the kitchen mystery. The hors d'oeuvres at Piccolo Mondo look ravishing, but all the flavors are generally on the same level. There are complete luncheons that cost from about $1.95 to $2.95; complete dinners from about $3.95 to $6.50. A la carte dishes at midday from about $1.50; in the evening from about $2.50. *Cocktails, wines. Dinner is served Saturday and Sunday from 1 p.m. Closed Monday.*
AE DC

PIERRE, HOTEL

Fifth Avenue at 61st Street TE *8-8000*

★★The Café Pierre has French cuisine in quiet and enormously pleasant surroundings. The food is very good; the service at times leaves something to be desired. All dishes are à la carte with main luncheon dishes from about $2.40 to $7.25; main dinner courses from about $5 to $8.

Cocktails; wines in bottle and in carafe. Supper is served from 10 p.m. to 2 a.m.
AE DC

★★**The Pierre Grill** is famous for its curries, and the reputation is justified. They are excellent. The remainder of the menu in this spacious, columned room is French and generally competent. All dishes are à la carte with main courses at midday from about $2.50 to $7.75 and at dinner from about $3.20 to $8.75. *Cocktails, wines.*
AE DC

★★ PIERRE AU TUNNEL

306 West 48th Street CO *5-9039*

This is another of New York's small, unpretentious French restaurants near the theater district. It is well worth a visit whether or not you are Broadway bound, because the kitchen is generally excellent and the menu is most engagingly priced. The luncheon menu is à la carte with main courses from about $1.50 to $4. The dinner menu is table d'hôte with complete meals from about $3.85 to $5.50. *Cocktails, wines. Dinner is served from 1 p.m. on Sunday. Closed Sunday during July and August.*

★★ PIERRE'S

52 East 53rd Street EL *5-4074*

This is a deservedly popular restaurant with French cuisine. The tables, however, seem uncomfortably close together, and at peak dining periods the noise level tends to be high. There are complete luncheons from about $4 to $4.90; complete dinners from about $6 to $7.50. *Cocktails, wines. Closed Saturday, Sunday, holidays and three weeks in August.*
AE DC

★★ PIETRO'S

201 East 45th Street MU *2-9760*

This is physically one of the least pretentious Italian restaurants in town. The food—whether pasta or chicken parmigiana—is prepared with admirable care and simplicity in an all-butter kitchen that is small but equipped with a sizable staff. The food is generally first-rate. And awesomely expensive. Both luncheon and dinner menus are à la carte with main courses at midday from about $3.50 for chopped steak to $5.25 for minute steak; in the evening from about $5.25 for shrimp marinara to $6 for lamb chops. *Cocktails, wines. On Saturday the restaurant opens at 6 p.m. Closed Sunday and, during the summer months, Saturday also.*

PILSNER RESTAURANT

406 East 73rd Street RE *4-9577*

A Czechoslovakian restaurant. Among the specialties of the house are an excellent roast duck and at times roast goose. The menu is both prix fixe and à la carte with complete meals from about $2.25 to $4.25; à la carte dishes from about $1.95 to $3. *Cocktails, wines. Open for dinner only: Monday through Friday from 5 p.m.; Saturday, Sunday and holidays from noon.*

DC

★★ PIRAEUS, MY LOVE

117 West 57th Street *757-1040*

This is a new and seemingly fashionable Greek restaurant that recently opened in New York. The decor simulates the deck of a rather large yacht, including a gangplank entrance with rope and a dining deck with genuine glass-centered portholes illuminated with lights in nautical blue. The waiters wear blue and white jerseys, and there is piped-in Greek music and the pleasant scent of cucumber. Some of the dishes are interesting including lamb in pastry with tomatoes, feta cheese and tomatoes.

The octopus in oil is excellent. If you like Greek dishes cooked in much oil, you will certainly enjoy the cold imam baldi, or eggplant goulash with onions and tomatoes. A vital disappointment at the restaurant was a main course of barbounia mesogiou listed on the menu as a fish flown in by the Greek airlines. At one dinner it was overcooked and tasted as though it had been frozen. Complete luncheons at Piraeus cost about $5; complete dinners about $7. There is an à la carte menu with main courses from about $3 to $5. *Cocktails, wines. Closed Sunday.*

AE CB DC

★ PIRO'S

1350 Madison Avenue LE *4-9664*
(between 94th and 95th Streets)

This is a relatively new neighborhood restaurant with an Italian menu. At its best the food is very good. There is, for example, an excellent eggplant dish stuffed with a soft creamlike cheese, and the scampi are appetizing. On the debit side, the sauces, particularly those made with tomato, seem a trifle sweet, and the antipasto is uninspired. Piro's has a seating capacity of about 25, and the restaurant is brightly lit. The cost of main dishes is from about $1.60 for spaghetti with garlic and oil to $4 for breast of chicken dishes. *There is no bar, but guests may bring their own wine or beer. Open for dinner only. From June 1 through Labor Day, the restaurant is closed Saturday and Sunday; otherwise it is closed Sunday and Monday. Closed Memorial Day, July 4, Labor Day, Thanksgiving, Christmas and Jewish holidays. Reservations frequently essential.*

★★ PIZZERIA ALLA NAPOLETANA

147 West 48th Street JU *6-9617*

This pizzeria is more commonly and affectionately known as Luigino's, and it may be the oldest established pizza house in the city. Luigino's is simply adorned, and guests sit in booths. There is the usual assortment of manicotti, veal with peppers, sausages and so forth, prepared in the old-fashioned New York manner. The cost of the food, all à la carte, is from about $1.50 for pizza with mozzarella and tomatoes to $3.75 for steak with peppers or mushrooms. *Wines, beer on tap. Closed New Year's Day, Thanksgiving and Christmas.*

★★★ P. J. CLARKE'S

915 Third Avenue (at 55th Street) PL *9-1650*

With all the building going on in that vicinity, someone should start a movement now to declare Clarke's a landmark for preservation. It is a friendly, colorful place with original turn-of-the-century furnishings, and many New Yorkers regard it as a second home. It is celebrated as the setting for that old movie classic, *The Lost Weekend*, with Ray Milland. Some of the best hamburgers and chili in town may be had at noon in the barroom, and the food in the rear dining room is, considering the small kitchen, very good. The blackboard menu lists such diverse fare as steak Diane, spinach and mushroom salad, zucchini Benedict, which is to say with hollandaise, and chili and meat balls. The cost, à la carte, is from about 90 cents to $3.25. *Cocktails, wines. Open Monday through Saturday from 8 a.m. to 4 a.m., Sunday from noon to 4 a.m.*

★ P. J. MORIARTY

213 West 33rd Street LO *3-3453*
(near Pennsylvania Station)

50 East 54th Street MU *8-6060*
(between Park and Madison Avenues)

Third Avenue at 61st Street TE *8-2438*

1690 York Avenue (at 88th Street) *249-7555*

Yankee and Irish cuisine, with steaks and chops as specialties of the house. All dishes are à la carte with main luncheon courses from about $2.90 to $6; main dinner

entrees from about $3.15 to $6. *Cocktails, wines. The restaurants on 33rd and 54th Streets are closed Saturday and Sunday.*
AE CB DC

★★ P. J. O'HARA
869 Third Avenue EL *5-8122 and* PL *5-8825*
(at 53rd Street)

The name may sound Irish, but the menu has such entries as veal parmigiana, curries and an English mixed grill. The food is simply done and generally very good whether it is roast beef or a basic tomato sauce for spaghetti. The fish and seafood dishes in particular are creditable. On the other hand, O'Hara's antipasto is dull and woefully overpriced. The restaurant's decor is pleasant with a long bar and a good deal of nouveau-art stained glass. Luncheons, including main courses with dessert, are from about $2.10 to $3.40. Dinners are à la carte with main courses from about $2.75 for half a broiled chicken to $5.95 for sirloin steak. *Cocktails, wines.*
AE CB DC

PLAZA HOTEL
59th Street and Fifth Avenue PL *9-3000*

★★Oak Room is a fine-looking room with a masculine appeal, and the food is of the same quality as that found in the Plaza's **★★Edwardian Room.** That is to say it is, by and large, competently prepared. The less complicated dishes come off best. The menu is all à la carte with main courses at midday from about $2.80 for an omelet to $8.45 for sirloin steak. Entrees in the evening from about $3.80 for half a broiled chicken to $8.45 for the sirloin. *Cocktails, wines. Open seven days. Luncheon is not served Saturday and Sunday during July and August.*
CB

★★Trader Vic's see page 257.

★ PLUSH BURGER

241 East 60th Street PL 2-0030

Although it may be America's favorite food, a good hamburger is hard to find. The Plush Burger has not only good hamburgers but also other assets to recommend it—the sesame buns, for example, and a neat decor that is as plush as the name implies. There is red carpeting and there are crystal chandeliers. The service is courteous. The warm apple pie is excellent. The cost of hamburgers is from 95 cents to $1.50; the cost of a steak sandwich plate $2.45. *No alcoholic beverages. Closed Sunday, New Year's Day, Memorial Day, July 4, Labor Day, Thanksgiving and Christmas.*

POMPEIAN CAFÉ AND RESTAURANT, THE

136 West Third Street GR 5-3942

This restaurant, with its balustrade, gurgling fountain and candlelight, has a certain physical charm. The cuisine is, of course, Italian and comes from a very small kitchen. There is a smorgasbord luncheon and dinner at $2.85 and a complete dinner at $4.85. A la carte entrees cost from about $2 to $7. The outdoor café is in use during the summer. *Cocktails, wines.*

AE CB DC

★ PORT ARTHUR

7 Mott Street WO 2-5890

The best thing about the Port Arthur, one of the oldest restaurants in Chinatown, is the decor. It is heavy and antique, with much use of mother-of-pearl, hand-carved wood and stained glass. The menu may seem on the stereotyped side, but the food is competently prepared. There is excellent shrimp broiled with bacon, for example, and boned duckling with almonds. The sauces seem a trifle thick. There are complete luncheons that are a bargain costing from 75 cents to $1.10. A la carte dishes cost from $2.40 to $4.25. *Cocktails, wines. Only à la carte items are available Saturday, from 11 a.m. Closed Sunday.*

★ PORTOFINO

206 Thompson Street GR 3-9752

The Portofino is a three-room Italian restaurant, one of several passably good ones in Greenwich Village. The food here is relatively inexpensive and served in abundance. The antipasto dishes tend to be robustly flavored, but the main courses, such as boneless chicken Portofino or scaloppine with butter and lemon, are very well cooked. The menu is à la carte with main courses from about $2.25 to $5.25. *Cocktails, wines. Open for dinner only, from 4 p.m. Closed Thanksgiving and Christmas.*

AE CB DC

PRESIDENT

Lexington Avenue at 41st Street MU 3-5555

A large and somewhat unimaginative dining room well favored by businessmen. The food is frequently referred to as "hearty." At midday main courses with vegetables cost from $2.50 to $3.75; in the evening from $2.75 to $5. The principal menu is à la carte with main dishes from about $2.75 to $5.75. The portions on the sandwich platters are generous. *Cocktails, wines. Closed Sunday, most major holidays and, during the summer months, Saturday also.*

AE CB DC

★ PRESS BOX

139 East 45th Street MU 2-9752

Predominantly American cuisine with steaks and chops as the prime entrees. Complete luncheons from about $3.95 to $5.45. The à la carte menu, available for luncheon and dinner, lists entrees from about $3.50 to $7.75. *Cocktails, wines. On Saturday the restaurant opens at 5 p.m. Closed Sunday and most major holidays.*

AE CB DC

★ PRIME BURGER

536 Madison Avenue PL *3-4214*
(between 54th and 55th Streets)
5 East 51st Street *759-4730*

In a city the size of New York it is remarkable how few enterprises offer first-rate hamburgers. The Prime Burgers' hamburgers are small but very good, and so is most of the other food. The menu lists such foods as eggs in several styles, salads, steak tartare and chili con carne. The two restaurants are frequently crowded and there is often a wait for a counter seat. The cost of the principal dishes ranges from about 75 cents for a hamburger to $1.35 for English-style fish and chips. The restaurants offer a take-out service. *No alcoholic beverages. Closed Sunday, New Year's Day, Washington's Birthday, Memorial Day, July 4, Labor Day, Thanksgiving and Christmas.*

PROOF OF THE PUDDING

1165 First Avenue (at 64th Street) *421-5440*

For want of a better word you might call this new edition of the Proof of the Pudding a "fun" restaurant. It has a modern look, with shiny plastic banquettes, marble table tops, mirrors and sconces and miniature candles. When the young and attractive owners describe the food, it sounds like heavenly relish, but the food itself is of a fantasy sort. For example, one dish, so help me Hannah, was made with shrimp, lemon, dill, noodles and a maraschino cherry in a cream sauce. How does that strike you as an ice cream sundae? The portions are large. When a waiter produced one order of overcooked lamb, it was with the greeting, "If you get through that, I say 'bon voyage' to you." Giving credit where it's due, a salmon steak with béarnaise at one lunch was good and in beautiful contrast to a rather tough shrimp appetizer, at the same table, with a lime sauce that smacked strongly of commercial mayonnaise. The cocktails, served in wine glasses, are gigantic. There is an outdoor dining terrace that was recently sorely

in need of a broom. All dishes are à la carte. Main dishes at midday cost from about $2.95 to $7.50; in the evening about $3.95 to $7.50. *Cocktails, wines. Open seven days a week.*
AE DC

★ PUBLICK HOUSE

917 Third Avenue PL *2-7930 and* PL *2-7931*
(near 55th Street)

In spite of a somewhat pretentiously worded menu, this is an interesting restaurant with dishes of Irish inspiration. It offers, for example, Irish stew and steak and kidney pie. Such foods are well prepared. As to atmosphere, there are red-jacketed waiters, red tablecloths and candlelight. The dishes are à la carte with entrees at luncheon from about $1.25 to $3.95; at dinner from about $1.25 to $5.75. Brunch, at $2.25, is served Saturday and Sunday from noon to 4 p.m., followed by dinner. *Cocktails, wines, beer on draught. Closed Election Day.*
AE CB DC

QUON LUCK RESTAURANT

66 Mott Street CA *6-4675*

This is a friendly restaurant in Chinatown with a competent but undistinguished menu and kitchen. Along with the moo goo gai pan and braised duck there are ample helpings of piped-in music from a local radio station. There are complete luncheons from about 95 cents for chicken chow mein to $2.95 for lobster Cantonese style; à la carte dishes from about $1.10 for chicken chow mein to $3.85 for shelled lobster Cantonese. *Cocktails, wines. Only à la carte items are available on Sunday.*

★★★★ QUO VADIS

26 East 63rd Street TE *8-0590*

The Quo Vadis not only has one of the finest kitchens in Manhattan, the management maintains the most rigid standards for the conduct of their admirable enterprise. The menu is scrupulously put together, from the fondue bruxelloise (fried cheese) and the exceptional specialty, eels in green sauce, through entrees and roasts, crêpes suzette and soufflés. The service is generally polished at Quo Vadis, and if there is to be the slightest criticism, it may be that the acoustics in the main dining room permit a certain din at peak dining periods. All dishes are à la carte with main courses at midday from about $3.50 to $4; in the evening from about $5 to $8. *Cocktails, wines. Luncheon is not served on Sunday. Closed holidays.*

AE CB DC

RAINBOW ROOM

30 Rockefeller Plaza PL *7-9090*

There is one thing to be said for certain about the Rainbow Room. The windows on a clear night open onto some of the most glorious views of the city. The food is another matter. The menu is broad and offers an extensive assortment of four courses for one fixed price, $9.75. Of several dishes sampled the most interesting was assorted hors d'oeuvres with cold curried chicken, head cheese, palm hearts and mushrooms. A watery lobster bisque lacked substance; the billi bi, at its best one of the most delectable of creamed soups, tasted as if it had been made with canned mussels; and a serving of beef that should have been hot was cold. Open seven days a week for dinner. Brunch, at $6, is served Saturday and Sunday from noon to 3 p.m. *Cocktails, wines.*

AE CB DC

★★ RAJMAHAL RESTAURANT

124 Fourth Avenue *473-9086*
(between 12th and 13th Streets)

This is a new and markedly unpretentious Pakistani-Indian restaurant in Greenwich Village. Specialties include bhunda dishes, thickened curries made of beef,

lamb, chicken and shrimp; birani dishes with a somewhat more delicate sauce; and kurma dishes made with sweet spices and yogurt. The Rajmahal has a kitchen that is generally excellent and offers in addition to main courses an assortment of breads and condiments. There is a complete luncheon that costs $1.25; complete dinners from $3 to $4.95. A la carte dishes are priced from $1.75 to $3. *Wines, beers. Luncheon is not served Sunday.*
AE DC

RATNER'S

111 Second Avenue (between 6th and 7th Streets) GR *3-7374*

Jewish cuisine. Menu is à la carte; dairy specialties from about $1.10; other main dishes from about $1.45. *No alcoholic beverages. Closed on Jewish holidays; otherwise open twenty-four hours a day.*

★ RATTAZZI

9 East 48th Street PL *3-5852*

This is a worthwhile and popular Italian restaurant. All food is à la carte with main luncheon dishes from about $2.65 to $5.75; dinner entrees from about $3.75 to $7. *Cocktails, wines. Closed Saturday, Sunday and holidays.*
AE CB DC

★★ RED COACH GRILL

784 Seventh Avenue (at 51st Street) CI *5-2500*

This grill, in the City Squire Motor Inn, has a pleasant atmosphere contrived to resemble an English rustic inn. The roast beef is of excellent quality, and the lobster and shrimp dishes are recommended particularly. There are special luncheons with soup, main course, salad and beverage that cost $1.85 to $2.95. Most of the items are à la carte with main courses from about $1.85 to $5.45. Complete dinners cost from about $4.70 to $5.45; à la carte main dishes from about $3.85 to $6.95. Supper,

served from 11 p.m. to 1 a.m., is à la carte with entrees from about $1.95 to $5.95. *Cocktails, wines. Closed Christmas.*
AE CB DC

RENATO

21 Van Dam Street AL *5-9899*

This is an Italian restaurant in Greenwich Village with a thoroughly respectable decor and a kitchen that is only fleetingly inspired. Complete luncheons cost from about $3.50 to $5.85; à la carte main dishes from about $2.50. Complete dinners cost from about $4.80 to $8.50; à la carte entrees from about $2.40. In summer there is an outdoor garden. *Cocktails, wines. On Saturday the restaurant opens at 5 p.m. Closed Sunday and national holidays.*
AE CB DC

★★ RENATO EAST

302 East 45th Street MU *6-0021*

The kitchen at Renato East is generally commendable. The dishes, whether osso buco, striped bass in brodetta or spaghetti with meat sauce, seem to be cooked with particular care. There are complete luncheons from about $2.75 to $3.75; à la carte entrees from about $2 to $6. Complete dinners from about $4.25 to $7.50; à la carte main dishes from about $2.25 to $6.50. *Cocktails, wines. Closed Sunday, New Year's Day, July 4 and Christmas.*
AE CB DC

RESTAURANT LAURENT

111 East 56th Street PL *3-2729*

It was remarkably like surrealism or Alice in Wonderland. There you are at a table in the vicinity of half a dozen waiters, captains, maîtres d'hôtel and so forth. You would like to order wine, and since the main dish is fish, you want it white and chilled. You wave in the direction of the service staff, but to no avail. A long time later courses start to arrive, and finally someone offers a

wine list. You order and the maître d'hôtel says in a reprimanding voice, "If you want that wine chilled, you should have ordered it half an hour ago." As to the food, there have been numerous disappointments from a kitchen formerly regarded as exceptionally good. On one occasion deviled ribs of beef listed on the menu were not available. An omelet was flat and overcooked; veal scallops were thick and had a pasty coating, and of several dishes only an order of small softshell crab is remembered with any particular pleasure. Complete luncheons from about $5; dinners are à la carte with main courses from about $5.25. *Cocktails, wines (those in carafe are decent). Luncheon is not served Saturday and Sunday. Closed most major holidays.*
AE CB DC

★★ REUBEN'S

6 East 58th Street PL *9-5650*

This celebrated landmark is best known for its cheesecake and sandwiches, both of which are inspired. Frequent entrees on the menu include cold gefüllte fish with pickled beets and horseradish, hot turkey drumstick and roast beef hash with poached egg. The main dining room is spacious, with a conservative decor. Complete luncheons from about $2.50 to $3.50. Dinners are à la carte with main dishes from about $2.50 to $5.50. *Cocktails, wines. The restaurant is open 24 hours a day Friday and Saturday, to 5 a.m. Monday through Thursday, to 3 a.m. Sunday. Reservations accepted.*
AE DC

★★ REX RESTAURANT

147 East 60th Street TE *8-2024 and* TE *8-9739*

The Rex has merit. The food is cooked with care, and the reception is warm. There are two indoor dining rooms, and when weather permits, the canopy-covered "garden" is open outside. Unfortunately, as in most New York restaurant gardens, when the weather is warm and the humidity high, the garden area tends to be a little sticky. The kitchen at the Rex is Italian. The luncheon menu is à la carte with main courses from about $2.50 for cannelloni milanese to $5.50 for sliced filet bordelaise. There are complete dinners from about $4.75 for chicken Tetrazzini to $6 for duckling with wild rice; à la carte entrees from about $2.75 to $7. The shrimp maison with mustard sauce is interesting. *Cocktails, wines. Closed Sunday, New Year's Day, Thanksgiving and Christmas.*

AE CB DC

★ RICK'S SEA FOOD HOUSE

871 Third Avenue EL *5-8605*
(between 52nd and 53rd Streets)

A small, unpretentious, modestly priced restaurant that is frequently crowded and noisy. The menu lists plain broiled fish of all kinds, from imported Dover sole to Boston scrod and smelts. All generally have good flavor but are sometimes overcooked. A number of au gratin fish dishes and lobster dishes are available. Complete luncheons of entree, dessert and coffee from $2.30 to $2.60. Main course entrees on the à la carte menu from about $1.95. Complete dinners from about $2.75. *Cocktails, wines.*

AE CB DC

★ RISTORANTE PUGLIA

189 Hester Street *226-8912*

This is a colorful, atmospheric establishment in Little Italy, and it is reminiscent of a waterfront restaurant in Naples. A visit to the Ristorante Puglia is an adventure. Most of the customers and all the staff speak in Italian, and the food is lusty. The hot appetizers include stuffed mushrooms, stuffed pepper, stuffed tomato and a delicious deep-fried potato croquette stuffed with melting cheese. The tiny shrimp in hot sauce are fiery. There is the usual assortment of pasta dishes, sautéed veal dishes and the like, plus such oddments as charcoal-grilled sheep's head.

The food, all in all, is tasty and robust. There is one menu and all the dishes are à la carte with main dishes from about 80 cents for pasta marinara to $2.50 for chicken parmigiana. *There is no bar, but apéritifs, wines and beers are available. Closed Monday.*

RITA DIMITRI'S LA CHANSONNETTE

890 Second Avenue (near 48th Street) PL 2-7320

La Chansonnette, whose decor looks more like a boudoir than a restaurant, is full of gusto when Miss Dimitri belts out songs, and the public seems to dote on it. The tables, compactly placed, are filled. The kitchen's fare is uneven, from excellent quality lamb noisettes, first brought to the table cold, to stuffed breast of chicken with mousseline sauce filled with stringy cheese. Many of the dishes are garnished with what seem like once-frozen noisette potatoes. The restaurant is open evenings only. The cost of complete dinners is from about $6.75 for trout amandine to $9.25 for tournedos Rossini. There are à la carte dishes from about $4.50 to $8. The menu also lists a "music charge, $1 per show." *Cocktails, wines. Closed Sunday, New Year's Day, July 4, Labor Day, Thanksgiving and Christmas.*

AE CB DC

★ ROCCO RESTAURANT

181 Thompson Street GR 3-9267

This restaurant, near several off-Broadway theaters in Greenwich Village, is of the genre sometimes referred to as "family-style Italian." The menu is South Italian style, and some of the dishes are industriously spiced with herbs and spices, such as garlic and oregano. The dishes are à la carte and include a very good put plain antipasto at $1.10, a special antipasto at $1.50, steamed clams marinara at $1.75 and—the most expensive entree—sirloin steak at $4.25. *Cocktails, wines.*

ROMA DI NOTTE

1528 Second Avenue (at 79th Street) RE *4-3443*

A dark and shadowy restaurant and bar with menus soiled and torn. The antipasto cart shows some imagination with its mussels, stuffed squid, stuffed mushrooms and so on, but some of these items look a little tired. The homemade tortellini and their broth were excellent, and a boneless breast of capon with prosciutto was creditable enough. A serving of stuffed veal loin tasted as though it had been cooked too far in advance. An arugula salad was well seasoned, but the restaurant's desserts go from run-of-the-mill to ghastly. The restaurant is open for dinner only, and the menu is à la carte. Main courses cost from about $4.80 to $7. *Cocktails, wines. Closed Sunday.*
AE DC

★ ROMEO SALTA

39 West 56th Street CI *6-5772*

This is one of New York's best-known Italian restaurants, and it has moments of eminence. The kitchen is wayward, and there is no guarantee of excellence. Complete luncheons from about $3.75 to $5.50. Dinners are à la carte with main courses from about $4 to $7.50. *Cocktails, wines. Closed Sunday and, during the summer months, for luncheon on Saturday. Closed New Year's Day, Memorial Day, July 4, Thanksgiving, Christmas and from August 15 through Labor Day.*

★ ROSETTA'S RESTAURANT

502 Avenue of the Americas YU *9-9442*
(near West 12th Street)

This is a small, fairly pleasant Italian restaurant in Greenwich Village. The food may not be distinguished, but it is nonetheless palatable and reasonably priced. Complete luncheons from about $2 to $2.50; à la carte dinner entrees from about $1.75 to $4. *Cocktails, wines.*

From September through June the restaurant is closed Monday; during July and August it is closed Saturday.

ROSOFF'S

147 West 43rd Street JU 2-3200

A 67-year-old restaurant in the Times Square area. The menu is American, the portions are copious and the boast of the menus is "All you can eat." There are complete luncheons from about $1.35 to $5.70; à la carte main courses from about $1.35 to $5.25. Complete dinners from about $2.95 to $6.75; à la carte entrees from about $2.25 to $6.05. *Cocktails, wines. Supper is served Saturday only, from 9:15 p.m. to 1 a.m.*

AE CB DC

★★ RUC RESTAURANT

312 East 72nd Street RH 4-9185

A small, frequently crowded Czechoslovak restaurant with a kitchen that is generally commendable. The veal goulash, pork chops à la Bratislava and roast duckling are well prepared. The palacinky, or Czechoslovak version of crêpes suzette, are distinctive and consequently very popular. The menu is both prix fixe and à la carte with complete meals from about $2.25 to $4.25; à la carte dishes from about $1.65 to $3.65. *Cocktails, wines. The restaurant is open from 4 p.m. to 10 p.m. Monday through Friday, and from noon until 10 p.m. Saturday and Sunday.*

★★ RUGANTINO

55 West 56th Street 581-5615

This is a dimly lit, neat and simply decorated dining spot with food better than that found in most small Italian restaurants. The cannelloni, tender noodles stuffed with meat vaguely seasoned with nutmeg, is especially good. And the osso buco, or veal bone, which occasionally appears on the menu, is recommended. Luncheon is à la carte with main courses from about $2.25 for spaghetti to

$5 for filet mignon. There are complete dinners from about $4.75 to $7.50; à la carte entrees from about $2.25 to $6.25. *Cocktails, wines. On Saturday and Sunday the restaurant opens at 4:30 p.m.*
AE CB DC

★★ RUNNING FOOTMAN, THE

133 East 61st Street 838-3939

This is a fashionable restaurant, the enterprise of Michael Pearman, the former owner of Michael's Pub. The decor is bright, interesting and offbeat. It is a three-level restaurant with a bar opening into a small dining area. This leads into a main dining room with walls painted "hot salmon" color. The lighting is dim, with chandeliers and globe lamps mounted on steer horns. The steaks and chops are excellent, and one of the most interesting dishes is listed as a chickenburger. There is a very good steak and kidney pie, but the quality of the steak could be better. The menus are à la carte. Main courses at dinner are priced from about $3.85 to $6.90; luncheon and supper dishes from $2.80 to $5.80. *Cocktails, wines. Closed Saturday and Sunday.*

RUSSIAN BEAR

139 East 56th Street PL *3-0465*

Russian food, embracing such dishes as chicken Kiev, shashlik and beef Stroganoff. A la carte dishes from $3.50 to $5.75; complete dinners from $5 to $7.75. *Cocktails, wines. The restaurant is not open for lunch.*
AE CB DC

★★ RUSSIAN TEA ROOM

150 West 57th Street CO *5-0947*

This is not a tearoom in the usual sense of the word, and it is probably the best Russian restaurant in the city. The kitchen does not have extraordinary merit and yet the food is generally good. Specialties of the house include such familiars as borscht with sour cream, blinis with red caviar and beef à la Stroganoff. One of the best dishes, served only at Wednesday luncheon, is the Siberian Pelmeny. These are ground beef balls flavored with dill, wrapped in pastry and cooked in broth, the Russian version of won ton or ravioli. They are available either served in broth or with a mustard sauce and sour cream. The cost of main luncheon dishes with dessert and beverage is from about $3 to $6. There are complete dinners from about $5.50 to $6.25; à la carte entrees from about $3.50 to $6.50. Supper is served from 9:30 p.m. to 1 a.m., Saturday to 2 a.m. *Cocktails, wines.*

AE CB DC

★ ST. GERMAIN RESTAURANT

36 West 48th Street JU *6-8997*

The St. Germain is more or less a carbon copy of several small French bistro-type restaurants in New York. There is the typical assortment of hors d'oeuvres—eggs à la russe, céleri rémoulade and pâté maison; among main courses, the usual coq au vin, omelets, London broil and tripe. The taste of the food will seem familiar to many Manhattan palates. The service by French waitresses is polite and attractive. The cost of complete luncheons is from $2.80 to $3.50; of complete dinners from $3.75 to $5. *Cocktails, wines. Closed Saturday and Sunday.*

AE DC

★★★ SAITO

131 West 52nd Street JU *2-7809*

The Saito was one of the first of Manhattan's luxury Japanese restaurants, and in its relatively new setting it remains a place with opulence, dignity and an excellent kitchen. Seating is according to customer choice, Western or Oriental, and there is a sukiyaki bar where the food is cooked directly before the guests. The most popular dish, of course, is sukiyaki, but the luncheon or dinner most highly recommended is the o-teishoku. This is a many-course affair, and the food is special. The cost of a complete luncheon is from about $2.50 to $4.50; of a complete dinner, from about $5.50 to $10. The à la carte menu lists dishes from about $4.20 to $5.80. *Cocktails, wines. Closed Sunday, New Year's Day and for luncheon on Memorial Day, July 4, Labor Day, Thanksgiving and Christmas.*

AE CB DC

★ SAM WO

39 Mott Street WO *2-8750*

There is no apparent end to the good restaurants in Chinatown with a clean but frowsy atmosphere. What would the place be without them? The Sam Wo is cordially recommended for all categories—noodles, pork, beef, poultry or fish. The restaurant is open day and night and guests might be asked to share their table. The menu is à la carte with main dishes from about 85 cents for roast pork lo mein (with noodles) to $4.30 for a chicken with lobster-meat dish. *There is no bar, but beer may be brought into the restaurant.*

★★★ SAN MARCO

52 West 55th Street CI *6-5340*

The San Marco has expanded its dining facilities and as a consequence has lost some of the personal ambiance it once enjoyed. Dishes that deserve it are not invariably prepared tableside these days, and one plate of pasta requested with truffles was returned for want of a truffle flavor. The San Marco remains, however, possibly the best Italian restaurant in New York. It has a well-rounded menu and the food is generally first-rate whether it is pasta, meat or fowl. It has been said that you can judge the quality of a restaurant by its veal, and judged on that alone the San Marco would be remarkable. The chef would do well, on the other hand, to make his own soup stock. The soups taste altogether as though they were made from a commercial base. There are complete luncheons from about $4.25 for vermicelli with tomato and garlic to $6.75 for various steaks Italian style. Dinners are à la carte with main dishes from about $3.75 to $7. *Cocktails, wines. Closed Sunday and, during July and August, for luncheon on Saturday. Closed New Year's Day, Memorial Day, July 4, Labor Day, Thanksgiving, Christmas and two weeks in August.*

AE CB DC

★★ SAN MARINO

236 East 53rd Street PL *9-4130*

At its best, and the best would include the marinara sauce for imported langostine and the broiled jumbo squab, the food at San Marino is excellent. And if the food in the main is very good, it is in contrast to the reception, which is at times indifferent, and the service, which, when the restaurant is crowded, is impatient and hurried. The cost of a full-course luncheon is from about $3.75 to $4.50. The dinner menu is à la carte with main courses from about $3 to $7.50. *Cocktails, wines. On Saturday the restaurant opens at 5 p.m. Closed Sunday, legal holidays and three weeks in August.*

SAN REMO

393 Eighth Avenue *565-6161*
(between 29th and 30th Streets)

This is a little Italian restaurant that seems to have a host of admirers from Seventh Avenue and other points about town. The food—mostly on the pasta side—is simply but earnestly prepared and it is inexpensive. All dishes are à la carte with main courses at noon from about $1.10 to $1.75; in the evening from about $1.40 to $3. *There is no bar, but wines and beer are available. On Saturday and Sunday the restaurant opens at 5 p.m.*

★★ SANTA LUCIA

160 West 54th Street CO *5-9719*

This is another of the noteworthy, small Italian restaurants of Manhattan with an interesting menu. Among the unusual first courses, for example, there is warm, sautéed escarole and cold, fried tripe with lemon. The sauces here are excellent. Three-course luncheons are from about $2.25 to $2.75; dinners are à la carte. The à la carte menu is available at all times, and main courses are priced from about $2.40 to $7.50. There is an open-air garden. *Cocktails, wines. On Saturday the restaurant opens at 5 p.m. Closed Sunday, New Year's Day, Memorial Day, July 4, Labor Day, Election Day, Thanksgiving and Christmas.*

AE CB DC

★★ SARDI'S

234 West 44th Street LA *4-0707*

This is almost without question the nation's most famous restaurant for celebrity-watching. The atmosphere is convivial, and all things considered, it is a reasonably priced restaurant with moderately good food. The best-known specialties are, perhaps, the cannelloni à la Sardi, hot shrimp à la Sardi and deviled beef bones. There are complete luncheons priced at $3.50; dinners are à la carte. A la carte items at both luncheon and dinner cost from about $3.25 to $8.50. *Cocktails, wines. Closed Sunday.*

AE CB DC

★★ SARDI'S EAST

123 East 54th Street PL *1-6655*

This is a convivial, spacious restaurant that is the East Side counterpart of the celebrity haunt in the Broadway area. Sardi's East is a pleasant place to dine, and the menu is a mélange of several cuisines, including Italian, American and Chinese. East or West, Sardi's hot shrimp is famous. All dishes are à la carte with main luncheon courses from about $2 to $6.95; main dinner entrees from

about $2.85 to $6.95; main supper entrees from about $2 to $5.95. *Cocktails, wines. Luncheon is not served Saturday, Sunday and holidays.*
AE CB DC

★ SAVOIA

477 Third Avenue MU *6-5848 and* MU *4-9782*
(between 32nd and 33rd Streets)

This is a simple, earthy and honest Italian restaurant of the "neighborhood" variety, and if you like that kind of place, it is altogether pleasant. The menu itself—with its pasta dishes, various veal dishes and so forth—will seem familiar, but the sauces are well seasoned and the food in general is cooked with care. Pizza is one of the most popular specialties of the Savoia, and it is very good. The menu, the same for lunch and dinner, is à la carte with main courses from about $1.30 for spaghetti with butter sauce to $6 for steak pizzaiola. *Cocktails, wines.*

★★ SAYAT NOVA

91 Charles Street OR *5-7364*

There are several points of interest about the Sayat Nova in Greenwich Village. The dining room is in a basement, the service is friendly and the Armenian food is generally excellent. Some of the dishes include very good small, stewed artichokes with potatoes and onions, a tasty soup with meat balls and lemon, and numerous dishes made with lamb, including several kebabs. Finding the Sayat Nova seems a trial for some New York taxi drivers, but it is worth the effort. The menu is à la carte with main courses from about $2.50 for lamb in grape leaves to $3.50 for lamb and mushroom kebab. *Cocktails, wines. Open for dinner only. Closed most major holidays.*

★★ SAY ENG LOOK

1 East Broadway *732-0796*

Almost all the restaurants of New York's Chinatown can claim one distinction or another. This one, however, has more than the accustomed share. Two excellent dishes are tiny shrimp cooked with sesame oil and crab with egg sauce. The crab dish is tedious to eat but delicious. There is a single menu for lunch and dinner; all dishes are à la carte with main courses from about $1.75 for shredded pork Shanghai style to $2.95 for sea cucumber with crab meat. Sea cucumber is a long, forbidding-looking ocean creature sometimes called sea slug. The service at the Say Eng Look wavers between friendly and indifferent. *No alcoholic beverages.*

★★ SCANDIA

227 West 45th Street (in the Piccadilly Hotel) CI *6-6600*

New York does not boast a Scandinavian restaurant to equal those of Denmark or Sweden, but this is one of the best the city has to offer. The restaurant is in the heart of the theater district. Before dining, guests should read the explanation on the back of the menu on how to enjoy a smorgasbord. Complete smorgasbord at luncheon is $3.25; at dinner $4.95; at supper (10 p.m. to 1 a.m.) $3.95. There are complete luncheons from $2.60 and à la carte entrees from $1.95. Complete dinners from $3.95. *Cocktails, wines, akvavit and Danish beer. Reservations accepted.* *AE CB DC*

★ SCHAEFER'S

1202a Lexington Avenue *734-9887*
(between 81st and 82nd Streets)

This German-American restaurant may not be much to look at, but it has "home-style" cooking that is inexpensive and good. The menu at times offers such bourgeois fare as homemade head cheese, oxtail ragout and breaded breast of lamb. Main dishes cost from about

$1.30 to $1.70, and the portions are copious. Schaefer's is a small restaurant with only four tables. There is also a dining counter. *There is no bar, but domestic and imported beers are available. Closed Sunday.*

★ SCHRAFFT'S RESTAURANTS

There are 34 Schrafft's Restaurants in the New York area, with many foods that should appeal to the young set—particularly the ice cream, which, over the course of a year, comes in about 40 flavors. The sundaes, notably hot fudge and butterscotch, seem to be special favorites. A day at the Central Park Zoo might include a visit to Schrafft's at 625 Madison Avenue. The Stock Exchange is next door to the restaurant at 48 Broad Street. The Schrafft's at 990 Madison Avenue is around the corner from the Metropolitan Museum. Luncheon is à la carte with main courses from about $1.20 to $2.95. Club dinners, without appetizer, are about $3.20 to $4; à la carte entrees from about $2.45 to $6.10. *Cocktails, wines. Closing days differ for the various restaurants; all are closed Christmas.*

AE DC

★★ SEA-FARE OF THE AEGEAN

25 West 56th Street LT *1-0540*

In view of the considerable financial outlay for this newest addition to the Sea-Fare restaurants, the decor is disappointing. The food is, however, in keeping with the usual Sea-Fare tradition, and the standards are high. The Sea-Fare restaurants generally are among the best sea-food restaurants in the city. All dishes are à la carte with main courses from about $2.95 to $9.50. There are also daily specials. Brunch, at $3.50, is served Sunday from 1 p.m. to 3 p.m. *Cocktails, wines. Closed Thanksgiving.*

AE CB DC

★★ SEA-FARE RESTAURANT

1033 First Avenue (at 57th Street) PL *9-4176*
44 West 8th Street AL *4-5646*

These are among three Manhattan seafood restaurants bearing the same name that can be relied upon to offer an adequate selection of fresh seasonal and year-round varieties of fish. All are simply but generally well prepared, without the common fault of overcooking. Long Island porgies, Boston scrod, sea and striped bass and red snapper are among the features. Service is friendly even though not always expert. Luncheon and dinner menus are à la carte with entrees from $2.75 for broiled porgy to $5.85 and up for lobster. There are also daily specials. Brunch, at $3.65, is served Sunday from noon to 3 p.m. *Cocktails, wines. Closed Thanksgiving.*
AE CB DC

SEA HUNT

67 West 44th Street MU *7-2376*

This is a recently opened seafood restaurant conveniently close to many Broadway theaters. It has a neat but garish decor and excellent clam broth and sesame sticks. The portions, such as the baked Panama shrimp, are enormous, and the service is friendly. Both the menu and the kitchen are conventional. All dishes are à la carte at luncheon with main courses from about $2.75 for sautéed sole to $5.25 for broiled miniature lobster tails. There are complete dinners from $3.95 to $6.95; à la carte entrees from about $3.50 for sole to about $7.95 for broiled live large stuffed lobster. *Cocktails, wines. On Saturday the restaurant opens at 4 p.m. Closed Sunday and legal holidays.*
AE DC

SEMPIONE

923 Second Avenue (at 49th Street) EL *5-8186*

Many of the dishes at the Sempione, a well-established Italian restaurant on the East Side, seem

seasoned at approximately the same taste level, and thus the food seems routine. The menu is generally run of the mill, with a predictable antipasto (anchovies, peppers, provolone and the like), veal parmigiana, veal and peppers and lobster fra diavolo. The menu is à la carte with main dishes from about $3.25 to $6.50. *Cocktails, wines. On Saturday the restaurant opens at 4 p.m. Closed Sunday.*
AE CB DC

SERENDIPITY 3 (offbeat)
225 East 60th Street TE *8-3531*

There is nothing in all New York like this Alice-through-the-looking-glass dining establishment. In the front of the building is a general store that sells everything from pillboxes to Tiffany lamps. Next comes a dining room that serves luncheons in the omelet style, dinners and late-hour coffees with desserts. Complete luncheons from $2.75 to $3.75; à la carte entrees from $1.75. Dinner is à la carte with main courses from about $2 to $7.50. Supper is served from 9:30 p.m. to 1 a.m. The restaurant is frequently crowded even through the coffee hour. *No alcoholic beverages. Closed Sunday, New Year's Day, Thanksgiving and Christmas.*

★ SEVILLA
62 Charles Street *929-3189 and 243-9513*

This is a friendly neighborhood Spanish café and bar in Greenwich Village. The kitchen is generally competent and the food is well seasoned. On the minus side, the ventilation is not the best in the world and the multihued jukebox can prove a distraction. All dishes are à la carte with main courses at luncheon from $1.50 to $3.90; at dinner from $2.75 to $4.50. *Cocktails, wines.*
AE CB DC

★ SHANGHAI CAFÉ

3217 Broadway MO *2-1990*
(between 125th and 126th Streets)

The luncheon menu at the Shanghai is as stereotyped as chop suey, but the à la carte dishes can be excellent. Complete luncheons from about $1.35 to $1.60; complete dinners from about $1.85 to $2.15; à la carte dishes throughout the day from about $1.05 to $3.25. Family dinners for two persons begin at $4.95. *No alcoholic beverages. Closed Thanksgiving.*

★ SHANGHAI D'OR

2519 Broadway (at 94th Street) AC *2-5500*

In the most essential thing, the food, the Shanghai d'Or ranks high. The menu is interesting with its beef or pork with mustard greens and chicken with peanuts and mushrooms in mustard sauce. There is a good relish too—pickled cabbage with a touch of sesame oil. The service is willing, but, particularly at noon, the restaurant seems understaffed. Main courses at noon cost from about $1.10 for chicken chow mein to $3 for lobster with black bean sauce. There are complete dinners from about $1.30 to $3.40. The à la carte menu lists dishes from about $1.25 to $3.75. *Cocktails, wines.*

SHANGHAI EAST

1059 Third Avenue TE *8-0850*
(between 62nd and 63rd Streets)

This is a spacious, conventional Chinese restaurant with a kitchen that produces a cuisine that is good but not memorable. The luncheon menu has its share of chow mein and egg roll, but there are more interesting dishes, such as pressed duck with almonds and chicken with almonds. The cost of a complete luncheon is from about $1.30 to $3.25. The dinner menu is à la carte with main dishes from about $2.25 to $7. *Cocktails, wines.*
AE CB DC

★ SHANGHAI GARDEN

140 West 4th Street *982-7670*

This is a new and in some respects laudable Chinese restaurant that is within walking distance of the ANTA Washington Square Theater. The food at its best seems exceptionally good. On one occasion the hot and sour soup, the fried dumplings and the chicken in hot sauce all had special merit. On another evening the soup came off far less well and an order of scallion pork was brought to the table cold. It should be added that the dishes are reasonably priced. There are complete luncheons that cost from 90 cents to $1.75. Dinners are à la carte. A la carte dishes cost from $1.60 to $3.50. *No alcoholic beverages. Only à la carte items are available Saturday and Sunday, from noon.*

★ SHANGHAI VILLAGE

23 Pell Street CO *7-2092*

The Shanghai Village has improved its interior with new lighting. It is an upstairs place with indifferent service, a menu with commendable variety and a good kitchen. Even the spring rolls have something to recommend them. The same menu serves throughout the day, although the prices are slightly higher in the evening. There are complete luncheons from about 95 cents to $2.45; complete dinners for two from about $4.35 to $5.10. A la carte dishes cost from about $1.35 to $3.50 at midday; from $1.50 to $3.50 in the evening. *Cocktails, wines.*

★★ SHEIK RESTAURANT, THE

132 Lexington Avenue MU *4-9143*
(between 28th and 29th Streets)

Some of the most gratifying restaurants in New York are the small ones, like The Sheik, that specialize in Middle Eastern cookery. The menu at The Sheik includes appetizers made with sesame paste, such as baba ganough, which is mashed eggplant, and hummus, which is puréed chick-peas. The main courses, such as the shish kebab, are made principally with lamb, and there are excellent stuffed vegetables. The restaurant is relatively inexpensive. A complete luncheon costs $1.75; a complete dinner, $3.75. The same menu, with à la carte main courses from about $1.35 to $3.95, serves throughout the day. *Cocktails, wines. Closed Sunday, New Year's Day, July 4, Thanksgiving and Christmas.*

★ SHUN LEE

119 East 23rd Street GR *3-4447*

A large, bustling and physically colorless Chinese restaurant with unadorned walls and artificial flowers. The food, however, even at its most conventional, is almost invariably appetizing, and with expert guidance it is possible to dine extremely well. There are run-of-the-mill luncheons priced from about $1.15 for chicken chow mein to $3.25 for lobster Chinese style. The à la carte menu is recommended. Dishes cost from about $1.45 for chicken yat gaw mein to $4.70 for squab in casserole. *Cocktails, wines. Only à la carte items are available Saturday and Sunday, from 11 a.m.*

★★★★ SHUN LEE DYNASTY

900 Second Avenue (at 48th Street) PL *5-3900*

This is a consistently excellent Chinese restaurant and decidedly one of the best in Manhattan. It has a decor by Russel Wright that becomes more and more agreeable with subsequent visits. There are shiny gold streamers that serve as room dividers and a Fongling, a circular device made with Chinese wind chimes, overhead. The menu doesn't change from one visit to the other, but the variety is admirable, from the assorted hot appetizers and hoisin chicken to Szechuan dishes. The latter, incidentally, may not be as highly spiced as they should be—a concession to public taste. The management will provide a hot

sauce on the side on demand. Complete luncheons cost from about $1.75 to $4.25; complete dinners cost $6.25. A la carte dishes at midday from about $1.75 to $4; in the evening from $3 to $5.25. *Cocktails, wines. Open seven days. Luncheon is not served on Saturday and Sunday.*
AE DC

SIGN OF THE DOVE
1110 Third Avenue (at 65th Street) UN *1-8080*

From the standpoint of decor this is one of New York's most enchanting restaurants. There are gas lamps, antique grillwork, Venetian glass and a garden. The menu includes cheese soufflé, fish dishes and charcoal-broiled meats, and the quality ranges from mediocre to very good. The table service at worst is lamentable. A la carte main courses at luncheon range from $3.75 to $6.75; à la carte dinner entrees from $6.95 to $10.50. *Cocktails, wines. Luncheon is not served Saturday. Closed July 4, Thanksgiving and Christmas.*
AE CB DC

★ SING WU
123 Second Avenue (near 7th Street) GR *5-7540*

The Sing Wu is an unpretentious and very good Chinese restaurant that boasts a Shanghai and Cantonese kitchen. As in almost all Chinese restaurants, it is best to order from the à la carte menu. There are special luncheons from 95 cents to $2.75; special dinners from $1.40 to $4.20. A la carte main courses cost from about 95 cents to $4.25. *Cocktails, wines.*

SIRO'S
58 East 53rd Street PL *3-8059*

The menu is French and runs a predictable gamut from sole amandine to duckling bigarade. Complete luncheons from about $3.25 to $3.95; à la carte main dishes from about $2.95 to $4.95. Complete dinners from about $6.25 to $7.25; à la carte entrees from about $3.25 to $6.25. *Cocktails, wines. On Saturday the restaurant opens at 5:45 p.m. Closed Sunday, most major holidays and, during the summer months, Saturday also.*

★ SIX HAPPINESS

130 East 56th Street PL *3-3371*

The cuisine here is Chinese, but the ambiance is East-meets-West. The dishes range from the ordinary (dim sim) to exceptional (butterfly shrimp). Luncheons with main course, tea and dessert from about $1.50 to $2.95. The à la carte entrees throughout the day cost from about $2 to $6. *Cocktails, wines. Only à la carte items are available on Sunday. Closed Thanksgiving.*

AE CB DC

★★ SIXTY EIGHT RESTAURANT

59 Fifth Avenue (between 12th and 13th Streets) *255-8744*

This restaurant has reportedly reverted to the original management of several years ago, and the change seems all to the good. Some of the dishes sampled came off remarkably well, including the very simply made broiled jumbo shrimp à la "68," which are tender and cooked with a lemon butter and herb sauce. Equally good were a rollatin of chicken—braised, rolled chicken with a well-seasoned filling—and green tagliarini with marinara sauce. The service is not polished, but it is done with some care. There are complete luncheons priced from $2.50 to $6.50. Complete dinners cost from $4.25 to $7.25. A la carte dishes from $2.75 to $6.25. *Cocktails, wines. Open seven days a week.*

AE

★ SLOPPY LOUIE'S

92 South Street BO *9-9821*

This is a raffish, rough-and-ready restaurant in the vicinity of the Fulton Fish Market. It has an ill-kempt look that is not without appeal, and it is well patronized. The fish—grilled, sautéed or turned into what the management calls bouillabaisse—is among the freshest in town. The "bouillabaisse" is a tasty mélange of fish and seafood, including squid, a bit overcooked. At Sloppy Louie's the customers share tables, and the clientele is primarily male, although ladies are welcome. All the foods are à la carte and reasonably priced. The average entree costs less than $2. *No alcoholic beverages. The restaurant closes at 8 p.m. Closed Saturday and Sunday.*

★ SMOKEHOUSE, THE

957 Third Avenue (between 57th and 58th Streets) *421-4040*

New York is probably the delicatessen capital of the world. The new Smokehouse rates average marks where the food is concerned, but it is unusually attractive physically, with its wood paneling, high ceilings and odd-shaped, four-square counters. The flavor of the foods, whether corned beef, chopped liver or sauerkraut, is good but notably bland, and thus without marked distinction. The cost of the food is from about 60 cents for an egg-salad sandwich to $2.45 for a delicatessen platter. *Cocktails, wines. Open seven days a week. Closed Yom Kippur and the first and last two days of Passover.*

★ SOLOWEY'S

431-433 Seventh Avenue *564-5602*
(between 33rd and 34th Streets)

This is a landmark of sorts in the heart of New York's famed garment district. The restaurant is noted for its sandwiches (the Seventh Avenue Special is a combination of lake sturgeon, chopped egg, anchovy, smoked salmon, sardines, onion, tomato and olives, served canapé style) and rich desserts. The menus are both prix fixe and à la carte with complete luncheons from $1.75 to $3; complete dinners from $3.95 to $7. A la carte items from

about $2.95 to $6.75. *Cocktails, wines. Closed Sunday during the summer months.*
AE CB DC

★ SON OF THE SHEIK

132 Greenwich Street BE *3-5240*

The Son of the Sheik has a name out of cinemaland, but the food is Syrian and very good. Many of the dishes, in the Middle Eastern tradition, are based on lamb, including the inevitable shish kebab and baked or raw kibbee. There is an excellent cucumber and yogurt salad and an eggplant salad. There is a complete luncheon or dinner that costs $2.25; otherwise the menu is à la carte with main courses from about $1.25 to $2.50. *There is no bar, but beer and wine are available. Closed Saturday and Sunday.*

★★★ SPANISH PAVILION, THE

475 Park Avenue (near 57th Street) *421-5690*

This is one of the most beautiful restaurants in Manhattan. It is as elegant and grand as a Spanish grandee, and the menu and the food are generally a delight. The restaurant is more or less rectangular in shape, one wall hung with a large 16th-century tapestry and a life-size portrait of the Spanish King Felipe IV. There are rich red banquettes and square-cut Jacobean chairs with hand-woven wool backs. The menus are printed on stiff parchment, and from appetizer to dessert the food is interesting. There is, for example, an excellent appetizer consisting of three egg halves neatly shaped to resemble whole eggs, but capped with minced seafood and various sauces, including mayonnaise and vinaigrette; an unaccustomed and interesting soup, castilla la vieja, made with slivers of almonds and bread. But best of all perhaps, there is a classic zarzuela de mariscos Costa Brava, which is made with an assortment of fresh seafood, including lobster, langostinas, mussels, clams and shrimp, in a delicate sauce vaguely flavored with tomato. Wonder of wonders, some of the most palate-seducing dishes are the desserts—the rich, fluffy natillas à la española, or Spanish custard, and the pine-nut cake in particular. There is less enthusiasm for a flaming banana with spirits sampled recently. The banana was both undercooked and underripe. The Spanish Pavilion is substantially priced along the lines of the town's luxury French restaurants. There is a complete luncheon that costs $7.50. A la carte dishes both at midday and in the evening cost from about $4.50 for broiled fish to $8 for the partridge. *Cocktails, wines. The restaurant is closed Sunday. Reservations are recommended.*

AE CB DC

★ SPARK'S PUB SOUTH

123 East 18th Street GR *5-9696*

If you have a taste for art nouveau and reasonably well-prepared Italian food, there might be much to your liking at Spark's Pub South. It is a long, narrow restaurant with dim lighting and posters pinned to the wall and a jukebox, which seems, oddly enough, appropriate to the mood of the place. If you sit close to the kitchen you will find it noisy. But the chefs make excellent soups, such as a consommé with egg, and minestrone. One of the recommended specialties is the cannelloni, made with a tomato, cheese and cream sauce. The routine spaghetti does not come off so well; it is at times overcooked. All dishes are à la carte. At luncheon they are priced from $1.25 to $1.75; at dinner from $1.75 to $3.95. *Cocktails, wines. On Saturday and Sunday the restaurant opens at about 5 p.m.*

★★ STAGE DELICATESSEN

834 Seventh Avenue (between 53rd and 54th Streets) CI *5-7334*

This is a relatively small restaurant with genuine character, an understandable favorite with men and women in the entertainment world. The sandwiches, whether a single-decker corned beef or a triple-decker with chopped liver, turkey and pastrami, are excellent. The delicatessen has such Jewish specialties as matzoh-ball soup and stuffed derma. The menu is à la carte with sandwiches from 50 cents to $2.40; hot main entrees from about $1.55. *Soft drinks and beer. Open 8 a.m. to 4 a.m. Closed for the Jewish New Year.*

★★ STEAK CASINO

33 University Place (at 9th Street) AL *4-7499*

This is a comfortable, well-run steak house in Greenwich Village, a neighborhood place, with paneled walls hung with replicas of various games of chance, and an odd assortment of chandeliers. There is a copper-hooded charcoal grill, and the steaks and chops are, by and large, of good quality. The menu is typical, with its seafood cocktails, grilled foods, baked potatoes in foil and salads with the usual choice of dressing—French, Russian or blue cheese. The blue cheese, incidentally, is good. All dishes are à la carte with main courses at midday from about $1.85 to $3.75; in the evening from about $3.50 to $6.95. *Cocktails, wines. Luncheon is not served Saturday and Sunday. Closed Thanksgiving and Christmas.*

AE CB DC

★★ STEAK JOINT, THE

58 Greenwich Avenue CH *2-0009*

This is a large restaurant and one of the best steak houses in Greenwich Village. It may have a touch too much of chrome and plastic for some tastes, but customers can count on well-done steaks well done (the management does not recommend it) and rare steaks rare. Added to that, the service is on the whole more cordial than one is accustomed to in New York. There are complete luncheons from about $2.60 to $3.95; otherwise the menu is à la carte with principal dishes from about $3.50 to $6.25. *Cocktails, wines. Dinners are served from noon on Sunday.*

AE CB DC

★ STEAK PLACE, THE

112 Central Park South CO *5-2470*
(near the Avenue of the Americas)

In the most essential thing, steak, The Steak Place ranks as excellent. The meat is of first quality, and it is grilled over charcoal with considerable expertise. The Steak Place smells like a New York steak place with its odor of smoke and charred meat. The decor is all red flocked wallpaper and poor lighting, and, in a word, it doesn't swing. The service, such as it is, is friendly but wishy-washy, and the restaurant seems to be understaffed. With its faults, The Steak Place is, nonetheless, recommended. A buffet lunch, served Monday through Friday from noon to 3 p.m., is $2.50. The dinner menu is à la carte with main courses from about $3.50 to $7.50. *Cocktails, wines.*

AE CB DC

STEINBERG'S

2270 Broadway (at 81st Street) EN *2-2030*

One of New York's several dairy restaurants with Jewish cuisine. "Dairy" implies that meats are never served, and the menu lists such foods as fish dishes, omelets and mushroom cutlets. There are club luncheons priced at $1.70 to $2.65. The principal specialties on the à la carte menu cost from about $1.65 to $2.15. *No alcoholic beverages. Closed for Jewish holidays.*

AE CB DC

★★ STOCKHOLM RESTAURANT

151 West 51st Street CI *6-6560*

The decor of this restaurant is nondescript and uninspired, but the smorgasbord, or Scandinavian feasting board, is one of the most interesting in New York. There is, of course, an assortment of herring, which is very good, as well as lobster, shrimp, salads, cold meats and hot dishes. Guests may return to the buffet as often as the

spirit moves them. The cost of the smorgasbord with dessert and coffee is $3.25 at midday and $4.95 in the evening. The restaurant's menus also list complete luncheons from about $2.65 to $5.50; complete dinners from about $3.75 to $7.50. *Cocktails, wines. Dinner is served Sunday from 1 p.m.*
AE DC

★★ STOUFFER'S

666 Fifth Avenue, downstairs PL *7-6662*
(between 52nd and 53rd Streets)

Among New York's reasonably priced restaurants this is one of the best. The menu is plain, but it shows imagination, and the food is almost consistently first-rate. There are many rooms in the restaurant, the surroundings are pleasant and the waitresses are courteous. A typical menu might include chicken pot pie with dumpling, or filet of fish with lemon, and excellent vegetable accompaniments, particularly the eggplant and spinach. There is a special luncheon priced at about $2; otherwise luncheons are à la carte with main courses from about $1.10 to $1.80. Dinners are à la carte with entrees from about $1.95 to $6. *Cocktails, wines. Closed Christmas.*
AE CB DC

STUDENT PRINCE

207 East 86th Street AT *9-8230*

German-American. Complete luncheons from $1.75; à la carte main courses from $1.50. Complete dinners from $3.75; à la carte entrees from about $2. *Cocktails, wines.*

★ SUEHIRO RESTAURANT

35 East 29th Street MU *4-9187*

New York has enjoyed a rash of new Japanese restaurants in recent years, but the Suehiro upstairs at this address has been here for many a moon. It is a simply decorated place, if it can be called decorated at all, but it is popular because the food is quite good and it is relatively inexpensive. One criticism of the restaurant could be that the tempura, although tasty, is a trifle oily. There are complete luncheons from about $1.95 to $2.75 and complete dinners from about $2.75 to $3.50. The à la carte menu throughout the day is priced from about 75 cents to $3.50. *There is no bar, but beer is available. Luncheon is not served Saturday. Closed Sunday.*

★ SULTAN'S TABLE, THE

130 East 40th Street MU *3-4770*

The Lebanese kitchen of The Sultan's Table is very good, whether it is preparing that excellent vegetable and wheat salad called tabooley or the mashed eggplant appetizer known as baba ghanouge. The kibbee, made with ground lamb and pine nuts, is good too. The same à la carte menu serves all day. Main courses are from from about $1.50 to $4.75. *Cocktails, wines. On Saturday and Sunday the restaurant opens at 5 p.m. Closed July 4 and Christmas.*

AE CB DC

★ SUN LUCK EAST

75 East 55th Street PL *3-4930*

A vast and somewhat lavish Chinese restaurant in midtown Manhattan. The menus for both luncheon and dinner are extensive. The cost of a complete luncheon is from about $1.55 to $3.85. The cost of main dishes on the à la carte menu is from about $2.95 to $6.50. *Cocktails, wines.*

AE CB DC

★ SUN LUCK GOURMET

157 West 49th Street JU *2-8182*

A neat, serviceable Chinese restaurant in the Broadway area. The kitchen is not invariably distinguished, but it is competent, and, as in most of the city's Chinese dining rooms, the luncheons are a bargain. There

are complete luncheons from about 95 cents to $3; complete dinners from about $2.25 to $3.70. Main courses on the à la carte menu range from about $2.15 to $6.25. *Cocktails, wines. Luncheon is not served on Sunday.*
AE CB DC

★ SUN LUCK IMPERIAL

935 Lexington Avenue (at 69th Street) LE *5-4070*

This edition of the Sun Luck restaurants is spacious and handsome with interiors of rich gold. The Chinese food, on the other hand, is more or less run-of-the-mill. The restaurant is also relatively expensive. There are complete luncheons from about $1.50 to $3.85. Dinners are à la carte with most main courses in the $3.75 to $6 category. *Cocktails, wines. Dinner is served Sunday from 1 p.m.*
AE CB DC

★★ SUN LUCK QUEENS

91-16 59th Avenue, Elmhurst, Queens *446-1166*

It seems that the farther Chinese restaurants are from Manhattan, the less Chinese they are in spirit. Long Island does not have a wealth of Chinese dining establishments, and this one, the latest addition to the expanding Sun Luck group, is welcome. The chef prepares food cued to what the management obviously considers local taste, but it is palatable nonetheless. The restaurant, frequently crowded, consists of two levels, but the service is willing. There are complete luncheons from about $1.30 to $1.90; complete dinners from about $1.90 to $2.80. A la carte dishes cost from about $1.60 to $4.75. *Cocktails, wines. Dinner is served Sunday from 1 p.m.*
AE CB DC

SUPREME MACARONI COMPANY

511 Ninth Avenue (between 38th and 39th Streets) *244-9314*

This restaurant, at the rear of a store that sells macaroni, has enjoyed a considerable vogue for a number of years, due no doubt to its colorful and offbeat nature. It is a seedy-looking establishment, with posters on the wall and some rather insistent music from a small radio. There is no menu, but the offerings include such dishes as eggplant, veal and breast of chicken parmigiana, spaghetti, scampi and steak pizzaiola. The food is quite edible, but ordinary. All dishes are à la carte, and the cost of main courses is about $1.50 for spaghetti to $5 for steak. *There is no bar, but beer and wines are available. Closed Sunday.*

SUSY WONG

1271 Lexington Avenue (near 86th Street) FI *8-4957*

This Chinese restaurant has a menu that is fairly standard. So is the kitchen. There are complete luncheons priced from about 99 cents to $3.95. There is always an à la carte menu with principal dishes from about $1.65 to $4.75. *Cocktails, wines. Only à la carte items are available on Sunday, from 1:30 p.m.*

SUTTER'S FRENCH CAFÉ

10th Street and Greenwich Avenue *255-0666*

Sutter's in Greenwich Village is something of an institution. It has excellent pastries, such as apple turnovers, assorted small cookies, brioches and croissants, all made with fresh butter and eggs. The management has opened a small café on the premises where these pastries are served along with sandwiches, ice cream and coffee. It is a fine idea, but unfortunately the sandwiches, with their untrimmed crusts and pedestrian fillings (liverwurst, American cheese and the like), are a disappointment. The cost of the fare is from about 35 cents for a brioche to 85 cents for a cream cheese and sliced ham sandwich with relish. *No alcoholic beverages. The café opens at 11 a.m.*

★★★ SWEET'S RESTAURANT

2 Fulton Street WH *4-9628*

There is no escaping the fact that this is one of New York's most engaging restaurants. The food is simply cooked and brought to the table sizzling hot, the waiters are models of men with a desire to please the customers, and there is no wonder the restaurant has been around since 1845. Fish and seafood are specialties of the house, but even the vegetables, particularly the deep-fried eggplant, are special. The tables are close together, Sweet's is frequently crowded, and oftentimes it is difficult to procure a table. The restaurant opens at 11 a.m., the kitchen closes at 8 p.m., and the same à la carte menu serves throughout the day. The cost is from about $2 for broiled haddock or flounder to $4.50 for broiled Maine lobster. *Cocktails, wines. Closed Saturday, Sunday, New Year's Day, Lincoln's Birthday, Washington's Birthday, Memorial Day, Labor Day, Thanksgiving, Christmas and the first two weeks in July.*

★ SWISS INN

355 West 46th Street CO *5-9283*

This is a reasonably good restaurant near the theater section, with one of the few Swiss kitchens in town. The restaurant offers such Helvetian fare as bundnerfleisch, the dried beef of the Grisons, cheese fondue and wurst, or sausage, salad. There are complete luncheons from about $1.90 for an omelet to $2.50 for beef bourguignon, with à la carte main dishes from about $1.70 to $3.80. The dinner menu is à la carte with main courses from about $2.60 for bratwurst to $5 for sirloin. *Cocktails, wines. Luncheon is not served Saturday. Closed Sunday and all holidays.*

TAI YAT LOW

22 Mott Street WO *2-3892*

Both the menu and the kitchen of this restaurant in Chinatown seem tailored for the American trade, but the food is tasty nonetheless. There are complete luncheons from about $1 to $2.50, and a full-course dinner that costs $3.75. The à la carte menu lists dishes from about $1.35 to $4.50. *There is no bar, but guests may bring their own beverages. Dinner is served Saturday and Sunday from noon.*

★★ TAKEDA RESTAURANT

58 West 56th Street JU *2-6153*

This is a most agreeable Japanese restaurant with a typical menu that lists the usual sukiyaki, tempura and teriyaki. Although the range is predictable, the food is well seasoned and interesting, and one dish that is cordially recommended is the katsu donburi, or sliced pork cutlet on rice. There are complete luncheons that cost from $1.85 to $3; complete dinners from $4 to $5.50. A la carte main dishes cost from $3.50 to $5. The restaurant is deservedly popular, frequently crowded, and the service at times tends to be slow. *Cocktails, wines. On Sunday the restaurant opens at 5 p.m.*

AE CB DC

TALISMAN, THE

55 Liberty Street BA *7-9944*

American cuisine. At lunchtime there is an à la carte menu that lists entrees from about $3.50. Complete dinners from about $3.80 to $5.95; à la carte main dishes from about $4. *Cocktails, wines. Dinner served until 8:45 p.m. Closed Saturday, Sunday and legal holidays.*

CB

★★ TAMURA RESTAURANT

106 Liberty Street *964-2247*

A very pleasant Japanese restaurant that opened recently in the Wall Street area. It is a long, simply decorated place with a well-conceived menu that also lists several Korean dishes including bulkoki (broiled marinated beef) and kalbi (broiled short ribs of beef). The kitchen produces excellent kushikatsu made with deep-fried pork and vegetables, a delicious shiwoyaki, or salt-broiled salmon, and there are numerous dishes cooked at the table including, of course, sukiyaki. Complete luncheons are priced from $2.50 to $3.25; à la carte entrees from $1.75. Complete dinners cost from $3.75 to $4; à la carte main dishes from $1.50 to $2.95. *Cocktails, wines. Closed Sunday.*

DC

★ TANT MIEUX

370 Bleecker Street CH *3-2474*

This is a curious little restaurant in Greenwich Village, with stark blue walls, an old poster advertising "Gone With the Wind" and about a dozen tables. It deals primarily in desserts, but there are main courses available, such as beef in red wine sauce, coq au vin and skewered lamb on rice. The beef sampled was very well cooked, but the lamb tasted as if it had been marinated in sugar and spice. The restaurant serves an excellent blue-cheese salad. The desserts, including various sundaes and banana splits, are as rich as all get-out. The cost of main dishes is $2.50; desserts range from 65 cents for a dish of ice cream to $1.25 for pêche melba. *There is no bar. A complimentary glass of wine is offered with the main courses, but guests may bring their own wines. The restaurant opens at 6 p.m. Closed Monday.*

TAVERN ON THE GREEN

Central Park at 67th Street TR *3-3200*

The best thing to be said of the Tavern on the Green is that it has the physical feel of Manhattan. There is an open terrace for dining, and it is pleasant enough on a cool night in midsummer. The kitchen and service are something else again. Among other regrettable items samples recently list a soggy ramekin of cheese, ordinary chopped liver, roast chicken served in lieu of broiled chicken that had been ordered (with the waiter or captain insisting that it was broiled chicken with stuffing) and a cold wedge of Brie cheese on the way to petrifaction. Complete luncheons without dessert cost from about $2.65 to $3.45; à la carte items at midday from about $1.25 to $2.95. Dinners are à la carte with main courses from about $3.25 to $5.95. *Cocktails, wines. Open seven days a week.*

AE CB DC

★ TEDDY'S RESTAURANT

219 West Broadway WO *6-2180*

The best-known features of this restaurant are the bountiful six-course dinners. In the evening there is no printed menu and waiters recite the main-course dishes. These determine the price of the meal, which is Italian throughout. The cost of the entire meal ranges from $7.50 to $9.50. There is an à la carte luncheon menu with entrees from about $2.75. The decor is modern, neat and quite stylish. *Cocktails, wines. Closed Sunday. Reservations recommended.*

AE DC

★ TEMPLE GARDEN, THE

16 Pell Street BE *3-5544*

The food is good at this rather recent addition to the roster of Chinatown restaurants. The restaurant is large and overly illuminated, but it is worth a visit. Complete luncheons from about 99 cents to $2.05. A la carte dishes from about $1.85 to $8. Chinese family dinners are $2.25 a person. *At the present time there are no alcoholic beverages.*

★ TEXAS CHILI PARLOR

215 West 10th Street 243-9221

The chili at this small, neat restaurant in Greenwich Village could stand more zip and zing, but the restaurant should be of interest to chili aficionados. Although the chili dishes are on the bland side, they are still obviously prepared with care and enthusiasm, and the place has an aura of charm without being coy. There are only three small tables and eight or so stools around a counter. The menu includes two kinds of chili—one with ground meat, the other with cubed meat—tamales, enchiladas and empanadas. There are also black-eyed peas with ham hock. The cost ranges from about 70 cents for a bowl of chili to $1.80 for tamales with chili. *There is no bar, but customers may bring their own wine or beer.*

37th STREET HIDEAWAY

32 West 37th Street WI *7-9462*

This second-floor restaurant, which was once a famous actor's apartment, looks comfortably old-fashioned. The menu is more or less French and Italian, and the kitchen has only moderate inspiration. Complete luncheons from about $2.95 to $4.50; à la carte entrees from $3.25 to $4.50. Complete dinners from about $3.95 to $6.50; à la carte main dishes from $2.75 to $6.25. Supper is served from 10:30 p.m. *Cocktails, wines. On Saturday the restaurant opens at 5 p.m. Closed Sunday, New Year's Day, Memorial Day, July 4, Labor Day, Thanksgiving and Christmas.*
AE DC

★ THREE CROWNS

12 East 54th Street PL *3-9692*

As far as atmosphere is concerned, this is one of the pleasantest Scandinavian restaurants in Manhattan. The herring on the smorgasbord is excellent, and other dishes are generally good. There are complete luncheon and dinner menus. The cost of the smorgasbord at noon is $3 with dessert and coffee; $4.50 at dinner. Complete luncheons from about $3.50; à la carte main courses from about $2. Complete dinners from about $4.50. *Cocktails, wines. Smorgasbord and dinner from 1 p.m. on Sunday.*

AE CB DC

THREE HUSSARS

1587 Second Avenue *744-9938*
(between 82nd and 83rd Street)

The Three Hussars has the distinction of being open from 6 in the morning. It is a Hungarian restaurant, and the best dishes are along the lines of stuffed cabbage and stuffed peppers. The roast duck is, or was on one occasion, a distinct disappointment and tasted as if it had been cooked the day before. All dishes are à la carte with main courses from about $1.20 to $3.25. *There is no bar, but wine may be brought in from the outside. Closed Wednesday.*

★★ TIEN TSIN

569 West 125 Street MO *6-5710*

A pleasant, bright Chinese restaurant in uptown Manhattan. The à la carte menu has a tempting range of dishes prepared with excellent taste, whether boiled dumplings as an appetizer or strips of chicken with preserved turnip. The cooking here is generally more exotic than is customary in most of the Chinese restaurants in town. There is, to be sure, a lot of chop suey and chow mein available. All the dishes are à la carte with main courses at noon from about 95 cents to $1.50; at dinner from about $1.35 to $3.50. *No alcoholic beverages. Closed for Chinese New Year.*

TIKI VILLAGE, THE

The Drake Hotel, 59 East 56th Street HA *1-5580*

The Tiki Village is another of those lushly decorated restaurants in the Polynesian style, but with a menu that is predominantly Chinese. There is a nice ambiance about the place, and the service is willing if at times ponderous and slow. The seasonings for many of the dishes are overly bland, as if the management underestimates the public's growing awareness of and liking for an authentic Chinese cuisine. All dishes are à la carte with main courses at midday from about $1.55 to $3.50; in the evening from $2.95 to $5.75. *Cocktails, wines. Dinner is served Sunday from 1 p.m.*

AE CB DC

★★ TIK TAK HUNGARIAN

1477 Second Avenue (at 77th Street) RH *4-9699*

This is another Manhattan restaurant that is extraordinary in that the food is both prepared with exceptional care and reasonably priced. The menu lists such Hungarian foods as goulash and paprikash, roast pork and an excellent braised veal shank. The cost of a complete luncheon is $1.75. Dinners are à la carte with main courses from about $2.50 to $4.25. *Cocktails, wines. Dinner is served Saturday and Sunday from noon. Reservations accepted.*

TINGHATSAK

21 Mott Street WO *2-8149*

One of many small, good but physically undistinguished restaurants in Chinatown. At midday it is a contender for the title of the least expensive restaurant in Manhattan, with a complete luncheon from 95 cents to $1.90. The evening prices are conventional, with à la carte dishes from about $1.25 for pork chop suey to about

$3 for lobster dishes. *There is no bar, but beer may be ordered from outside. Only à la carte items are available on Sunday, from noon.*

★★ TIN LIZZIE RESTAURANT, THE

140 West 51st Street JU *2-3535*

If you are fascinated by "fun" places, camp surroundings and art nouveau, you will no doubt be enchanted with The Tin Lizzie. It is an amusing restaurant with assorted tongue-in-cheek trappings that include an antique automobile, a whole stuffed peacock with feathers, a giant simulated stained-glass window between the lengthy bar and the main dining room, a polished barber chair and photographs and art held over from the nineteen-thirties. The menu lists such entrees as ask-the-waiter soup and, for a real gag, roast owl with truffle sauce served on St. Swithin's Day only. That will give you an idea of The Tin Lizzie. The dishes are along the lines of grilled foods, oversize salads, omelets and eggs Benedict. The food is competently prepared, although one order of Tin Lizzie special steak with freshly grated horseradish left a little to be desired. The steak had an excellent flavor and was cooked to a turn, but the meat, alas, was chewy. All dishes are à la carte with main courses at midday from about $2.25 for an open club sandwich to $6.25 for grilled sirloin; in the evening from about $4.25 for broiled chicken with spareribs to $7.95. *Cocktails, wines. The menu, in fact, advertises a quart of martinis for $6. Luncheon is not served on Saturday. Closed Sunday during the summer.*

AE CB DC

TIP TOE INN

Broadway and 74th Street SU *7-2000*

The Tip Toe Inn is a roomy, tall-ceilinged restaurant with a Jewish and American menu. It lists such dishes as chopped lox, fried chicken à la Maryland, blintzes and Irish stew. The food is not bad, but neither is it distinguished. One of the most popular dishes is the stuffed cabbage Hungarian style. This is very good. There are complete luncheons from about $1.50 to $3.25; complete dinners from about $3.40 to $4.95. The à la carte menu lists entrees from about $1.75 to $3.10. *Cocktails, wines.*

TOKYO SUKIYAKI HOUSE

144 West 55th Street CO *5-6075*

The food in this Japanese restaurant is rather tasty, and there is an added advantage of being close to Carnegie Hall, the Coliseum and several movie houses. The principal dishes are sukiyaki made with beef, chicken or pork; tempura, which is fried shrimp; and teriyaki, which is beef, chicken or pork dipped in a soy-spiced sauce and grilled. On the negative side, the restaurant has a slight ventilation problem. There are complete luncheons from $2.75 to $3.25; complete dinners from $3.50 to $4. A la carte dishes cost about $1.25 to $2.80. *Cocktails, wines. Dinner is served Saturday and Sunday from 11:30 a.m.*

TOLEDO RESTAURANT

66 West 55th Street *581-0464*

New York seems to be getting more Spanish by the hour, and this is one of the most opulent of the city's new restaurants. The decor is busy, with a Spanish tiled bar, Spanish tiled floors, large chandeliers, wooden grillwork. It is handsome, nonetheless. The dining room is relatively small, with only 18 tables or so, and it enjoys a good deal of popularity. There are some curious faults about the menu and the food. With rare exceptions the food on the luncheon menu is hardly Spanish. There are shrimp salad, chicken salad and broiled dishes, grilled fish and veal scaloppine. Spanish dishes might include the gazpacho and black bean soup and a flan. The dinner menu is not much more Iberian. There is, however, a zarzuela, a concoction of seafood and fish bathed in a tomato sauce. It is quite ordinary and the fish and seafood

on a recent evening were overcooked. So was the braised partridge with salt pork and onions. There is a complete luncheon that costs $6.50. The dinner menu is à la carte with main dishes from about $4.50 to $9. *Cocktails, wines. Luncheon is not served on Saturday; closed Sunday.*
AE CB DC

★★ TOMALDO RESTAURANT

812 Third Avenue (at 50th Street) EL *5-8368*

Neat and spacious, Tomaldo's ranks with the best of midtown's inexpensive, middle-class Italian restaurants. Luncheon is à la carte with main dishes from $2. A la carte dinner entrees from about $2.50; complete dinners are $4.25. There is a garden for outdoor dining May through September. *Cocktails; wines by the bottle and by the glass. On Saturday the restaurant opens at 5 p.m. Closed Sunday, New Year's Day, July 4, Labor Day, Thanksgiving and Christmas. Reservations accepted.*
AE CB DC

TOM'S GARDEN RESTAURANT

305 First Avenue (between 17th and 18th Streets) *473-6750*

To judge from the hordes of people who go in and out of Tom's Garden for take-out orders of Chinese food, the management must be doing something right. The bulk of the menu is routine and runs to such dishes as chop suey, fried rice and chow mein. Moo goo means mushrooms, gai means chicken and pan means sliced. Tom's moo goo gai pan needs more moo goo, more gai and fewer vegetables. Complete luncheons cost from 95 cents to $3; complete dinners from $1.50 to $3.25. A la carte dishes are priced from about $2.50 to $4.25. *No alcoholic beverages. Dinner is served Sunday from 11 a.m.*

★★ TOM'S SHANGRI-LA

237 Madison Avenue MU *3-0996*
(between 37th and 38th Streets)

One of the handsomest Chinese restaurants in all of Manhattan. The luncheon menu can be as dreary as an egg roll, but the à la carte menu, by contrast, can be rewarding. A la carte luncheon entrees from about $1.40 to $3.25; main dinner courses from about $2.35 to $14 (Peking duck). *Cocktails, wines. The restaurant is open until 2 a.m.*

AE DC

★ TONKATSU

9 East 52nd Street *889-5385*

The customers at the Tonkatsu are primarily young Japanese businessmen, and that in itself is an indication that the restaurant must be worthwhile. The food is commendable, whether it is sashimi, tonkatsu (a breaded pork cutlet dish), noodle soup, teriyaki or sukiyaki. The service at times is disoriented, but the waitresses are bright and smiling. The restaurant is open for luncheon only, and the menu is both prix fixe and à la carte. The cost of a complete meal is from about $2.25 to $2.50, with à la carte dishes priced from about $1.50 to $2. *No alcoholic beverages. Closed Saturday, Sunday and holidays.*

★★ TONY'S ITALIAN KITCHEN

212 West 79th Street TR *4-9017*

The best thing to be said about Tony's is that the pasta is freshly made and the vegetables are freshly cooked. And that is saying a lot. The tomato sauces are good, the meat sauce standard. The food on the whole is competently prepared, whether it be lasagne or boneless chicken parmigiana. The portions are enormous. There is an extensive hot and cold antipasto table. At noon all dishes are à la carte, and the à la carte menu has dishes from $1.75

to $5. Complete four-course dinners cost from $4.25 to $4.90. *Cocktails, wines.*
AE DC

★★ TONY'S WIFE

150 East 55th Street EL *5-4506*

Tony's Wife is a New York institution with a host of devoted patrons, and the enthusiasm is not misplaced. It is a small, intimate restaurant with a kitchen that is at times outstanding, particularly in grilled dishes such as royal squab and mutton chops. It may also have more waiters per capita than any other restaurant in the city. Nevertheless the restaurant falls short of perfection. There are plastic flowers, pictures hung askew, and a serving of prosciutto on one occasion was sliced from the impoverished side of the ham. There are complete luncheons from about $3.75 to $4.50. Dinners are à la carte with main courses from about $2.75 for half a broiled chicken to $6.50 for sirloin steak. *Cocktails, wines. Closed Saturday Sunday, July 4 and Labor Day.*

★★ TOOTS SHOR

33 West 52nd Street JU *2-6000*

If Manhattan restaurants were judged solely on the basis of a fraternal, gregarious atmosphere, Toots Shor's would come off with the grand laurel. At midday there are three mammoth dining rooms on separate levels with standing room only and a noise level to equal that of Babel. The menu goes along the lines of London broil, browned roast beef hash, mixed grill and the inevitable Rock Cornish game hen. The food isn't bad, but it is certainly not distinguished. All dishes are à la carte, with main courses at midday from about $3.25 to $7.25; at dinner from about $3.75 to $7.25; at supper (10 p.m. to 1 a.m.) from $3 to $7.25. *Cocktails, wines. Open at 5 p.m. on Saturday. Closed Sunday, New Year's Day, Christmas.*
AE CB DC

★ TOP OF THE SIX'S

666 Fifth Avenue (near 53rd Street) PL *7-6662*

For a city that towers architecturally, Manhattan has astonishingly few restaurants that swing aloft to take advantage of the views. The Top of the Six's offers breathtaking vistas and is therefore well worth a visit. The decor displays trappings from a French château, and it has lost some of its luster in the past few years. The food varies in quality, although it is rather simply prepared, with such dishes as grilled chops and steaks, French-fried shrimp and baked chicken in something called Dinners Provencial. The word "provencial" is the management's own coinage, and they are welcome to it. Luncheons are à la carte with entrees from about $2.50 to $3.55. There are complete dinners that cost $6.75 and à la carte entrees from about $6.75 to $7.75. Supper is served from 10:30 p.m. to 1 a.m., with entrees from $2.75 to $7.50. *Cocktails, wines. On Sunday the restaurant opens at 4 p.m. Closed Christmas.*
AE CB DC

★ TORTILLA FLAT

85 Washington Place *477-9401*
(two blocks south of 8th Street, off the Avenue of the Americas)

This is a dimly lit Greenwich Village restaurant that, at first sight, may seem a bit forbidding. It isn't, and the Mexican food is exceptionally good. Tortilla Flat is frequently crowded with well-behaved "bohemians," bearded gentlemen and young women in miniskirts. There is candlelight, a jukebox and sawdust on the floor, and considering the traffic, the waitresses do a remarkable job in getting the food to the tables. There are tamale plates and taco plates and combination plates, and the cost is from about $1.35 for chili con carne with rice and beans to $2 for an enormous combination plate with six dishes. Customers who do not enjoy raw onions beware. One unfortunate note: the margheritas at Tortilla Flat are not made with fresh lime or lemon juice, and they are not very good. *Cocktails, wines. Closed Christmas.*

TOUT VA BIEN

311 West 51st Street CI *7-8622*

An enormously informal bistro type of place with a jukebox and a somewhat routine menu, but with fairly good food nonetheless. The roster of dishes includes coq au vin and omelets. The cost of dinner is from about $3 to $5.50 à la carte; $4.50 prix fixe. The restaurant is close to several Broadway theaters. *Cocktails, wines. Luncheon is not served.*

★★ TOWER SUITE

Time and Life Building, Rockefeller Center JU *6-2100*

The view from this restaurant at the top of the Time and Life Building is spectacular. The quality of the cuisine varies, but Sunday brunch, served until 3 p.m., is a joy. It offers fresh juices, fine breads, smoked fish, oysters, clams, soups, a fine assortment of main courses and desserts. The cost for the entire menu is $6. The single price for dinner is $8.50. The Tower Suite has a fine collection of wines that are reasonably priced. *Cocktails, wines. Open only for dinner weekdays; from 11:30 a.m. to 3 p.m. Sunday.*

AE CB

TOWN HOUSE, THE

108 East 38th Street LE *2-6727*

An extensive menu and relatively plain cuisine. The choicest dishes are, perhaps, the grillades. The menus are à la carte with main luncheon courses from about $3.25 to $6.50; dinner entrees from about $3.95 to $7.50. *Cocktails, wines. Closed Sunday and holidays.*

AE CB DC

★★ TRADER VIC'S

Plaza Hotel, 59th Street at Fifth Avenue PL *9-3000*

There is an undeniable appeal about Trader Vic's, the first of the big-time Polynesian restaurants. In its present location in the Plaza Hotel, it may seem a touch less lush and overblown than formerly, but there is still an amplitude of fishing nets, hunting spears, tapa cloth and the like. The food, principally of Chinese inspiration, is competently prepared and the public loves it. Reservations are frequently essential and sometimes difficult to obtain. All the menus are à la carte with main courses at noon from about $2.75 to $3.50; in the evening from about $2.95 to $6.50. *Cocktails, wines. Open seven days a week.*

CB

TRATTORIA

45th Street entrance to the Pan Am Building MO *1-3090*

If only it were possible to eat the scenery and ignore the kitchen of a few Manhattan restaurants! This is a handsome place with its candy-striped Venini globes overhead, its multicolored posters on the wall, mahogany bar and mosaic-faced rotunda. The menu is extensive, and the food is hopelessly mediocre. There is a vast assortment of appetizers including stuffed artichokes, stuffed mushrooms and the like, and it is amazing how the chef makes everything taste alike. The pasta dishes are ordinary and so are the sauces that grace them. The mozzarella in carrozza is a poor and overcooked joke. The desserts at the Trattoria, however, are excellent. All dishes are à la carte. During the day the cost of main courses is from about $1.10 to $3.95. In the evening entrees are priced from about $1.35 to $5.75. *Cocktails, wines. Reservations are accepted for dinner Monday through Friday and for both luncheon and dinner Saturday and Sunday.*

AE CB DC

★ TREFNER'S RESTAURANT

619 Lexington Avenue (at 53rd Street) PL *9-6527*

The menu at Trefner's is as down to earth as homemade apple pie. The food is Yankee style and good and most reasonably priced. The menus are table d'hôte. The cost of a complete luncheon is from about $1.55 to $1.95; of a complete dinner $1.85 to $2.95. *No alcoholic beverages. Closed New Year's Day, Thanksgiving and Christmas.*

★★ TRINI

271 Amsterdam Avenue (near 72nd Street) TR *4-8950*

Anyone with a penchant for excellently prepared Latin American food in a restaurant that may be short on decor will probably find Trini to his liking. It does not smack of elegance either in the physical surroundings or in the service, but the food is good, whether it is a combination Mexican plate with tamale, tacos, rice and beans ($1.90) or the spiced chopped meat stew known as picadillo à la española ($1.70). The Venezuelan hallacas ($1.95), with its meat and olives in a steamed cornmeal coating with cheese, is also especially good. What's more, there are complete luncheons for 99 cents with soup, main course, dessert and beverage. Trini's is small, and at peak dining hours there may very well be a wait for a table. *Beer and wines only. Only à la carte items are available Saturday and Sunday, from noon. Closed Monday and the last two weeks of July.*

★ TROLL SMOREBROD SHOPPE

64 West 38th Street *736-1276*

This is one of the tiniest restaurants in New York, and it has a certain amount of charm. There are only a dozen seats, and the specialties of the house are Scandinavian sandwiches prepared by two young women from Norway. They are the staff. The assortment of sandwiches is interesting and includes rullepolse, the spiced veal dish, homemade liver loaf and Norwegian cheese. Each day there are one or two main dishes available, and there are also homemade soups and cakes. The soups are outstanding. The restaurant is open for breakfast, brunch and lunch from 8 a.m. to about 5:30 p.m., and, considering the size of the establishment, heaven knows what would happen if they were deluged with customers. The cost of sandwiches is from 65 cents to $1.05. A main dish, beef stew, for example, costs $1.25. *No alcoholic beverages. Closed Sunday, New Year's Day, Memorial Day, July 4, Labor Day, Thanksgiving and Christmas.*

TSURUYA

239 West 105th Street RI *9-9400*

This is a long-established Japanese restaurant that attracts a respectable following from members of the Japanese community, the faculty and students of Columbia University and so on. The food is adequately prepared but not equal to that of the best Japanese restaurants in midtown Manhattan. There is very good teriyaki and tempura, but the batayaki, a combination of beef, mushrooms, onions and watercress simmered in butter, was a disappointment. The slices of beef were cooked from a frozen state and were, therefore, dry. The ginger sauce for the dish was also bland. There is a single menu that lists complete dinners from $2.50 to $4.50. A la carte dishes cost from $1 to $4. *Cocktails and beers. The restaurant opens at 4 p.m. Tuesday through Friday, at noon Saturday and Sunday. Closed Monday.*

★★ "21"

21 West 52nd Street *582-7200*

This New York institution founded by Jack Kriendler and Charlie Berns dates from Prohibition days and is adored by many of the world's elite. It is as much of a club, without formal membership rites, as a restaurant can be. One chronicler of the New York scene bull's-eyed the establishment in noting that "21" "is now run by brothers of Jack and Charlie . . ., who also possess the founders' talent for gemütlichkeit and for making the simple act of being admitted seem an enviable achievement." The atmosphere of "21" is primarily masculine with its dark paneling and silver, a gregarious bar on the main floor and an elegant dining room above. The menu at "21" has some interesting dishes including terrapin Maryland and, on occasion, fresh game, but the food is for the most part quite ordinary. It is complemented by the service. The man at the door of "21", whose favor should be curried for entrance into the hallowed halls, is Chuck Anderson. The menus are à la carte. The cost of main courses at midday is from about $3.50 to $5; in the evening from about $4.50 to $6; at supper (11 p.m. to 1 a.m.) from about $3 to $7.50. *Cocktails, wines. Closed Sunday and, during the summer months, Saturday also. Closed New Year's Day, Memorial Day, July 4, Labor Day and Christmas.*

★★ UNICORN, THE

324 East 57th Street *751-4455*

This is one of several new and fashionable restaurants recently opened that seem to reflect the mood, if not the madness, of Manhattan in the mid-sixties. This one has a table tent that says "JUKE BOX—We have a juke box in the foyer. Please feel free to play anything that you will enjoy hearing. If you want something that is not 'in the box' bring it in and we'll put it on for you." If you can accept the decibels (and you certainly can't ignore them), the Unicorn is not an unattractive restaurant from a standpoint of decor, food or service. In the center of the main dining room is a massive statue, and the walls are hung with oils. There are red-checked tablecloths, a unicorn tapestry and leaded glass hurricane lamps that illuminate the tables. Among the appetizers there are excellent hot stuffed mushrooms and scampi Lucienne, tiny, tender shrimp sautéed quickly in a butter sauce lightly flavored with garlic and parsley. The steaks and

many of the main courses Italian style are good. All dishes at the Unicorn are à la carte and the cost of main courses at dinner is from $4.25 to $7. Supper dishes cost from about $2.50 to $3.75. *Cocktails, wines. The restaurant is closed Monday.*
AE DC

★ UNIVERSITY RESTAURANT, THE

25 West 8th Street OR *3-0721*

This small restaurant in Greenwich Village is within walking distance of the ANTA Washington Square Theater. The restaurant is as neat as a pin, the walls are hung with oils and there is piped-in music. The menu is simple and the food is good if not distinguished. The chicken Athenian, a specialty of the house, is an interesting idea with tomatoes and mushrooms but dully lacking in seasonings. The restaurant's grilled meats can be excellent. One thought occurs about the University's shrimp cocktail: Among the appetizers listed, why should there be an additional charge of 85 cents for four shrimp, even if they are perfectly cooked? On a recent visit they were overcooked and watery. The cost of a complete luncheon at The University Restaurant is from $1.75 to $2.85; of a complete dinner from $3.75 to $6.50. A la carte dishes cost from $2.75 to $5.50. *Cocktails, wines. Closed Sunday.*
AE DC

★ UN RINCÓN ARGENTINO

1626 Broadway (near 50th Street) CI *5-2580*

There is an undeniable appeal about the informal nature of this Argentine restaurant, and the price is right. There are, for example, platters of grilled luncheon dishes (available Monday through Friday) that include pork sausages and empanadas (listed as gaucho pie) for 99 cents. A grilled half chicken with salad is listed for the same price. The à la carte menu, available throughout the day, has entrees from about $1.95 for skirt steak cooked on skewers to $3.50 for "assorted typical Argentine broilings." The flavor of the steak is good, but it may be a trifle chewy. *Beers, wines. Dinner is served Saturday and Sunday from noon.*

★ VALENTINO'S

355 West 39th Street LO *5-8710*

Anyone who enjoys "discovering" small, pleasant, so-called family-style restaurants may well be pleased with Valentino's. The dishes are made with basic sauces in a small kitchen and are simply prepared. There is no menu. The restaurant's soups are outstanding. One of the nicer specialties of the house is chicken breast stuffed with ham and cheese, available in the evening. Some of the dishes are mediocre—the veal with peppers, for example, and the salad. The cost of a representative luncheon entree is about $2.50; of a dinner entree about $3.50. There are fewer than a dozen tables, and the walls are adorned with photographs and memorabilia of the motion-picture actor. *There is no bar, but some very ordinary wines are available. On Saturday the restaurant opens at 6 p.m. Closed Sunday.*

★★ VASATA

339 East 75th Street RH *4-9896*

This is perhaps the best Czechoslovak restaurant in New York. The atmosphere is crisp and clean and the dining room is well staffed with waiters who seem anxious to please. The food is of a high order, with such entrees as roast duck, roast pork, chicken paprika and various schnitzels. The schnitzels, which are veal, are recommended in particular. The cost of complete luncheons is from about $1.10 to $1.45; of complete dinners from about $2.45 to $5.95. In the evening the à la carte entrees are from about $1.85 to $5.35. *Cocktails, wines. Dinner is served from noon on Sunday. Reservations are frequently imperative.*
AE

★★ VESUVIO RESTAURANT

163 West 48th Street CI *5-6138*

The Vesuvio has a commendable Italian kitchen, certainly one of the best in the Broadway area, where there are many. The fish and seafood dishes are particularly interesting. The service, on the other hand, is, or was on one occasion, disheveled, slow and frustrating. All dishes are à la carte with main luncheon entrees from about $1.75 to $3.50; main dinner courses from about $1.75 to $8. *Cocktails, wines.*

AE CB DC

★★ VIA MARGUTTA

24 Minetta Lane AL *4-7630*

There are numerous Italian restaurants in Greenwich Village, and the Via Margutta is one of the best. It has a bit more sophistication than some of the others, and the menu is well varied. The cannelloni Via Margutta is recommended in particular. There are complete dinners from about $3.95 for the cannelloni to $5.75 for minute steak; à la carte dishes from about $2.50 to $5.75. *Cocktails, wines. Open for dinner only. Closed Monday, New Year's Day and Christmas.*

AE DC

★★ VIA VENETO

56 West 56th Street CI *5-8969 and* JU *6-7812*

The chef of the Via Veneto seems to exercise more care in the preparation of his menu than many other chefs in small Italian restaurants. The pasta, whether it is linguine with clams or fettucine with truffles, seems special. A fault in the restaurant is that it is crowded and the tables are almost touching. There is a complete luncheon priced from $2.75 for homemade lasagna to $5.75 for breast of chicken with truffles. Complete dinners cost from about $4.50 to $7.50, with à la carte dishes from about $2.75 to $5.75. *Cocktails, wines. On Saturday, dinner is served*

from noon. Closed Sunday, New Year's Day, July 4, Labor Day, Thanksgiving and Christmas.
AE CB DC

★★ VICTOR'S CAFÉ

240 Columbus Avenue (at 71st Street) TR 7-7988

Anyone with a passion for Cuban food would look hard in this city to find a more auspicious source than Victor's. This is a neat, friendly place, and the food is generally excellent, whether arroz con pollo, arroz con mariscos marinera (rice with seafood) or shredded beef à la Cubana. The soups are excellent, including the fabada asturiana, or white bean soup. On Saturdays and Sundays there is roast pig. The menu is à la carte with main dishes from about $1.75 to $3.95. *No alcoholic beverages.*

★ VILLA DORIA

1460 Second Avenue LE 5-9310
(between 76th and 77th Streets)

This is a pleasant enough Italian restaurant neatly decorated with wine vats, heralds, shields, crossed swords and the like. The food is reasonably good, and more care is put into it in the evening than at midday. At noon, for example, the antipasto tastes refrigerated and left over. The Villa Doria has a very good dish called cannelloni gastronomica, made with ground meats, spinach and cheese, and a creditable osso buco, when it is available. Luncheons (main course, dessert and coffee) from $2.25 to $4.25. There are complete dinners from about $4.75 to $7.25; à la carte dishes from about $2.50 to $6.25. *Cocktails, wines. On Sunday the restaurant opens at 4:30 p.m. Closed Monday, New Year's Day, July 4, Labor Day, Thanksgiving and Christmas.*
AE CB DC

★★ VILLA PENSA

198 Grand Street *226-8830*

This is an engaging, popular and colorful Italian restaurant near the heart of Little Italy. It is also one of the best Neapolitan restaurants in town. The food is robust, and although it may not appeal to the most fastidious palates, it is exceptionally good. There are numerous hot appetizers, many of them garlic-scented, including shrimp, stuffed clams and eggplant. The mussels, when available, are excellent in a rich tomato sauce. The main dishes are very good too, particularly those made with chicken. All dishes are à la carte with main dishes at midday from about $1.25 to $3.50; in the evening from about $1.60 to $3.50. *Cocktails, wines. Closed Wednesday.*

DC

★★ VINCENT PETROSINO

100 Greenwich Street (near Rector) BA *7-5398*

Petrosino's has for many years enjoyed a certain fame among people who enjoy fresh seafood cooked to order Italian style, and it has recently opened at a new address. The restaurant is located at the rear of Petrosino's fish market, where customers may stand at the counter and eat shrimp in the shell or other seafoods with cocktail sauce. The main dining room is a casually run, friendly place, and the food, some of it robustly seasoned, can be excellent. There are chowders, broiled fishes, fish fries, sautées and salads. The specialties include lobster, shrimp or crab meat marinara, creamed finnan haddie and oyster broil. All dishes are à la carte with main courses from about $1.75 to $3.25. *There is no bar, but beers are available. The restaurant closes at 5:30 p.m. Closed Saturday and Sunday.*

★ VINCENT'S CLAM BAR

119 Mott Street CA *6-8133*

This is a raffish, offbeat and curiously compelling restaurant noted for a single specialty, a hot and peppery tomato sauce that may be too hot for some palates. On weekends there may be a line of customers waiting for a seat at the bar or in the nondescript dining room. Vincent's serves the hot sauce with wonderfully fresh steamed scungilli (conch), squid, mussels and clams. The accompaniment is a hard roll dipped quickly into boiling water to soften it. The cost of one serving of any specialty is about $1. *Cocktails, wines.*

★ VOISIN

30 East 65th Street LE *5-3800*

When a restaurant of the established stature of the Voisin does not live up to its promise it is a disappointment indeed. It is one of the handsomest restaurants in the city, with Wedgwood-blue-and-white appointments. But the food is the thing and, when last observed, the portion of egg en gelée was gross, the hot shrimp marseillaise was overcooked although in an excellent spiced sauce, and the grilled sweetbreads Rose Marie tasted unpleasantly of smoke. A service of English sole Duglère was very good although not a culinary triumph. Spaghetti with red clam sauce seems an odd item for a grand luxe restaurant. The pastries, on the other hand, are above average for the city. There is a prix fixe luncheon for $6 and an à la carte menu at midday with main courses from about $2.75 to $9.50. The complete dinner is $10.25, with à la carte entrees in the evening priced from about $4 to $9.50. *Cocktails, wines. Closed Monday.*

AE CB DC

VORST'S CENTURY SEA GRILL

127 Columbus Avenue TR *4-8760*
(between 65th and 66th Streets)

There is a certain charm about the turn-of-the-century look of Vorst's, and more, it is near the Lincoln Center for the Performing Arts. The specialty of the house is seafood, although the menu also lists such diverse fare as stuffed cabbage, sauerbraten and boiled beef. The kitchen is conventional, which is to say that the food is palatable but not distinguished. The menus are à la carte with main courses at midday from about $2 for broiled fish to $4 for tenderloin steak; in the evening from about $2.85 for broiled fish to $5.60 for sirloin. *Cocktails, wines. Dinner is served Sunday from 11:30 a.m. Closed New Year's Thanksgiving and Christmas.*

★★ WAH KEE RESTAURANT

16 Doyers Street BE *3-8582*

Wah Kee has remained through the years one of Chinatown's consistently good restaurants. Like most of its counterparts in the area, it is physically nothing fancy, but the chef seems to know what he is doing. One of the most interesting dishes, although it is not listed on the menu, is lemon chicken. It is breaded and fried and has a lemon flavor. The same à la carte menu serves for luncheon and dinner. The cost of main courses ranges from about $1.30 for roast pork with Chinese vegetables to $4 for squab with oyster sauce. There are also Chinese family dinners from $2.50 a person. *Cocktails, wines.*

WALDORF-ASTORIA

301 Park Avenue (between 49th and 50th Streets) EL *5-3000*

The Bull and Bear: A masculine, handsome decor and a clublike atmosphere at noon on weekdays, when the restaurant is open to men only. Women are invited after 3 p.m. and all day Saturday and Sunday. The portions are hearty and the bill of fare lists grilled dishes,

stews and generous sandwiches. All dishes are à la carte with main dishes at both luncheon and dinner from about $3.75 to $8. *Cocktails, wines.*
CB

WALSH'S STEAK HOUSE

158 East 23rd Street 228-7400

The feeling about Walsh's is that it should be a good deal better than it is. The old-fashioned decor is too bright, and, although the steaks are of good quality, they are not invariably cooked to the doneness asked for. The tendency seems to be in the direction of overcooking. The luncheon menu lists such dishes as mixed grill and browned beef stew, and it is à la carte with main courses from $1.85 to $6.50. The à la carte menu in the evening has entrees from about $2.35 to $6.50. *Cocktails, wines. Dinner is served Saturday from noon and Sunday from 1 p.m*
AE CB DC

★ WARDS BLACK BASS

11 East 32nd Street MU *4-2817*

Lit by flickering candles even at lunchtime, this restaurant with its shadowed, lofty ceiling and enormous dark pictures has an atmosphere that is vaguely medieval. The food is good and well served. Specialties are shrimp and mushrooms in garlic butter and Charleston Meeting Street crab meat (crab in a sherry-flavored sauce topped with cheese). Desserts include pecan pie and Pontchartrain ice cream pie. Luncheon is à la carte with main courses from $2.75 to $3.95. Complete dinners are $5.50; à la carte entrees from $4.25 to $6.75. *Cocktails, wines. Closed Saturday, Sunday, New Year's Day, July 4, Labor Day, Thanksgiving and Christmas.*
AE DC

WASHINGTON SQUARE INN

Fifth Avenue at 8th Street 674-5007

When a dining room is understaffed the service in any restaurant can be wildly disorganized and unpleasant, as it was recently at the Washington Square Inn. A captain, waiters and a bus boy ran hither and yon to small purpose. The result was long lapses between courses and lukewarm omelets. The menu at the Inn is fairly simple, and the food at its best is respectably good, particularly the lentil soup and certain casserole dishes. On the other hand, a recent dish of Alaska king crab au gratin was grainy. Complete luncheons cost from about $2.15 to $2.75, with à la carte dishes at midday from $3.75 to $6.50. Complete dinners cost $5, with à la carte dishes from $3.50 to $6.50. *Cocktails, wines. Luncheon is not served Saturday and Sunday.*

AE DC

★ WHITE HOUSE RESTAURANT

1464 First Avenue (between 76th and 77th Streets) 744-9342

There is a wealth of Hungarian restaurants in the vicinity of the East 70's, and this is a good one. The menu includes such dishes as goulash, things paprikash and roast duck. The chopped chicken liver, an appetizer, resembles a pâté maison and it is exceptional. The foods overall tend to be well prepared although somewhat bland. The menu is à la carte with main courses from about $2.50 to $2.95. *Cocktails, wines. Luncheon is not served. Open seven days a week.*

WHITE'S SEA FOOD RESTAURANT

102 West 43rd Street LO 5-9048

In an over-all sense White's is no more distinctive than several other fish and seafood restaurants in Manhattan, but the fish is palatable and the complete luncheons are reasonably priced. The Manhattan clam chowder at White's is very good as contrasted with the deep-fried, crinkle-cut potatoes, which taste as though cooked in overworked fat. Complete luncheons from $1.45 to $1.95; à la carte entrees from $1.50 to $5.25. Complete dinners from $2.90 to $6; à la carte main dishes from $1.50 to $5.25. *Cocktails, wines. Closed Sunday and, during the summer months, Saturday also. Closed New Year's Day, July 4, Labor Day, Thanksgiving and Christmas.*

★ WHYTE'S

344 West 57th Street JU *6-7900*

Whyte's menu offers a wide selection of fish dishes including the restaurant's year-round specialty of finnan haddie, prepared in three different ways. There are two dining areas here, one in a high-ceilinged main dining room with an Edwardian atmosphere and, during warm weather, one on a covered terrace. The à la carte menu is essentially the same at luncheon and dinner, with main courses from about $2.50 to $6.95. *Cocktails, wines. Closed Sunday.*

AE CB DC

★★ WHYTE'S DOWNTOWN

145 Fulton Street CO *7-2233*

There is an engaging turn-of-the-century charm about this branch of Whyte's, and the fish, particularly the finnan haddie in heavy cream (listed as à la Whyte), is remarkably good. Dishes other than fish and seafood are not of equal stature. There is an à la carte menu for both lunch and dinner with main courses from about $2.50 to $6.95. *Cocktails, wines. Closed Saturday and Sunday.*

AE CB DC

★ WO KEE

11 Doyers Street WO *2-8155*

This is another of those abundant, small, downstairs restaurants in Chinatown with food that is generally excellent. True, the menu is stereotyped, but even such standards as Cantonese lobster and shrimp with mushrooms (canned) are appealing. The fried squab, not listed on the menu, is delicious with its spiced salt served on the side and a squeeze of fresh lemon. Some of the champions of the Wo Kee declare that it has the best won ton in town. It is good. The same menu serves throughout the day and it is all à la carte. The cost of main dishes is from $1.25 to $3.75. *No alcoholic beverages.*

★★ WO PING

24 Pell Street RE *2-0847 and* WO *2-8172*

Wo Ping in Chinatown is noisy as a gong and earthy as a ginger root, but the restaurant is a great favorite with those who enjoy snails, crabs and other seafood Chinese style. The snails and crabs, in particular, can be delicious if a trifle inelegant to eat, since they both demand fingers in the sauce. There are complete luncheons from 80 cents to $1.20; family dinners for two priced at $4.80 and for six at $14.40. Main courses on the à la carte menu from $1.50 to $4.55. *No alcoholic beverages. Dinner is served Sunday from 1:30 p.m.*

★★ XOCHITL MEXICAN RESTAURANT

146 West 46th Street PL *7-1325*

One of the best known and best of New York's Mexican restaurants. The kitchen offers a typical assortment of tamales, enchiladas, tacos and tostadas, and the dishes are generally made with care. The Xochitl has fewer than 20 tables, and at peak dining hours there may be a wait for a seat. The service is of the smiling but take-it-or-leave-it category. The same à la carte menu serves throughout the day with entrees from about $1.10 for chili con carne with beans to $4 for a combination plate. *Cocktails, wines, Mexican beers. On Sunday the restaurant is open from 2 p.m. Closed Thanksgiving and, during July and August, on Sunday.*

★ YELLOWFINGER'S BUTCHERIA

60th Street and Third Avenue *752-1460*

This is a relatively new and bustling restaurant that is far more interesting in concept than in execution. There are tables on the sidewalk and, inside, counters where guests may stand and dine while sipping beer or soft drinks. The dining and service areas are strikingly designed with inlaid Mexican tile. The Butcheria's menu is well varied with grilled hot and sweet Italian sausages, white sausages, hamburgers and shish kebab. There is one station where excellent Brittany crêpes are made and filled with such oddments as cheese, ham and cheese, or jelly. The quality of the food over-all is first-rate. There are two faults with the restaurant. The ventilation is poor and the service behind the counters is disorganized, desultory and generally lacking in efficiency. The cost of most items is about 90 cents. The cost of the shish kebab, the least interesting item on the menu, is $1.35. *Beers and soft drinks.*

YEN KING

247 Third Avenue (at 20th Street) GR *5-6622*

A neat, pleasant Chinese restaurant vaguely in the Stuyvesant Town–Kips Bay area. At its best, and this would include the Yen King shrimp with ham and chicken, it is excellent. On the other hand, the routine dishes on the menu are as uninspired as the watery won ton soup and the overcooked Cantonese-style chicken. There is a complete luncheon from about $1.40 for pork chow mein to $3.50 for lobster Cantonese. The à la carte menu, always available, is priced from about $2 for you-know-what to $5.95 for Yen King steak. *Cocktails, wines. Only à la carte items are available on Sunday, from 1 p.m.*
AE DC

★ YEN LUCK

497 Third Avenue MU *5-1933*
(between 33rd and 34th Streets)

This is a perfectly adequate Chinese restaurant with food that is good but not unusually distinguished. The stuffed chicken wings are well prepared among the appetizers, and so are the dem sem, or steamed dumplings. When a choice of main dishes was left to the discretion of a captain, he produced two containing seafood, which is rather bizarre, but the service in general seems nervous and detached. There are complete luncheons that cost from $1.40 to $3.50. A la carte main dishes are priced from $2.10 to $4.95. *Cocktails, wines. Only à la carte items are available on Sunday, from 1 p.m.*

AE DC

★★ YE OLDE CHOP HOUSE

111 Broadway RE *2-6119*

A restaurant in the city's financial section that is well worth remembering, particularly for lunch. The establishment has a chop-house atmosphere, and at their best the grilled dishes, such as English mutton chop ($5), are excellent. This is also one of the few places in town where genuine Smithfield ham ($3.75), hot from the grill, is available. For the unaccustomed the ham may be overly salty, but for the initiated it is delicious. The same menu serves for luncheon and dinner, and all dishes are à la carte. Main courses cost from $3.60 to $7.50. When in season, game is available. *Cocktails, wines. Open until 7:30 p.m. Closed Saturday, Sunday and all major holidays.*

AE CB DC

★ YE WAVERLY INN

16 Bank Street CH *3-9396*

Visitors to New York or even the natives would be hard put to find a restaurant more typically American than Ye Waverly Inn. It is atmospheric too, with low ceilings, antique floors and an outdoor garden. The restaurant is said to date from the 19th century. The food is what is commonly called "home style," and entrees include such dishes as roast beef, baked meat loaf, fried porgy and grilled ham steak. There is a luncheon that costs $1.10 and complete luncheons from about $1.10 to $1.95. Dinners cost from about $2.25 to $3.50. *There is no bar, but patrons may bring their own wine. Luncheon is not served Saturday and Sunday.*

★ YING'S

108 Fifth Avenue (at 16th Street) *929-0842*

This is a new, brightly lighted and routine-looking Chinese restaurant on lower Fifth Avenue. The menu is rather heavy in the chop suey–chow mein department, but the chef can prepare some very good dishes including Ying's boneless chicken and various noodle dishes. The food is, by and large, reasonably priced. There are complete luncheons from $1.10 to $3.50; complete dinners from $1.95 to $3.95. A la carte items from about $1.25 to $5.25. *No alcoholic beverages. Luncheon is not served on Sunday.*

YOUNG CHINA

35 West 8th Street GR *5-8654*

This is a small, neat and clean Chinese restaurant in Greenwich Village. The food is palatable, but the menu offers few surprises. There are the usual soups and the usual combination plates. Complete luncheons cost $1.10 to $1.80; complete dinners for two $5.40. A la carte dishes are priced from $1.30 to $3. *No alcoholic beverages. Dinner is served Sunday from noon.*

★★ ZETTI HUNGARIAN RESTAURANT

1574 Second Avenue *734-9134*
(between 81st and 82nd Streets)

There are numerous Hungarian restaurants in New York, and this is one of the most engaging. It is relatively small, the decor is neat and unpretentious, but the food is excellent. There is an especially good appetizer called lecso, made with peppers and sausage, and the roast duck is first-rate. The waitresses are pleasant and, except when the restaurant is crowded, admirably efficient. There is a complete luncheon for $1.50. Complete dinners are about $2.75 to $3.50. The à la carte menu lists entrees from about $2 to $2.50. Reservations are recommended. *Cocktails, wines. Open seven days a week.*

★ ZOE CHASE

115 East 60th Street TE *8-6983*

The cuisine of Zoe Chase is as emphatically plain as the decor. The over-all atmosphere of the restaurant is like a tearoom, but the food is appetizing and moderately priced. Single guests are asked at times to share tables. Luncheons with dessert and beverage cost from about $1.20 to $1.75. There is a snack luncheon for 99 cents. Complete dinners cost from about $2.55 to $4.50. *No alcoholic beverages. Closed Saturday and Sunday.*

★★ ZUM ZUM

45th Street entrance to the Pan Am Building *974-6786*

Lexington Avenue at 45th Street *974-4876*

74 Broad Street *269-2955*

The first of these agreeable beer-and-wurst establishments opened about four years ago in the Pan Am Building. It is a casual restaurant, standing room only at peak dining periods, with white tile and chopping-block decor, and many kinds of sausages hanging from the ceiling. The other two branches follow the same policy. You can dine rather well for a very small sum, and a typical lunch with soup, sandwich, salad and dessert can be had for $1.50. The specialties are various kinds of sausages from frankfurters and liverwurst to bauernwurst and bratwurst. Most are served on a bun with either sauerkraut or onion sauce, and the cost is from about 35 cents for a frankfurter to 95 cents for roast beef with bacon and potato salad. The soups are, incidentally, made with first-class ingredients and they are generally outstanding. *There is no bar, but the cold beer in steins is delicious. The restaurant in the Pan Am Building is open from 7:30 a.m. until 10 p.m. Monday through Friday, until 8 p.m. Saturday; closed Sunday. The one at Lexington and 45th is open from 7:00 a.m. until midnight Monday through Saturday; closed Sunday. The Broad Street restaurant is open from 7:30 a.m. until 10 p.m. Monday through Friday, until 5:00 p.m. Saturday; closed Sunday.*

INDEX

CRAIG CLAIBORNE

Craig Claiborne, food news editor of THE NEW YORK TIMES, *was born 47 years ago in Mississippi. After receiving a degree in journalism from the University of Missouri in 1942, he joined the Navy, serving in World War II and the Korean War. He lived in Paris and Chicago after World War II and after the Korean War in Switzerland. There he entered a hotel school and was trained in French cuisine and service. It was, he claims, the greatest adventure of his life. Mr. Claiborne now lives in New York's Greenwich Village and East Hampton, where he spends most of his week ends enjoying his hobby, cooking. His other books are* THE NEW YORK TIMES COOKBOOK, AN HERB AND SPICE COOKBOOK *and* THE NEW YORK TIMES MENU COOKBOOK.